REVIEWING

BIOLOGY

THE LIVING ENVIRONMENT

WITH SAMPLE EXAMINATIONS

SECOND EDITION

Carl M. Raab

Former Director of Academic Initiatives for the
Office of School Programs and Support Services
New York City Board of Education, NY
Former Assistant Principal, Supervision Science
Fort Hamilton High School, Brooklyn, New York

Revised by
Michael F. Renna

Assistant Principal, Supervision Science
Hillcrest High School, Queens, New York
Lead AP Science, Queens Superintendency
Coordinating Biology Mentor, NYS

AMSCO

Amsco School Publications, Inc.
315 Hudson Street / New York, N.Y. 10013

The publisher wishes to acknowledge the helpful contributions
of the following consultants in the preparation of this book:

Marilou Bebak
Biology Teacher
Nardin Academy High School
Buffalo, New York
Coordinating Biology Mentor, NYS

Lane Schwartz
Former Principal (Retired)
Glen Cove High School, Glen Cove, New York
Former Assistant Principal, Science
John Jay High School, New York City, New York

Bart Bookman
Assistant Principal, Science
Adlai E. Stevenson High School
Bronx, New York
Coordinating Biology Mentor, NYS

Martin Solomon
Science Teacher / Programmer
Daniel Carter Beard Junior High School 189Q
Queens, New York

Barbara Poseluzny
Assistant Principal, Science
A. Philip Randolph High School
New York City, New York
Lead AP Science, Manhattan Superintendency
Coordinating Biology Mentor, NYS

Text and Cover Design: Howard S. Leiderman
Composition: Nesbitt Graphics, Inc.

Science, Technology, and Society features written by Christine Caputo.

Please visit our Web site at: ***www.amscopub.com***

When ordering this book, please specify:
either **R 741 P** *or* REVIEWING BIOLOGY: THE LIVING ENVIRONMENT,
SECOND EDITION

ISBN: 0-87720-049-1

Note to the Teacher

The newly revised, second edition books of this series—*Reviewing Biology: The Living Environment, Reviewing Earth Science: The Physical Setting, Reviewing Chemistry: The Physical Setting,* and *Reviewing Physics: the Physical Setting*— offer an innovative format that comprehensively reviews the new National Science Standards-based Core Curriculum. Each book is readily correlated with the standard textbooks for the high school level. This series is specifically geared to the needs of students who want to refresh their memory and review the material in preparation for final exams.

The material in *Reviewing Biology: The Living Environment, Second Edition* is divided into eight chapters, each of which is subdivided into major topic sections. The book is abundantly illustrated with clearly labeled drawings and diagrams that illuminate and reinforce the subject matter. Important science terms are **bold-faced** and defined in the text. Other science terms that may be unfamiliar to students are *italicized* for emphasis. In addition, the large work-text format and open design make *Reviewing Biology: The Living Environment, Second Edition* easy for students to read.

Within each chapter are several sets of multiple-choice, short-answer (constructed response), and essay (extended constructed-response) questions that test the students' knowledge and reasoning while provoking thought. Topical reading comprehension passages with question sets appear at the end of each chapter, giving students further opportunity to refine their science reading and writing skills. Tables, graphs, and diagrams that aid in interpreting, reviewing, and testing the material often accompany the questions. The more than 750 questions found in the text can be used for topic review throughout the year, as well as for exams and homework assignments. The four sample examinations at the back of the book can be used as final exams or practice for the final exam.

A section called *Laboratory Skills* follows the eight chapters. This special section reviews the scientific skills and methods that all students should master in the course of completing one year of biology instruction at this level. *Reviewing Biology: The Living Environment, Second Edition* also contains a full Glossary, where students can find concise definitions of the bold-faced scientific terms. Students can use the extensive Index to locate the text discussions of these and other important biological terms.

Also included in *Reviewing Biology: The Living Environment, Second Edition* are eight new *Science, Technology, and Society* features that explore current controversial issues in biological science, society, and technology. Reading comprehension, constructed response, and research questions presented at the end of each feature encourage students to evaluate the issues and to make their own decisions about the impact of science and technology on society, the environment, and their lives.

Contents

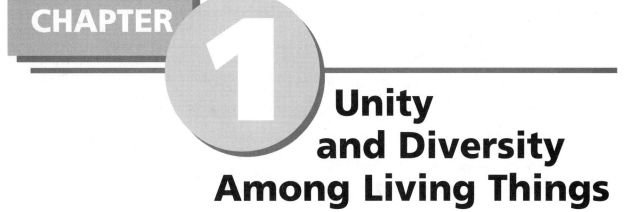

Unity and Diversity Among Living Things

CONCEPT OF LIFE

Scientists have not yet agreed on a single definition of life. Thus, life is often defined in terms of certain activities, or life functions, that are performed by all living things.

Life Functions

All living things, or **organisms**, carry on several basic life functions. First of all, *regulation* involves the control and **coordination** of the life functions. The process of **nutrition** provides all the substances that are used by an organism for the growth and repair of its **tissues**. Nutrition includes the activities involved in *ingestion* (obtaining food from the environment), **digestion** (processing food for use by the organism), and *egestion* (removal of solid wastes). *Transport* includes the absorption of materials through cell membranes and the **circulation**, or distribution, of materials to all the cells of the organism. After the materials are delivered to the cells, the process of **respiration** can occur. Respiration includes the chemical activities that release energy from organic molecules for use by the cells. During respiration, the chemical bonds of **glucose** are broken down, and the energy released is stored in the compound **ATP**. An organism uses the energy in ATP to perform its life functions. ATP functions much like a rechargeable battery—when it gets "run down," it is recharged by the breakdown of glucose.

Other chemical reactions are involved in building, rather than breaking down, **molecules**. During **synthesis** reactions, small molecules combine to form larger ones. *Growth* is an increase in size brought about by increases in cell size and cell number. The products of synthesis are the raw materials that are used for growth. The process of **excretion** includes all those activities that are involved in the removal of cellular

waste products from the organism. These wastes include **carbon dioxide**, water, salts, and nitrogen-containing compounds. The life function of **reproduction** results in the production of new individuals. However, since each organism has a limited life span, reproduction is necessary more for the survival of each **species** (a group of like organisms) than for the individual organism itself.

Metabolism. All the chemical activities that an organism must carry on to sustain life are its *metabolism*, or **metabolic** activities. The breaking apart of glucose molecules to release their energy and the growth and repair of tissues to maintain a functioning body are both examples of metabolic activities.

Homeostasis. The maintenance of a stable internal environment in spite of changes, or **deviations**, in the external environment is known as **homeostasis**. An example of homeostasis is the maintenance of a constant body temperature in spite of temperature fluctuations in the external environment.

Questions

Multiple Choice

1. The tendency of an organism to maintain a stable internal environment is called   (1) homeostasis   (2) nutrition   (3) reproduction   (4) synthesis

2. The energy available for use by the cell is obtained from the life function of   (1) reproduction   (2) respiration   (3) transport   (4) synthesis

3. The chemical process by which complex molecules of protein are made from simple molecules is called   (1) regulation   (2) respiration   (3) synthesis   (4) excretion

4. Which life function includes the absorption and circulation of essential substances throughout an organism? (1) transport (2) excretion (3) ingestion (4) nutrition

5. Which term includes all of the chemical activities carried on by an organism? (1) regulation (2) metabolism (3) digestion (4) respiration

6. Which life activity is *not* required for the survival of an individual organism? (1) nutrition (2) respiration (3) reproduction (4) synthesis

7. In an ameba, materials are taken from its environment and then moved throughout its cytoplasm. These processes are known as (1) absorption and circulation (2) food processing and energy release (3) energy release and synthesis (4) coordination and regulation

8. In an organism, the coordination of the activities that maintain homeostasis in a constantly changing environment is a process known as (1) digestion (2) regulation (3) synthesis (4) respiration

Short Answer
(Constructed Response)

9. Which life function provides the substances that are used by an organism for its growth and for the repair of its tissues? Explain.

10. Why are such different things as amebas and humans both considered to be organisms?

CELLULAR STRUCTURE OF LIVING THINGS

All living things are composed of **cells**. Some organisms consist of only one cell, while others consist of billions of cells. The processes that are essential for the survival of an organism are performed by its cells.

The Cell Theory

The *cell theory*, which is one of the major theories of biology, can be stated as follows: (a) Every organism is made up of one or more cells; (b) the cell is the basic unit of structure and function in all living things (for example, cells make, or synthesize, proteins and release energy); and (c) all cells come only from preexisting cells (that is, new cells are formed when previously existing cells divide).

Development of the Cell Theory.
During the last four centuries, improvements in the microscope and the development of other techniques have made it possible for biologists to observe and study cells. The cell theory was developed from the work of a number of scientists. First, *Anton van Leeuwenhoek* (1632–1723) made powerful simple microscopes (magnifying glasses) that he used to study living cells; he was the first person to observe sperm cells, bacteria, and protozoa. Then, *Robert Hooke* (1635–1703) made compound microscopes (microscopes with two or more lenses) that he used to observe thin slices of cork; he used the term "cells" to describe the small compartments that make up cork tissue. In 1831, *Robert Brown* concluded from his studies that all plant cells contain a nucleus. Later, in 1838, *Matthias Schleiden* concluded that all plants are made up of cells and, in 1839, *Theodor Schwann* concluded that all animals are made up of cells. Finally, in 1855, *Rudolph Virchow* concluded that all cells arise only from preexisting cells. These last three ideas formed the basis of the cell theory.

Exceptions to the Cell Theory. Recent discoveries have led scientists to identify several exceptions to the cell theory. For example, mitochondria and chloroplasts, which are cell organelles, contain genetic material (DNA) and can duplicate themselves within living cells. Another exception is the **virus**, which is not a living cell. It consists of an outer coat of protein surrounding a core of DNA or RNA. A virus can reproduce while inside a living host cell, but outside the host cell, it shows no sign of life. As such, viruses are not included in any of the five **kingdoms** of living things. And, finally, the first living cells on Earth must have developed from noncellular matter (not from preexisting cells).

Cell Structure. Cells contain a variety of small structures, called **organelles**, which perform specific functions (Figure 1-1).

The **cell membrane**, or *plasma membrane*, surrounds and protects the cell and separates the cell contents from the environment. The membrane consists of a double lipid layer in which large protein molecules float. The cell membrane is *selectively permeable*; this means that some substances can pass through it, while others cannot. In this way, the membrane regulates the passage of materials into and out of the cell and controls the cell's chemical makeup.

The **cytoplasm** is the fluidlike material that fills the space between the cell membrane and the nucleus. Many metabolic reactions occur in the cytoplasm, which consists mainly of water. The organelles are suspended in the cytoplasm.

Animal Cell

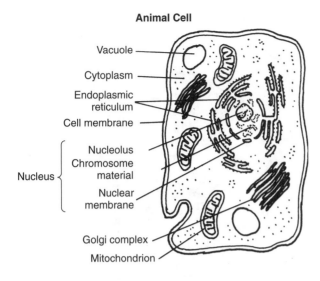

Vacuole
Cytoplasm
Endoplasmic reticulum
Cell membrane
Nucleolus
Chromosome material
Nucleus
Nuclear membrane
Golgi complex
Mitochondrion

Plant Cell

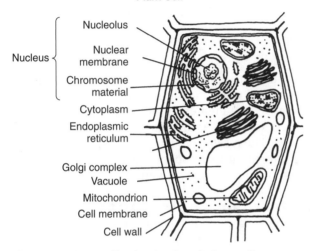

Nucleolus
Nuclear membrane
Nucleus
Chromosome material
Cytoplasm
Endoplasmic reticulum
Golgi complex
Vacuole
Mitochondrion
Cell membrane
Cell wall

Figure 1-1. Generalized animal and plant cells.

The **nucleus** is the control center of the cell. It is surrounded by a nuclear membrane and contains the genetic material, which is found in the **chromosomes**. The chromosomes are made of **DNA** (**deoxyribonucleic acid**) and protein.

The **ribosomes** are tiny organelles that are suspended in the cytoplasm and attached to the membranes of the endoplasmic reticulum. Protein synthesis takes place at the ribosomes.

The **mitochondria** are the sites of most reactions of aerobic **cellular respiration**, the process by which energy is released from nutrient molecules (such as glucose). Most of the ATP produced by aerobic respiration is synthesized in the mitochondria.

The **vacuoles** are fluid-filled organelles surrounded by membranes. In one-celled organisms, digestion occurs in food vacuoles and excess water collects in contractile vacuoles, which pump it out of the cell. Plant cells contain very large vacuoles that may fill much of the cell's interior. In

animal cells, there are relatively few vacuoles, and they are small.

The **chloroplasts** are small, pigment-containing organelles found in the cytoplasm of plants, algae, and some protists. Photosynthesis takes place in the chloroplasts.

The *cell wall* is a nonliving structure found outside the cell membrane of plant, algal, and fungal cells. It provides strength and rigidity, but does not interfere with the passage of materials into or out of the cell.

Questions

Multiple Choice

11. The unit of structure and function of all living things is (1) an organ (2) an atom (3) a cell (4) a nucleolus

12. According to the cell theory, which statement is correct? (1) Viruses are true living cells. (2) All cells are basically unalike in structure. (3) Mitochondria are found only in plant cells. (4) All cells come from preexisting cells.

13. Chloroplasts and mitochondria are examples of (1) cells (2) tissue (3) organelles (4) organs

14. The term "selectively permeable" is used in reference to the (1) nucleus (2) cell wall (3) cytoplasm (4) cell membrane

15. The part of a cell that is in most direct contact with the environment is the (1) nucleus (2) cell membrane (3) mitochondrion (4) vacuole

16. Plant cell organelles that contain photosynthetic pigments are (1) chloroplasts (2) ribosomes (3) chromosomes (4) cell walls

17. An observable difference between onion skin cells and cheek cells is that the onion skin cells have a (1) cell membrane (2) nucleus (3) vacuole (4) cell wall

18. The sites of protein synthesis in the cytoplasm are the (1) ribosomes (2) chromosomes (3) nuclei (4) vacuoles

19. The watery environment in which most life activities of a cell take place is the (1) cell membrane (2) chloroplast (3) cytoplasm (4) vacuole

20. Transport of materials into and out of a cell is most closely associated with the (1) nucleus (2) cell wall (3) ribosome (4) cell membrane

21. Which organelle contains genetic material and controls most cell activities? (1) nucleus (2) cell membrane (3) vacuole (4) endoplasmic reticulum

22. The cell organelles that are the sites of aerobic cellular respiration in both plant and animal cells are the (1) mitochondria (2) vacuoles (3) chloroplasts (4) nuclei

23. An increase in the concentration of ATP in a muscle cell is a direct result of which life function? (1) respiration (2) reproduction (3) digestion (4) excretion

24. A nonliving cell structure is a (1) cell membrane (2) nucleus (3) cell wall (4) mitochondrion

Short Answer
(Constructed Response)

25. In a complete sentence, give one example of how technology has enhanced our understanding of the structure of living things.

26. In two full sentences, explain why scientists have difficulty including viruses in the category of living organisms.

TOOLS AND METHODS OF CELL STUDY

There are various scientific tools and methods that enable the up-close study of cell structures and functions. These different techniques and types of equipment are used to study cells and cell parts at varying levels of magnification and in different conditions. For example, some tools are used for the study of live cells while others can be used only for the examination of preserved (dead) cells. Some of these tools and techniques are described below.

Compound Light Microscope
A microscope that uses two lenses or sets of lenses to form an enlarged image is called a *compound light microscope*. Light passes through the specimen, the objective lens, and the ocular lens, or *eyepiece*, before reaching the eye. The objective lens produces a magnified image that is further enlarged by the ocular lens. The main parts of a compound light microscope are shown in Figure 1-2. The functions of these parts are listed in Table 1-1 on page 5.

The amount of enlargement of an image produced by the lenses of a microscope is its *magnifying power*. For a compound microscope, magnifying power is found by multiplying the magnifying power of the objective lens by the magnifying power of the ocular lens. For example, if the magnifying power of the objective is 40×

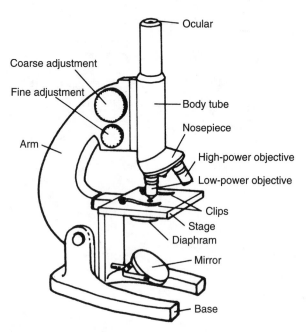

Figure 1-2. The compound light microscope.

(40 times) and that of the ocular is 10× (10 times), the total magnification is 40 × 10 = 400× (400 times). The greater the magnification of a specimen, the smaller the field of vision, or observable area. The *resolution*, or resolving power, is the capacity of the microscope to show, as separate, two points that are close together.

Other Types of Microscopes
A microscope that has an ocular lens and an objective lens for each eye is called a binocular or *dissecting microscope*. Dissecting microscopes, which produce a three-dimensional image, have relatively low magnifying power and are used for viewing fairly large, opaque specimens. For more magnifying power and the ability to observe unstained, living cells, a *phase-contrast microscope* is used; it makes visible parts that cannot be seen with an ordinary light microscope. The most powerful kind of microscope is the *electron microscope*, which can magnify an object more than 400,000×. Unlike other microscopes, the electron microscope uses an electron beam focused by electromagnets, instead of light and lenses. One disadvantage of the electron microscope is that only dead specimens can be viewed with it.

Techniques of Cell Study
Tiny instruments that can be used, with the aid of a microscope, to remove or transfer the parts of a cell are *microdissection* instruments. For example, with the use of microdissection instruments, a nucleus can be transferred from one cell to another. The laboratory instrument that is used to

Table 1-1. Parts of the Compound Light Microscope and Their Functions

Part	Function
Base	Supports the microscope
Arm	Used to carry microscope; attaches to the base, stage, and body tube
Body tube	Holds the objective lens and eyepiece
Stage	Platform on which the glass slide with the specimen is placed (over the hole in the stage through which light passes)
Clips	Hold the slide in position on the stage
Nosepiece	Holds the objective lenses; rotates so that the different objective lenses can be moved in line with the specimen and eyepiece
Coarse adjustment	Larger knob used for rough-focusing with the low-power objective
Fine adjustment	Smaller knob used for focusing with the high-power objective and for final focusing with the low-power objective
Mirror	Directs light to the specimen (on the stage)
Diaphragm	Controls the amount of light reaching the specimen
Objective lenses	Lenses mounted on the nosepiece
Ocular lens	Lens at the top of the body tube; commonly called the *eyepiece*

separate small particles or materials on the basis of density is the *ultracentrifuge*. In fact, various cell organelles can be isolated by the process of ultracentrifugation. The ultracentrifuge spins the sample in a test tube at very high speeds so that particles of different densities settle to the bottom of the test tube in layers. In addition, cell structures can be made clearly visible by the use of various *staining* techniques. Depending on its specific chemical makeup, a particular stain will be absorbed only by certain parts of the cell. For example, methylene blue and iodine are stains that are absorbed by the nucleus. Other parts of the cell can be made visible with other stains.

The unit used in measuring structures that can be viewed with a compound light microscope is the *micrometer* (μm). One micrometer equals 0.001 millimeter; 1000 micrometers equal 1 millimeter. The diameter of the low-power field of a compound light microscope is commonly about 1500 μm. A paramecium is about 250 micrometers (0.25 millimeter) long. (Measurement with a microscope is discussed in greater detail in the section on Laboratory Skills.)

Questions

Multiple Choice

27. Which of the following plant cell structures could not be seen using the 10× objective of a compound microscope? (1) nucleus (2) cell wall (3) cytoplasm (4) endoplasmic reticulum

28. A microscope reveals one hundred similar cells arranged end-to-end in a space of 1 millimeter. The average length of each cell must be (1) 0.1 micrometer (2) 10 micrometers (3) 100 micrometers (4) 1000 micrometers

29. Which instrument would provide the most detailed information about the internal structure of a chloroplast? (1) a compound light microscope (2) a phase-contrast microscope (3) an electron microscope (4) an ultracentrifuge

30. If the low-power objective and the eyepiece both have a magnifying power of 10×, the total magnifying power of the microscope is (1) 10× (2) 100× (3) 1× (4) 20×

31. To separate the parts of a cell by differences in density, a biologist would probably use (1) a microdissection instrument (2) an ultracentrifuge (3) a phase-contrast microscope (4) an electron microscope

32. Which microscope magnification should be used to observe the largest field of view of an insect wing? (1) 20× (2) 100× (3) 400× (4) 900×

33. The diameter of the field of vision of a compound light microscope is 1.5 millimeters. This may also be expressed as (1) 15 micrometers (2) 150 micrometers (3) 1500 micrometers (4) 15,000 micrometers

34. To transplant a nucleus from one cell to another cell, a scientist would use (1) an electron microscope (2) an ultracentrifuge (3) microdissection instruments (4) staining techniques

35. A student used a compound microscope to measure the diameters of several red blood cells and found that the average length was 0.008 millimeter. What was the average length of a single red blood cell in micrometers? (1) 0.8 (2) 8 (3) 80 (4) 800

36. A student using a compound microscope estimated the diameter of a cheek cell to be about 50 micrometers. What is the diameter of this cheek cell in millimeters? (1) 0.050 mm (2) 0.500 mm (3) 5.00 mm (4) 50.9 mm

37. A student has a microscope with a 10× eyepiece and 10× and 40× objectives. She observed 40 onion epidermal cells across the diameter of the low-power field. How many cells would she observe under high power? (1) 1 cell (2) 40 cells (3) 10 cells (4) 4 cells

38. After examining cells from an onion root tip under high power, a student switches to the low-power objective without moving the slide. He would most likely see (1) more cells and less detail (2) more cells and more detail (3) fewer cells and less detail (4) fewer cells and more detail

39. A slide of the letters F and R is placed on the stage of a microscope in the position shown in the diagram below. How would the image of the letters appear when the slide is viewed under the lower power of a compound light microscope?

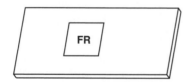

(1) RF (2) ꓭꓧ (3) ꟻꓤ (4) ꓤꟻ

40. The diagram below represents the field of vision of a microscope. What is the approximate diameter of the cell shown in the field? (1) 50 micrometers (2) 500 micrometers (3) 1000 micrometers (4) 2000 micrometers

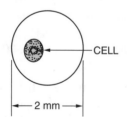

CELL

2 mm

Short Answer
(Constructed Response)

41. Select any three parts that are labeled in the diagram below and, for each part selected, (a) identify the part, and (b) in a complete sentence, state the function of that part.

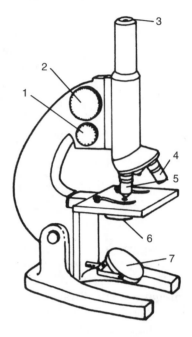

Answer the following question based on the information and the table below.

42. A lab microscope has two interchangeable eyepieces and four objective lenses. The table shows various combinations of the eyepiece and objective lenses and the apparent magnification of the specimen image produced. Use the information provided in the table to complete the missing data.

Eyepiece Lens	Objective Lens	Magnification of Image
10×		100×
	40×	400×
15×	90×	
10×		150×
		900×

43. In a complete sentence, explain how a biology student can calculate the magnification of a specimen when the powers of the eyepiece lens and the objective lens are known.

Essay
(Extended Constructed Response)

44. In a brief paragraph, describe how the development of the compound microscope and other magnifying instruments greatly advanced the science of biology.

BIOCHEMISTRY

The chemical reactions necessary to sustain life take place in the cells. The study of the chemical reactions of living things is called *biochemistry*.

Elements

A substance that cannot be broken down into simpler substances is called an *element*. Examples of elements include hydrogen, oxygen, sodium, and potassium. The most abundant elements in living things are **carbon, hydrogen, oxygen**, and **nitrogen**. Elements found in lesser amounts in living things include sulfur, phosphorus, magnesium, iodine, iron, calcium, chlorine, potassium, and others.

Atoms

All elements are made up of particles called **atoms**. Each element has a different kind of atom. The atoms of different elements differ in the numbers of protons, neutrons, and electrons they contain. A *compound* is formed when two or more elements combine chemically. For example, water (H_2O) is formed by the chemical combination of two hydrogen atoms and one oxygen atom.

Chemical Bonding

The formation of compounds involves either the transfer or the sharing of electrons between atoms, resulting in the formation of chemical bonds. When atoms lose or gain electrons, they become electrically charged particles called ions, and an *ionic bond* is formed. When atoms share electrons, a *covalent bond* is formed. When a compound forms, it has properties that are different from those of the elements that make it up.

Inorganic and Organic Compounds

There are two basic classes of chemical compounds: inorganic compounds and organic compounds. Both types are found in living things.

Compounds that do not contain both carbon and hydrogen atoms are **inorganic** compounds. Inorganic compounds found in cells include water, salts, carbon dioxide, and inorganic acids, such as hydrochloric acid (HCl).

Compounds that contain both carbon and hydrogen atoms are **organic** compounds. Because carbon atoms can form four covalent bonds with other atoms, organic compounds are often large and complex. The major categories of organic compounds are carbohydrates, proteins, lipids, and nucleic acids. (The nucleic acids—DNA and RNA—are discussed in Chapter 6.)

Carbohydrates

Sugars and starches, which are used primarily as sources of energy and as food-storage compounds, are *carbohydrates*. These substances are made up of carbon, hydrogen, and oxygen, and the ratio of hydrogen to oxygen is always 2 to 1. The simplest carbohydrates are the *monosaccharides*, or **simple sugars**. Glucose, galactose, and fructose, each with the formula $C_6H_{12}O_6$, are simple sugars.

Some carbohydrates, such as maltose and sucrose (both $C_{12}H_{22}O_{11}$) are known as *disaccharides*, sugars whose molecules are made up of two monosaccharide molecules bonded together. For example, a maltose molecule is formed from two glucose molecules that are bonded together.

The complex carbohydrates that are made up of chains of monosaccharides are called *polysaccharides*. Starch, cellulose, and glycogen are polysaccharides that are made up of chains of glucose molecules. In plants, **starch** is a food storage compound and cellulose makes up the cell walls. In animals, glycogen is the food-storage compound.

Proteins

Enzymes, hormones, and various structural parts of organisms are **proteins**. Proteins are made up of smaller **subunits** called **amino acids**.

Structure of Amino Acids. Amino acids contain the elements carbon, hydrogen, oxygen, and nitrogen. Some also contain sulfur. Figure 1-3 shows the generalized structure of an amino acid.

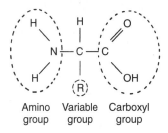

Figure 1-3. Generalized structure of an amino acid.

The –NH$_2$ is an amino group; the –COOH is a carboxyl, or acid, group; and the *R* represents a variable group. The *R* group is the part of the amino acid structure that differs from one amino acid to another. Twenty different amino acids are found in the cells of living things.

Like carbohydrates, amino acids combine chemically to form more complex molecules. When two amino acids combine, they form a *dipeptide*. The bond that holds the amino acids together is called a *peptide bond*. More amino acids may combine with a dipeptide to form a *polypeptide*. A protein is made up of one or more polypeptide chains. There are a great many types of protein molecules in living things. These molecules differ in the number, kinds, and sequences of amino acids they contain.

Lipids

Fats, oils, and waxes belong to a class of organic compounds called **lipids**. They serve mainly as sources of energy and as components of structures such as cell membranes. Lipids that are solid at room temperature are *fats*, while those that are liquid are *oils*. Lipids contain carbon, hydrogen, and oxygen. The ratio of hydrogen atoms to oxygen atoms is greater than 2 to 1 and varies from one lipid to another. The building blocks of lipids are fatty acids and glycerol.

Questions

Multiple Choice

45. What is the principal inorganic solvent in cells? (1) salt (2) water (3) alcohol (4) carbon dioxide

46. Fats that are stored in human tissue contain molecules of (1) glycerol and fatty acids (2) amino acids (3) monosaccharides and disaccharides (4) nucleotides

47. One of the carbon compounds found in a cell has twice as many hydrogen atoms as oxygen atoms. This compound most likely belongs to the group of substances known as (1) nucleic acids (2) lipids (3) proteins (4) carbohydrates

48. Which formula represents an organic compound? (1) NH$_3$ (2) H$_2$O (3) NaCl (4) C$_{12}$H$_{22}$O$_{11}$

49. Starch is classified as a (1) disaccharide (2) polypeptide (3) nucleotide (4) polysaccharide

50. Which organic compound is correctly matched with the subunit that composes it? (1) maltose—amino acid (2) starch—glucose (3) protein—fatty acid (4) lipid—sucrose

Short Answer
(Constructed Response)

51. There are only 20 different amino acids found in living things, yet there are thousands of different proteins. In a full sentence, explain why this is possible.

52. In one or two complete sentences, explain why starch molecules and protein molecules are both called polymers.

53. Examine each of the four molecular structures shown below. Identify each molecule as organic or inorganic and explain, in a full sentence, why it is classified as organic or inorganic.

Base your answer to the following question on the information and table below.

54. A lab was set up for students to analyze three unknown samples of organic molecules—a lipid, a carbohydrate, and a protein. The results of their lab tests are shown in the table. Based on these results, identify each sample as a protein, carbohydrate, or lipid, and then state the reason for your identification of each molecule as such.

Unknown Sample	Elements Contained	Molecular Characteristics
A	C, H, O, and N	Polymer, high molecular mass
B	C, H, and O	Very little oxygen, much hydrogen
C	C, H, and O	Twice as much hydrogen as oxygen

Essay
(Extended Constructed Response)

55. There are four major types of organic molecules that are important in living things; these are carbohydrates, lipids, proteins, and nucleic acids. Select any two and, for each one chosen, describe the structure of the molecule and state two ways that the molecule is useful to living organisms.

ENZYMES

Role of Enzymes

Chemical reactions occur continuously in living things. Each reaction requires the presence of a special protein called an **enzyme**, which regulates the rate of the reaction. In general, enzymes speed up the rate of a reaction. Enzymes are **catalysts**, substances that change the rate of a chemical reaction but are themselves unchanged by the reaction.

Enzymes are named after their *substrates*, the substances they act on. The name of an enzyme generally ends in *ase*. For example, a lipase acts on lipids, a protease acts on proteins, and maltase acts on the sugar maltose.

Enzyme Structure

An enzyme is a large, complex protein that consists of one or more polypeptide chains. In addition to the protein, some enzymes contain a nonprotein component called a coenzyme. If the coenzyme part is missing, the enzyme will not function. *Vitamins* often function as coenzymes.

The polypeptide chains that make up an enzyme are folded in a highly specific way, forming pockets on the enzyme surface into which the substrate molecule or molecules fit. The specific part of the enzyme where the substrate fits is called the *active site*.

Lock-and-Key Model of Enzyme Action

The mechanism of enzyme action can be explained on the basis of a lock-and-key model. The active site on an enzyme has a unique three-dimensional shape that can form a complex only with one type of substrate. The substrate fits an active site as a key fits a lock (Figure 1-4).

For an enzyme to affect the rate of a chemical reaction, the substrate must become attached to the active site of the enzyme, forming an *enzyme-substrate complex*. The enzyme's action occurs while the enzyme and substrate are bound to-

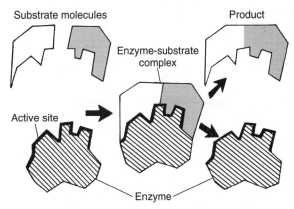

Figure 1-4. The lock-and-key model of enzyme action.

gether. At this time, bonds of the substrate may be weakened, causing it to break apart, or bonds may form between substrate molecules, joining them together. After the reaction is complete, the enzyme and product(s) separate, and the enzyme molecule becomes available to act on other substrate molecules.

Factors Influencing Enzyme Action

The rate of enzyme action is affected by temperature, concentrations of enzyme and substrate, and pH.

Temperature. The rate of enzyme action varies with temperature. Up to a point, the rate increases with increasing temperature (Figure 1-5). The temperature at which the enzyme functions most efficiently is called the optimum temperature. If the temperature is raised above the optimum, the rate of enzyme action begins to decrease. The decrease in enzyme action occurs because the higher temperature destroys the three-dimensional shape of the enzyme protein. In this process, known as *denaturation*, the shape of the enzyme's active site is altered so that it no longer fits the substrate. In humans, the normal

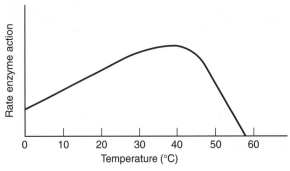

Figure 1-5. The effect of changing temperature on the rate of enzyme action.

body temperature of about 37°C is also the optimum temperature for most human enzymes. Denaturation of these enzymes begins at about 40°C, upsetting the body's homeostasis.

Enzyme and Substrate Concentrations.

The rate of enzyme action varies with the amount of available substrate. With a high concentration of enzyme and a low concentration of substrate, the rate of enzyme action increases as the substrate concentration increases (Figure 1-6). At the point where all enzyme molecules are reacting, the rate levels off, and addition of more substrate has no further effect.

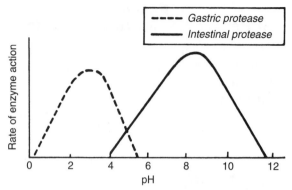

Figure 1-8. The effect of pH on the rate of enzyme action.

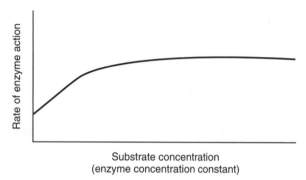

Figure 1-6. The effect of changing substrate concentration on the rate of enzyme action.

pH.

The rate of enzyme action varies with the pH of the environment. The **pH** scale is a measure of the hydrogen ion (H^+) concentration of a solution. Solutions with a pH of 7 are neutral. Those with a pH below 7 are acids, while those with a pH above 7 are bases (Figure 1-7).

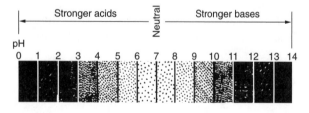

Figure 1-7. The pH scale ranges from acidic to basic.

Each enzyme has a particular pH at which it functions most efficiently. For example, most enzymes in human blood function best in neutral solutions. However, pepsin, an enzyme in the stomach, works best at a pH of 2 (a very high **acidity** level), and trypsin, an enzyme in the small intestine, works best at a pH of 8 (Figure 1-8).

Questions

Multiple Choice

56. Which of the following is characteristic of an enzyme? (1) It is an inorganic catalyst. (2) It is destroyed after each chemical reaction. (3) It provides energy for any chemical reaction. (4) It regulates the rate of a specific chemical reaction.

57. The "lock-and-key" model of enzyme action illustrates that a particular enzyme molecule will (1) form a permanent enzyme-substrate complex (2) be destroyed and resynthesized several times (3) interact with a specific type of substrate molecule (4) react at identical rates under all conditions

58. An enzyme-substrate complex may result from the interaction of molecules of (1) glucose and lipase (2) fat and amylase (3) sucrose and maltase (4) protein and protease

59. The part of the enzyme molecule into which the substrate fits is called the (1) active site (2) coenzyme (3) polypeptide (4) protease

60. A nonprotein molecule necessary for the functioning of a particular enzyme is called a (1) catalyst (2) polypeptide (3) coenzyme (4) substrate

61. Which of the following variables has the *least* direct effect on the rate of an enzyme-regulated reaction? (1) temperature (2) pH (3) carbon dioxide concentration (4) enzyme concentration

Base your answers to questions 62 through 64 on the following graph and on your knowledge of biology. The graph represents the rate of enzyme action when different concentrations of enzyme are added to a system with a fixed amount of substrate.

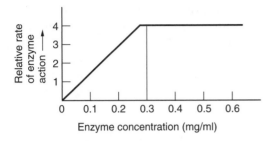
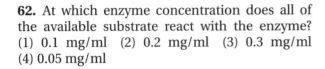
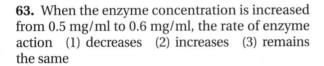
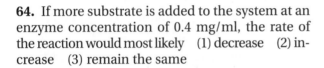
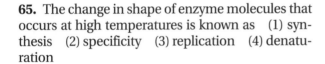

62. At which enzyme concentration does all of the available substrate react with the enzyme? (1) 0.1 mg/ml   (2) 0.2 mg/ml   (3) 0.3 mg/ml (4) 0.05 mg/ml

63. When the enzyme concentration is increased from 0.5 mg/ml to 0.6 mg/ml, the rate of enzyme action (1) decreases   (2) increases   (3) remains the same

64. If more substrate is added to the system at an enzyme concentration of 0.4 mg/ml, the rate of the reaction would most likely   (1) decrease   (2) increase   (3) remain the same

65. The change in shape of enzyme molecules that occurs at high temperatures is known as   (1) synthesis   (2) specificity   (3) replication   (4) denaturation

Base your answers to questions 66 and 67 on the following graphs. Graph I shows the relationship between temperature and the relative rates of activity of enzymes *A* and *B*. Graph II shows the relationship between pH and the relative rates of activity of enzymes *A* and *B*.

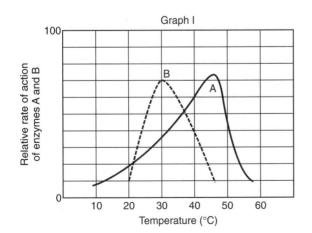

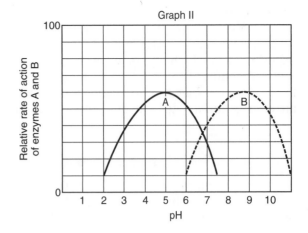

66. Under which conditions is enzyme *A* most effective?   (1) at 40°C and a pH of 5   (2) at 45°C and a pH of 5   (3) at 45°C and a pH of 9   (4) at 50°C and a pH of 9

67. The optimum environment for enzyme *B* is (1) a basic medium   (2) an acidic medium (3) either an acidic or a basic medium   (4) a neutral medium

Short Answer
(Constructed Response)

68. Draw a diagram in which you show how the enzyme maltase combines with two glucose molecules to form maltose. Label the enzyme, substrate, enzyme-substrate complex, and end product.

Use your knowledge of enzymes and biology to answer questions 69 and 70. Write your answers in complete sentences.

69. Fresh pineapple contains an enzyme that digests proteins. Adding fresh pineapple to gelatin (a protein) prevents it from setting or jelling. Adding cooked or canned pineapple does not have this effect and the gelatin can set normally. Explain why these different effects occur.

70. When an apple is cut open, the inside soon turns brown. This is because enzymes that are released from the cut cells react with certain molecules in the apple. Rubbing lemon juice (which contains citric acid) on the cut apple prevents it from browning. Explain why this is so.

Essay
(Extended Constructed Response)

71. The enzyme catalase is found in almost all living tissues. This enzyme catalyzes the breakdown of harmful hydrogen peroxide in the body.

Liver tissue is particularly rich in catalase content. Like all enzymes, catalase is affected by temperature fluctuations. Design and describe an experiment in which a person can study the activity of catalase over a range of temperatures, from 0°C to 80°C. Be sure to include an appropriate control and a data table in your experimental design.

Reading Comprehension

Base your answers to questions 72 through 75 on the information below and on your knowledge of biology. Source: *Science News* (March 25, 2000): vol. 157, no. 13, p. 207.

Coagulation Factor XI Boosts Clot Risk

Coagulation factors are proteins that guide the thinning and clotting of the blood. Their simple names—many are known only by Roman numerals—belie their importance and the specificity of their roles. One of them, factor XI, contributes to the formation of the enzyme thrombin, which in turn helps make a protein called fibrin, a key clotting agent in the blood.

Dutch researchers now report in the March 9 New England Journal of Medicine that people who have had a major blood clot in a vein—a condition called deep venous thrombosis—are about twice as likely as healthy people to harbor high concentrations of factor XI. Comparing 473 clot patients with 474 healthy participants matched for age and other characteristics, the researchers found that 92 of the patients but only 47 of the volunteers had factor XI concentrations exceeding 121 percent of normal.

Deep venous thrombosis strikes roughly 1 in 100 elderly people, causing pain and swelling, usually in a leg. These clots aren't the fat-based ones that cause heart attacks. But coagulation-based clots sometimes wind up in the heart, get pumped into the lungs, and clot an artery there—a potentially fatal condition.

Having excessive amounts of factor XI itself may not be enough to lead to such a troublesome clot, says study coauthor Joost C. M. Meijers, a biochemist currently at the Academic Medical Center in Amsterdam. Rather, extra factor XI might combine with other risk factors to result in clots, he says.

Drugs that diminish the activity of factor XI might work to ease clotting without causing side effects—such as bleeding—that complicate current anticlotting drug therapy, Meijers says.

72. What important role does factor XI normally play in the blood-clotting process?

73. What is observed about the levels of factor XI in the blood of people with major blood clots?

74. How might factor XI be involved in the formation of these blood clots in the veins?

75. How might doctors treat people with elevated factor XI levels so that clots do not develop?

CHAPTER 2

Maintenance in Living Things

Most living organisms perform the same life functions. They obtain and process food, and distribute nutrients and other essential materials to the cells. They get rid of wastes produced by cell metabolism. All of the life functions must be regulated.

Different kinds of organisms have specific structures and behavioral patterns that enable them to perform the life functions efficiently within their physical surroundings, or *environment*. These structures and behavioral patterns are called **adaptations**.

NUTRITION

Nutrition includes those activities by which organisms obtain and process food for use by the cells. The cells use **nutrients** from foods for energy, growth, repair, and regulation. Nutrition may be autotrophic or heterotrophic. In **autotrophic** nutrition, the organism can synthesize organic substances (nutrients) from inorganic substances obtained from the environment. In **heterotrophic** nutrition, the organism must ingest needed organic substances from other organisms in the environment.

Photosynthesis
The most common type of autotrophic nutrition is **photosynthesis**, which occurs in all plants and in some **bacteria** and protists (including all **algae**). In photosynthesis, the organism uses carbon dioxide and water taken from the environment and energy from sunlight to synthesize the organic compound glucose. Most of the chemical energy available to living organisms comes directly or indirectly from photosynthesis. Also, most of the oxygen in the air comes from photosynthesis.

Photosynthetic Pigments.
Photosynthesis requires the presence of certain colored substances called *pigments*, which "trap" light energy and convert it to a form of chemical energy that can

be used by living things. *Chlorophylls* are the green photosynthetic pigments found in photosynthetic organisms. In most of these organisms, the chlorophyll is found in organelles called chloroplasts (Figure 2-1). In addition to the chlorophylls, chloroplasts may contain a variety of other pigments.

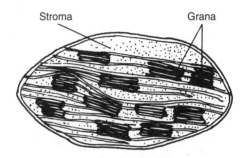

Figure 2-1. Structure of a chloroplast.

Chemistry of Photosynthesis.
The process of photosynthesis is complex, involving several series of reactions. However, it can be summarized by the following equation:

$$\text{carbon dioxide} + \text{water} \xrightarrow[\substack{\text{chlorophyll} \\ \text{enzymes}}]{\text{light energy}} \text{glucose} + \text{water} + \text{oxygen}$$

Carbon dioxide and water are the raw materials of photosynthesis. Light energy absorbed by the chlorophyll is converted to chemical energy, which is used to synthesize glucose from the raw materials. Water and oxygen are released as waste products of photosynthesis.

The glucose produced by photosynthesis is used, when needed, as an energy source in cellular respiration. It can also be converted to starch, an insoluble food storage compound. Before starch can be used in any cellular process, it must first be broken down by enzymes within the cell to glucose. The glucose can be used in the synthesis of other organic compounds, such as lipids and proteins.

Questions

Multiple Choice

1. By which process are CO_2 and H_2O converted to carbohydrates?   (1) transpiration   (2) respiration   (3) fermentation   (4) photosynthesis

2. The conversion of light energy into chemical bond energy occurs within the cells of   (1) molds   (2) yeasts   (3) algae   (4) grasshoppers

3. Glucose molecules may be stored in plants in the form of   (1) oxygen   (2) starch   (3) nucleic acids   (4) amino acids

4. Knowing that red glass transmits mainly red light, green glass mainly green light, yellow glass mainly yellow light, and orange glass mainly orange light, a student set up an experiment to determine the effect of light color on glucose production. She selected jars of each of the above colors and grew a bean plant in each jar under controlled conditions in the presence of natural light. The greatest amount of glucose would most likely be produced by the bean plant growing in the jar whose color was   (1) red   (2) yellow   (3) green   (4) orange

5. Organisms capable of manufacturing organic molecules from inorganic raw materials are classified as   (1) autotrophs   (2) heterotrophs   (3) aerobes   (4) anaerobes

6. The basic raw materials for photosynthesis are   (1) water and carbon dioxide   (2) oxygen and water   (3) sugar and carbon dioxide   (4) carbon dioxide and oxygen

7. Which word equation represents the process of photosynthesis?
(1) carbon dioxide + water → glucose + oxygen + water
(2) glucose → alcohol + carbon dioxide
(3) maltose + water → glucose + glucose
(4) glucose + oxygen → carbon dioxide + water

8. Autotrophic activity in plant cells is most closely associated with the organelles called   (1) mitochondria   (2) ribosomes   (3) vacuoles   (4) chloroplasts

9. In terms of nutrition, the functional difference between animals and plants is that green plants are able to   (1) synthesize glucose   (2) break down carbohydrates   (3) carry on aerobic respiration   (4) form ATP molecules

Short Answer
(Constructed Response)

Use the following information and your knowledge of biology to answer question 10.

10. Bromthymol blue turns to bromthymol yellow in the presence of carbon dioxide. When the carbon dioxide is removed, the solution returns to a blue color. Two green water plants were placed in separate test tubes, each containing water and bromthymol yellow. Both test tubes were corked. One tube was placed in the light, the other in the dark. After several days, the liquid in the tube exposed to the light turned blue. In a complete sentence, explain the results of this demonstration. What does it illustrate about the activity of plants during photosynthesis? What do you think occurred in the tube that was placed in the dark?

Use the information below and your knowledge of biology to answer question 11.

11. A suspension of chloroplasts from spinach leaves was kept under a bright light at a temperature of 25°C. Another suspension was kept in a dark corner of the same room. Each container had attached to it a small pipette by which the amount of oxygen released by the chloroplasts could be measured. The data table shows the volume of oxygen produced by each suspension over a 24-hour period.

Total Volume Oxygen Produced by Chloroplast Suspension (mL)

Time (hours)	Incubated in Light	Incubated in Dark
0	0.00	0.00
6	0.42	0.01
12	0.96	0.01
18	1.78	0.01
24	2.36	0.01

a) Describe the difference recorded in the amount of oxygen produced by the two chloroplast suspensions.
b) Explain the reason for the difference observed in the volume of oxygen produced by the two chloroplast suspensions.
c) Give a scientifically reasonable explanation for why the chloroplasts incubated in the dark produced just 0.01 mL of oxygen.
d) On a sheet of graph paper, make a line graph showing the results of the experiment. Use different colors to plot the data for each of the two suspensions.
e) State one change in the experimental procedure that would provide more reliable results.

Essay
(Extended Constructed Response)

12. Describe the roles of light, chlorophyll, carbon dioxide, and water in the process of photosynthesis.

13. Photosynthesis can be called one of the most important processes that occurs on Earth. In a paragraph or two, justify this statement citing specific examples where appropriate.

Adaptations for Photosynthesis

Algae and green plants are autotrophic organisms that carry on photosynthesis. A large percentage of Earth's photosynthesis occurs in unicellular algae present in the oceans. The raw materials necessary for photosynthesis are absorbed directly from the water into the cells of the algae. Most photosynthesis in terrestrial (land-dwelling) plants occurs in leaves.

Structure of Leaves. Most leaves are thin and flat, providing the maximum surface area for the absorption of light. The outermost cell layer of the leaf is the *epidermis*, which protects the internal tissues from water loss, mechanical injury, and attack by fungi (Figure 2-2). In some plants, the epidermis is covered by a waxy coating, called the cuticle, which provides additional protection against water loss and infection.

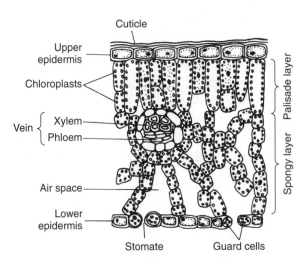

Figure 2-2. Cross section of a typical leaf.

There are many tiny openings in the epidermis and cuticle, mainly on the undersurface of the leaf. These openings, called stomates, allow the exchange of carbon dioxide, oxygen, and water vapor between the environment and the moist, inner tissues of the leaf. Each stomate is surrounded by a pair of chloroplast-containing guard cells. By changing shape, the guard cells open or close the stomate opening.

Beneath the upper epidermis is the *palisade layer*, which is made up of tall, tightly packed cells filled with chloroplasts. Most of the photosynthetic activity of the leaf occurs in this layer. The cells of the epidermis are clear, so that light striking the leaf passes through to the chloroplasts in the palisade layer.

Between the palisade layer and the lower epidermis of the leaf is the *spongy layer*, which is made up of loosely arranged cells separated by interconnecting air spaces. The air spaces are continuous with the stomates. Gases from the environment enter the leaf through the stomates and diffuse from the air spaces into the cells. Other gases diffuse out of the cells into the air spaces and then out of the leaf through the stomates. The cells of the spongy layer contain chloroplasts and carry on some photosynthesis.

The conducting tissues of the leaf are found in bundles called *veins*. The conducting tissues carry water and dissolved minerals from the roots through the stems to the leaves, and they carry food from the leaves to the rest of the plant.

Questions

Multiple Choice

14. Water is lost from the leaves of a plant through (1) spongy cells (2) root hairs (3) veins (4) stomates

15. The waxy covering over the surface of a leaf is the (1) cuticle (2) epidermis (3) palisade layer (4) spongy layer

Base your answers to questions 16 through 19 on the following diagram, which shows a leaf cross section, and on your knowledge of biology.

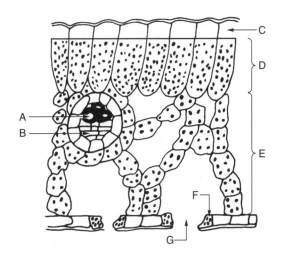

16. Which letter indicates the principal region of food manufacture? (1) *E* (2) *B* (3) *C* (4) *D*

17. Which letter indicates the area where carbon dioxide passes out of the leaf? (1) *A* (2) *G* (3) *C* (4) *D*

18. Which letter indicates a structure that regulates the size of a stomate? (1) *A* (2) *B* (3) *F* (4) *G*

19. Water and dissolved nutrients are carried by the tissues labeled (1) *D* and *E* (2) *C* and *D* (3) *A* and *B* (4) *E* and *F*

Short Answer
(Constructed Response)

Refer to the following diagrams of three different leaf types to answer question 20.

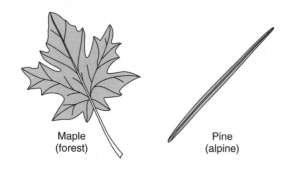

Maple
(forest)

Pine
(alpine)

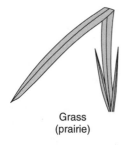

Grass
(prairie)

20. How is each leaf adapted to carry out photosynthesis in the particular habitat in which the plant lives? (See diagrams for typical habitat of each leaf type.) State one adaptation for each leaf.

21. A woman placed one of her tropical houseplants outside on her porch during the summer to receive some natural sunshine. A few days later, a rubbish fire broke out in a nearby vacant lot, spreading soot all over the neighborhood. Within two weeks, the plant's leaves started to turn yellow and drop off the stem. In one or two complete sentences, give two scientifically valid explanations of how the soot may have negatively affected the plant.

Essay
(Extended Constructed Response)

22. In a brief paragraph, explain why a cactus's leaves are not broad and flat but are reduced in size to the form of spines.

23. How is the typical leaf adapted for carrying out photosynthesis? Include the roles of the parts of a leaf in your answer.

Heterotrophic Nutrition

Organisms that cannot synthesize organic molecules from inorganic raw materials are *heterotrophs* and must obtain preformed organic molecules from the environment. Heterotrophic organisms include most bacteria, some protists, and all **fungi** and animals. Heterotrophic nutrition involves the processes of ingestion, digestion, and egestion. It generally begins with the mechanical breakdown of food, during which large pieces of food are broken down into smaller pieces by cutting, grinding, and tearing. The smaller pieces provide greater surface area for the action of enzymes during chemical digestion.

Digestion. In some heterotrophs, chemical digestion is *intracellular*—it occurs within the cell (or cells) of the organism. In most heterotrophs, however, digestion is *extracellular*—it occurs in a sac or a tube outside the cells. The end products of digestion are then absorbed into the cells.

Adaptations for Heterotrophic Nutrition

Heterotrophs obtain nutrients in a variety of ways.

Protists. In protists, such as the ameba and paramecium, digestion is intracellular. In the ameba, food particles are surrounded and engulfed by extensions of the cell called *pseudopods*. This process is known as *phagocytosis*. Within the cell, the food particle is enclosed in a food vacuole. In the paramecium, food particles are ingested through a fixed opening called the oral groove. They are moved into this opening by the beating of tiny "hairs" called *cilia*. The food particles are then enclosed in a food vacuole, which circulates in the cytoplasm (Figure 2-3).

In both the ameba and paramecium, the food vacuole merges with a *lysosome*, which is an organelle that contains digestive enzymes. The food within the vacuole is digested by these enzymes,

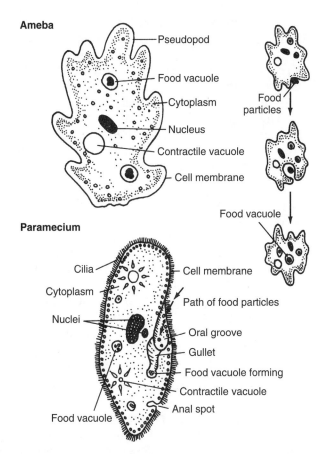

Ameba

- Pseudopod
- Food vacuole
- Cytoplasm
- Nucleus
- Contractile vacuole
- Cell membrane

Food particles

Food vacuole

Paramecium

- Cilia
- Cytoplasm
- Nuclei
- Cell membrane
- Path of food particles
- Oral groove
- Gullet
- Food vacuole forming
- Contractile vacuole
- Anal spot
- Food vacuole

Figure 2-3. Nutrition in ameba and paramecium.

and the end products of digestion are then absorbed into the cytoplasm. In the ameba, wastes are expelled from the cell through the cell membrane. In the paramecium, wastes are expelled through a fixed opening called the anal pore.

Humans. The human digestive system is essentially like that of most other **multicellular** (many-celled) animals. Food moves in one direction through a tube, and specialized organs carry out its mechanical breakdown and chemical digestion.

Questions

Multiple Choice

24. Based on their pattern of nutrition, all animals are classified as (1) autotrophic (2) heterotrophic (3) photosynthetic (4) phagocytic

25. Digestion that occurs in a sac or a tube is referred to as (1) phagocytic (2) intracellular (3) extracellular (4) heterotrophic

26. A fruit fly is classified as a heterotroph, rather than as an autotroph, because it is unable to (1) transport needed materials throughout its body (2) release energy from organic molecules (3) manufacture its own food (4) divide its cells mitotically

27. The principal function of mechanical digestion is the (1) storage of food molecules in the liver (2) production of more surface area for enzyme action (3) synthesis of enzymes necessary for food absorption (4) breakdown of large molecules to smaller ones by the addition of water

28. In the paramecium, most intracellular digestion occurs within structures known as (1) ribosomes (2) endoplasmic reticula (3) mitochondria (4) food vacuoles

29. Which organism ingests food by engulfing it with pseudopods? (1) grasshopper (2) paramecium (3) ameba (4) earthworm

Short Answer
(Constructed Response)

30. In one or two complete sentences, explain how mechanical digestion aids the process of chemical digestion.

31. Briefly define intracellular digestion and extracellular digestion.

32. Use the information below and your knowledge of biology and experimental procedures to answer the following questions.

A student performed an experiment to determine the rate of digestion by protease (a protein-digesting enzyme) on cooked egg white. He set up three sets of six test tubes each. Into the first set, he placed the same amount of water and pepsin plus two grams of cooked egg white into each test tube. The egg white was left in one piece in each tube. To the second set, he added the same amounts of water, pepsin, and egg white, but this time he cut the two grams of egg white into eight small pieces before placing it into each test tube. The third set of test tubes also received the same amounts of water, pepsin, and egg white, but the egg white was finely chopped up before being placed into each test tube.

a) What hypothesis was the student most likely testing?
b) Predict what should occur in each setup and give a scientifically valid explanation for your prediction.
c) The student omitted a control in his experiment. Describe an appropriate control that could be used in conducting this investigation.

TRANSPORT

Transport involves the absorption of materials through an organism's cell membranes and into its body fluids, and the circulation of materials throughout its body.

The Cell Membrane

The cell membrane surrounds the cell and regulates the passage of materials into and out of the cell.

Structure of the Cell Membrane. The currently accepted model of the structure of the cell membrane is called the *fluid mosaic model*. According to this model, the cell membrane consists of a double layer of lipid in which large protein molecules float (Figure 2-4).

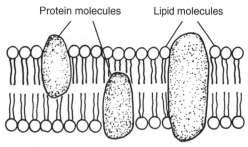

Protein molecules   Lipid molecules

Figure 2-4. The fluid mosaic model of cell membrane structure.

Function of the Cell Membrane. The cell membrane selectively regulates the passage of substances into and out of the cell. Small molecules, including water, carbon dioxide, oxygen, and the soluble end products of digestion, pass easily through the cell membrane. Most larger molecules, such as proteins and starch, cannot pass through the cell membrane. However, molecular size is not the only factor that affects passage through the cell membrane.

Diffusion and Passive Transport

All ions and molecules are in constant, random motion. When such particles collide, they bounce off each other and travel in new directions. As a result of their motion and collisions, the particles tend to spread out from an area of high concentration to an area of low concentration, a process known as **diffusion**. The difference in concentration between two such areas is known as the *concentration gradient.*

Molecules and ions that can pass through a cell membrane tend to move into or out of the cell by diffusion. The direction of diffusion depends on the relative concentration of the substance in-

side and outside the cell and usually results in a balance, or **equilibrium**, in the substance's concentration. Diffusion is a type of *passive transport*; it occurs because of the kinetic energy of the molecules and ions and does not require the use of additional energy by the cell.

The diffusion of water through a membrane is called *osmosis*. In osmosis, water molecules move from a region of higher concentration of water to a region of lower concentration of water until they reach an equilibrium.

Active Transport

Processes that require **active transport** involve the movement of particles through a membrane with the use of energy by the cell. In some cases, substances are moved by active transport from a region of lower concentration to a region of higher concentration (against the concentration gradient). In active transport, protein molecules embedded in the cell membrane act as carriers that aid in the transport of materials across the membrane.

Pinocytosis and Phagocytosis

Large, dissolved molecules can pass through a cell membrane by the process of pinocytosis (Figure 2-5). In pinocytosis, the cell membrane folds inward. The outer surface of the cell membrane then closes over, and the large molecule is enclosed in a vacuole inside the cell. In contrast, phagocytosis is the process by which a cell engulfs large, undissolved particles by flowing around them and enclosing them in a vacuole. For example, amebas engulf food particles by phagocytosis (with their pseudopods).

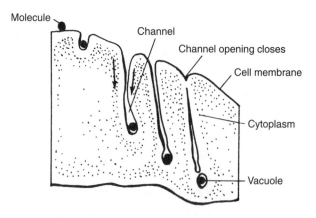

Molecule
Channel
Channel opening closes
Cell membrane
Cytoplasm
Vacuole

Figure 2-5. Pinocytosis.

Circulation

Circulation involves the movement of materials both within cells and throughout multicellular organisms. The movement of materials within a cell, *intracellular circulation*, takes place by diffusion and by *cyclosis*. Cyclosis is the natural streaming of cytoplasm that occurs within all cells. Intracellular circulation may also involve the movement of materials through the channels of the endoplasmic reticulum. The transport of materials throughout multicellular organisms is called *intercellular circulation*. Depending on the complexity of the organism, intercellular circulation may occur by diffusion or it may involve a specialized circulatory system with conducting, or vascular, tissues.

Questions

Multiple Choice

33. Which process would describe the movement of sugar molecules through a membrane from a region of higher concentration to a region of lower concentration? (1) osmosis (2) cyclosis (3) passive transport (4) active transport

34. In the human body, the potassium ion can pass easily through cell membranes, yet the potassium ion concentration is higher inside many cells than it is outside these cells. This condition is mainly the result of (1) passive transport (2) active transport (3) osmosis (4) pinocytosis

35. Chemical analysis indicates that the cell membrane is composed mainly of (1) proteins and starch (2) proteins and cellulose (3) lipids and starch (4) lipids and proteins

36. The flow of materials through the membrane of a cell against the concentration gradient is known as (1) passive transport (2) active transport (3) osmosis (4) pinocytosis

37. A biologist observed a plant cell in a drop of water and illustrated it as in diagram *A*. He added a 10% salt solution to the slide, observed the cell, and illustrated it as in diagram *B*. The change in appearance of the cell resulted from more (1) salt flowing out of the cell than into the cell (2) salt flowing into the cell than out of the cell (3) water flowing into the cell than out of the cell (4) water flowing out of the cell than into the cell

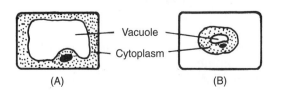

(A)   (B)

Vacuole
Cytoplasm

38. The natural streaming of the cytoplasm that occurs within all cells is called (1) pinocytosis (2) phagocytosis (3) osmosis (4) cyclosis

39. When a cell uses energy to move materials across its membrane, the process is known as (1) osmosis (2) active transport (3) diffusion (4) passive transport

40. The diffusion of water molecules into and out of cells is called (1) cyclosis (2) pinocytosis (3) osmosis (4) active transport

41. The net movement of molecules into cells is most dependent on the (1) selectivity of the cell membrane (2) selectivity of the cell wall (3) number of vacuoles (4) number of chromosomes

42. A red blood cell placed in distilled water will swell and burst due to the diffusion of (1) salt from the red blood cell into the water (2) water into the red blood cell (3) water from the blood cell into its environment (4) salt from the water into the red blood cell

Base your answers to questions 43 and 44 on your knowledge of biology and on the diagram below, which illustrates a process by which protein molecules may enter a cell.

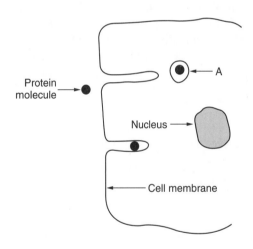

Protein molecule

A

Nucleus

Cell membrane

43. Which process is illustrated in this diagram? (1) pinocytosis (2) osmosis (3) diffusion (4) passive transport

44. Structure *A* is most likely a (1) ribosome (2) mitochondrion (3) nucleolus (4) vacuole

45. The process by which amebas ingest food particles is called (1) pinocytosis (2) osmosis (3) phagocytosis (4) cyclosis

Short Answer
(Constructed Response)

46. In two or more complete sentences, describe the differences between active transport and passive transport. Give one example of each type of transport.

Use the information in the paragraph and table below to answer question 47.

47. A biology student was attempting to determine the percent of water present in the cells of elodea (an aquatic plant). She placed leaves of elodea in varying concentrations of saltwater solutions and observed when plasmolysis (cell shrinking) occurred. The table summarizes the results of her experiment.

Solution Concentration	Observed Plasmolysis
0.5% NaCl	None
1.0% NaCl	None
1.5% NaCl	None
2.0% NaCl	Very slight
2.5% NaCl	Pronounced
3.0% NaCl	Pronounced

a) According to the data in the table, what percent of elodea cells is water? In a full sentence, explain how you arrived at this conclusion.

b) Give a scientifically valid explanation for what caused the cells to shrink at a certain concentration of salt water. What process causes plasmolysis of the cells?

Essay
(Extended Constructed Response)

48. Research and describe some circumstances in which human body cells perform active transport.

49. Freshwater protozoa (one-celled organisms) live in an environment that is very close to 100% water. The inside of the cell (cytoplasm) is about 90% water. Explain the problem these protozoans face in their environment with respect to maintaining homeostasis. Describe how they are adapted to deal with the problem.

Transport in Plants

The transport of materials in plants involves cyclosis, osmosis, diffusion, and active transport. Some plants contain specialized transport, or *vascular*, tissues while others do not.

Roots. Roots are structures that are specialized for the absorption of water and minerals from the soil and the conduction of these materials to the

stem. Roots also anchor the plant in the soil and may contain stored nutrients in the form of starch.

The surface area of the root is increased (for greater absorption) by the presence of *root hairs* just behind the growing tip (Figure 2-6). Water and minerals from the soil are absorbed through the membranes of the root hairs by osmosis, diffusion, and active transport. Materials are transported throughout the plant by two kinds of vascular tissues, *xylem* and *phloem*.

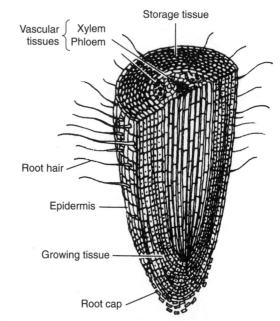

Figure 2-6. Structure of a root tip.

Stems.   Although the structure of stems is more complex than that of roots, the xylem and phloem of the stem are continuous with the xylem and phloem of the roots.

Leaves.   The xylem and phloem of the leaves, which are in bundles called veins, are also continuous with the xylem and phloem of the roots and stem.

Transport in Protists

Protists and other unicellular organisms have no specialized transport system. Materials enter and leave the cell by diffusion and active transport, and are circulated within the cell by diffusion and cyclosis (Figure 2-7).

Transport in Animals

Simple multicellular animals, whose cells are in direct contact with the surrounding water, have no specialized transport system. All other (that is, more complex) multicellular animals do have a specialized system for the transport of materials.

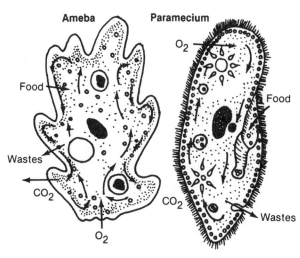

Figure 2-7. Transport in ameba and paramecium.

Humans. The human circulatory system is a closed system. Blood is moved through vessels by the pumping action of the heart (Figure 2-8). Human blood contains the pigment *hemoglobin*, which carries oxygen to the body tissues.

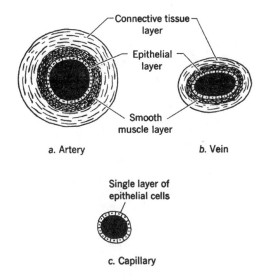

Figure 2-8. The three types of blood vessels.

Questions

Multiple Choice

50. The primary function of the root hairs in a plant is to (1) prevent excessive loss of water (2) provide increased surface area for absorption (3) conduct water and minerals upward (4) conduct organic food materials upward and downward

51. Which structures are found in the veins of a maple leaf? (1) phloem cells (2) guard cells (3) chloroplasts (4) capillaries

52. A circulatory system in which the blood remains within vessels is called (1) a closed circulatory system (2) an open circulatory system (3) an internal circulatory system (4) an external circulatory system

Short Answer
(Constructed Response)

53. The epidermal (outermost) cells of a plant's roots can continue to absorb water even when the concentration of water in the soil is very low, even lower than that in its cells. In one or two full sentences, explain the biological process that enables the root epidermal cells to do this.

54. In two or three complete sentences, compare and contrast the circulatory systems of a protist and a human. How are protists able to transport materials? How do humans transport materials?

RESPIRATION

The life processes of all organisms require energy. There is potential energy in the chemical bonds of organic molecules such as glucose. However, this energy cannot be used directly in cell metabolism. During cellular respiration, these bonds are broken and the energy that is released is temporarily stored in the bonds of the energy-transfer compound ATP (adenosine triphosphate). This process occurs continuously in the cells of all organisms.

Cellular Respiration

Cellular respiration involves a series of enzyme-controlled reactions in which the energy released by the breakdown of the chemical bonds in glucose is transferred to the high-energy bonds of ATP. When ATP is broken down by hydrolysis (the addition of water), ADP (adenosine diphosphate) and phosphate (P) are produced, and energy is released for use by the cell.

The conversion of ATP to ADP is a reversible reaction catalyzed by the enzyme ATP-ase. In living organisms, ATP is constantly being converted to ADP, and the energy released is used for the reactions of cell metabolism. The ADP is then converted back to ATP by the reactions of cellular respiration.

$$H_2O + ATP \underset{\text{ATP-ase}}{\overrightarrow{\hspace{2cm}}} ADP + P + \text{energy}$$

Anaerobic Respiration. In most organisms, cellular respiration requires the presence of free oxygen, and the process is known as *aerobic respiration*. In a few kinds of organisms, free oxygen is not used, and the process is known as *anaerobic respiration*, or *fermentation*. Some cells, such as muscle cells, which normally carry on aerobic respiration, can carry on anaerobic respiration in the absence of oxygen. Other cells, such as yeast and some bacteria, which carry on anaerobic respiration, lack the enzymes necessary for aerobic respiration. There is a net gain of only two ATP molecules for each molecule of glucose used in anaerobic respiration.

Aerobic Respiration. In aerobic respiration, glucose is broken down completely to carbon dioxide and water by a series of enzyme-controlled reactions. These reactions, which take place mainly in the mitochondria, produce a net gain of 36 ATP molecules.

$$\text{glucose} + \text{oxygen} \xrightarrow{\text{enzymes}} \text{water} + \text{carbon dioxide} + ATP$$

$$C_6H_{12}O_6 + 6O_2 \xrightarrow{\text{enzymes}} 6H_2O + 6CO_2 + 36\ ATP$$

Adaptations for Respiration

The oxygen used in aerobic cellular respiration comes from the environment, and the carbon dioxide produced must be excreted into the environment. Although the chemical processes of respiration are similar in most organisms, living things show a variety of adaptations for the exchange of these respiratory gases.

Protists. In simple organisms, such as protists, all or most of the cells are in direct contact with the environment. So the exchange of respiratory gases takes place by diffusion through the thin, moist cell membranes (Figure 2-9).

Plants. In plants, respiratory gases are exchanged through the leaves, stems, and roots. The exchange of respiratory gases occurs by diffusion through the cell membranes of internal cells, which are surrounded by intercellular spaces. The intercellular spaces open to the environment through the stomates, openings on the undersurface of the leaf.

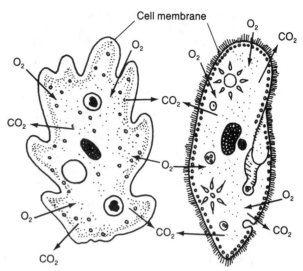

Figure 2-9. Respiration in ameba and paramecium.

Humans. In humans, the exchange of respiratory gases takes places at thin, moist membranes within the lungs. Hemoglobin aids in the transport of oxygen in the blood. Carbon dioxide and oxygen are carried between the respiratory surface in the lungs and the environment by a system of air tubes.

Questions

Multiple Choice

55. Most animals make energy available for cell activity by transferring the potential energy of glucose to ATP. This process occurs during (1) aerobic respiration only (2) anaerobic respiration only (3) both aerobic and anaerobic respiration (4) neither aerobic nor anaerobic respiration

56. In animal cells, the energy to convert ADP to ATP comes directly from (1) hormones (2) sunlight (3) organic molecules (4) inorganic molecules

57. The organelles in which most of the reactions of aerobic cellular respiration take place are the (1) ribosomes (2) chloroplasts (3) lysosomes (4) mitochondria

58. The substances that most directly control the rate of reaction during cellular respiration are known as (1) enzymes (2) phosphates (3) monosaccharides (4) disaccharides

59. Which end product is of the greatest benefit to the organism in which respiration occurs? (1) glucose (2) carbon dioxide (3) ATP molecules (4) water molecules

Base your answers to questions 60 through 64 on the diagram below, which represents a cellular process in animals, and on your knowledge of biology.

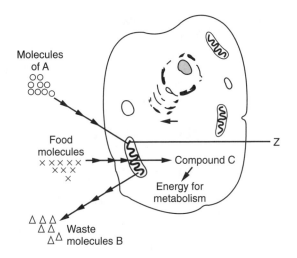

60. The items labeled as food molecules most likely represent (1) starch (2) glucose (3) phosphate (4) chlorophyll

61. Compound *C* most likely represents some molecules of (1) oxygen (2) glucose (3) ATP (4) DNA

62. If this cell is carrying on aerobic respiration, *B* represents molecules of a waste product known as (1) carbon dioxide (2) ATP (3) ethyl alcohol (4) phosphate

63. If this represents a kidney cell from the human body, the molecules of *A* are most probably (1) carbon dioxide (2) enzymes (3) lipids (4) oxygen

64. The cell organelle labeled *Z* is called a (1) chloroplast (2) mitochondrion (3) nucleolus (4) vacuole

65. Protists obtain oxygen from their environment through (1) stomates (2) cell membranes (3) vacuoles (4) mitochondria

66. In humans, respiratory gases are exchanged between the lungs and the environment through (1) air tubes (2) hemoglobin (3) vacuoles (4) stomates

Short Answer
(Constructed Response)

67. In one or two full sentences, explain why all organisms must carry out cellular respiration.

Base your answers to question 68 on the following information and on your knowledge of biology.

68. A biologist was culturing some muscle cells from a mouse (an aerobic organism) in a petri dish. He was interested in measuring the amount of ATP produced by the muscle cells when the cells were supplied with glucose. At the beginning of the experiment, the cells were producing large quantities of ATP. He then added a substance called malonic acid to the cell culture, and the amount of ATP produced fell to near zero.

a) Which organelles in the muscle cells were most likely affected by the malonic acid?
b) Why did the ATP production fall to near zero but not actually zero?
c) Propose a testable hypothesis concerning respiration in cells treated with malonic acid.
d) Predict the effect of malonic acid on an anaerobic organism and explain your prediction.

Essay
(Extended Constructed Response)

69. Compare and contrast the process of cellular respiration in anaerobic and aerobic organisms. Discuss the role of oxygen, where the reactions occur, and the net gain of ATP molecules.

EXCRETION

The metabolic activities of living cells produce waste materials. The life process by which the wastes of metabolism are removed from the body is called excretion.

Wastes of Metabolism

The wastes of various metabolic processes are shown in Table 2-1. Some wastes are **toxins** (compounds that are poisonous to body tissues), while other wastes are nontoxic. In animals, toxic wastes are excreted from the body. In plants, toxic wastes are sealed off and stored, sometimes in vacuoles. Some nontoxic wastes are excreted, while others are recycled and used in metabolic activities.

Table 2-1. The Waste Products of Metabolism

Metabolic Activity	Wastes
Respiration	Carbon dioxide and water
Dehydration synthesis	Water
Protein metabolism	Nitrogenous wastes
Certain metabolic processes	Mineral salts

Nitrogenous, or nitrogen-containing, wastes are produced by the breakdown of amino acids. Different kinds of organisms produce different kinds of nitrogenous wastes, including *uric acid*, which is nontoxic; *urea*, which is moderately toxic; and *ammonia*, which is highly toxic.

Adaptations for Excretion

In the simplest organisms, wastes pass from the cells directly into the environment. More complex organisms have a specialized excretory system.

Protists. In general, the excretion of wastes in protists is accomplished by diffusion through the cell membrane (Figure 2-10). In freshwater protozoans, such as the ameba and paramecium, water continuously enters the cell by osmosis. In these organisms, the excess water collects in organelles called *contractile vacuoles*. The contractile vacuoles burst at the surface of the cell, expelling the water back into the environment. This process involves active transport.

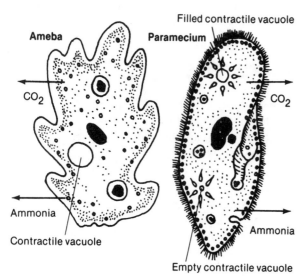

Figure 2-10. Excretion in ameba and paramecium.

In freshwater protozoans, the nitrogenous waste product is ammonia. Although it is very toxic, ammonia is also very soluble in water, and thus it can be easily excreted from the cells of these organisms.

In photosynthetic protists, such as algae, some of the carbon dioxide produced by cellular respiration can be recycled and used in photosynthesis. Some of the oxygen produced by photosynthesis can be used in cellular respiration.

Plants. In plants, as in algae, some of the waste gases produced by photosynthesis and cellular respiration are recycled. Excess gases diffuse out of the plant through stomates on the leaves, tiny openings on the stems, and epidermal cells on the roots.

Humans. In humans, carbon dioxide is excreted by the lungs. Water, salts, and urea are excreted by the kidneys. These waste products are passed out of the body through various specialized tubes, or passageways.

Questions

Multiple Choice

70. Metabolic wastes of animals most likely include   (1) water, carbon dioxide, oxygen, and salts   (2) carbon dioxide, nitrogenous compounds, water, and salts   (3) hormones, water, salts, and oxygen   (4) glucose, carbon dioxide, nitrogenous compounds, and water

71. Which activity would most likely produce nitrogenous waste products?   (1) protein metabolism   (2) glucose metabolism   (3) lipid metabolism   (4) starch metabolism

72. The leaf structures that are closely associated with both respiration and excretion are the (1) root hairs   (2) stomates   (3) waxy surfaces   (4) epidermal cells

73. Protists can function without an organized excretory system because their cells   (1) do not produce wastes   (2) change all wastes into useful substances   (3) remove only solid wastes   (4) are in direct contact with a water environment

74. Which statement best describes the excretion of nitrogenous wastes from paramecia?   (1) Urea is excreted by nephrons.   (2) Uric acid is excreted by nephrons.   (3) Urea is excreted through tiny tubules.   (4) Ammonia is excreted through cell membranes.

75. Most toxic products of plant metabolism are stored in the   (1) stomates   (2) vacuoles   (3) root cells   (4) chloroplasts

76. In freshwater protozoans, the organelles involved in the maintenance of water balance are (1) food vacuoles   (2) mitochondria   (3) contractile vacuoles   (4) pseudopods

Short Answer
(Constructed Response)

77. In one or two complete sentences, explain what job the kidneys perform in maintaining homeostasis in a human.

Base your answer to question 78 on the table below and on your knowledge of biology.

78. The table compares three nitrogenous waste products, their toxicity levels, their solubility in water, and the habitats in which the organisms that produce them typically live.

Type of Waste	Toxicity	Solubility	Habitat of Organism
Ammonia	Very high	Very good	Aquatic (in water)
Urea	Moderate	Good	Land, most generally
Uric acid	Low	None	Land, often desert

a) What connection exists between the habitat of an organism and the toxicity of its nitrogenous waste?

b) What connection exists between the solubility of each nitrogenous waste and its toxicity?

c) Based on your answers to *a* and *b* above, state a possible biological benefit of the connections among waste toxicity, waste solubility, and an organism's habitat.

Essay
(Extended Constructed Response)

79. Organisms produce waste products as a result of their metabolic activities. These wastes include carbon dioxide; water; nitrogenous wastes such as ammonia, urea, and uric acid; and mineral salts. Why must these wastes be removed from an organism? Select any three of the metabolic waste products listed and describe how they are produced in an organism.

REGULATION

Regulation involves the control and **coordination** of life activities. In all organisms, there are chemicals that regulate life activities. In multicellular animals, there is nerve control in addition to chemical control. Both nerve control and chemical control aid organisms in their maintenance of homeostasis.

Nerve Control

Nerve control depends mainly on the functioning of **nerve cells**, or *neurons*, which are specialized for the transmission of impulses from one part of the body to another.

Structure of a Nerve Cell. The three parts of a nerve cell are the *dendrites*; the cell body, or *cyton*; and the *axon* (Figure 2-11). Dendrites are composed of many branches, but the axon has branches mainly at the end that is farthest from the cell body. Impulses are received by the dendrites and passed to the cell body, which contains the nucleus and other organelles. From the cell body, impulses pass along the axon to its terminal (end) branches.

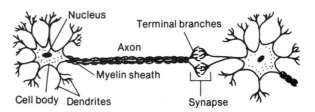

Figure 2-11. Structure of a typical nerve cell.

Impulses. An *impulse* is a region of electrical and chemical, or *electrochemical*, change that travels over the membrane of a nerve cell. When electrochemical impulses reach the terminal branches of an axon, they stimulate the release of chemicals called *neurotransmitters*.

Neurotransmitters and Synapses. The junction between adjacent nerve cells is called a *synapse*. At the synapse, the nerve cells do not touch; there is a small gap between them. When impulses reach the terminal branches of the axon of one nerve cell, they stimulate the release of neurotransmitters, such as acetylcholine, which diffuse across the gap of the synapse. The neurotransmitter stimulates impulses in the dendrites of the second nerve cell. In this way, impulses pass from one nerve cell to another (Figure 2-12, page 26).

The axons of some nerve cells have junctions with a muscle or a gland. In such cases, the chemicals released by the terminal branches of the axon stimulate contraction of the muscle or secretion by the gland.

Stimulus and Receptors. Any change in the external or internal environment that initiates impulses is called a **stimulus** (plural, *stimuli*). Stimuli are detected by specialized structures called **receptors**. Each kind of receptor is sensitive to a particular kind of stimulus; for example, eyes are sensitive to light, ears to sound, and so on.

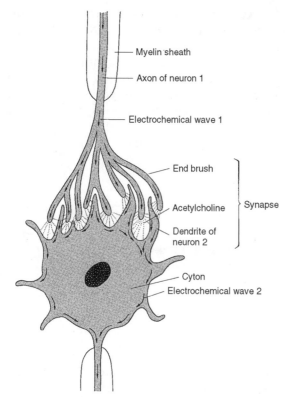

Myelin sheath

Axon of neuron 1

Electrochemical wave 1

End brush

Acetylcholine ⎤
⎬ Synapse
Dendrite of ⎦
neuron 2

Cyton

Electrochemical wave 2

Figure 2-12. Nerve impulses are transmitted from one nerve cell to the next by chemicals that diffuse across the gap (at the synapse).

Responses and Effectors.   The reaction of an organism to a stimulus is called a **response**. The response to a stimulus is carried out by *effectors*, generally the muscles or glands.

Adaptations for Nerve Control

Even the simplest animals have some type of nerve cells that transmit impulses.

Simple Animals.   In some animals, there is no brain, but there is a structure called a *nerve net* that transmits messages throughout the body. In other animals, there is a primitive brain, a *nerve cord* that runs the length of the body, *peripheral nerves* that serve all parts of the body, and in some, sense receptors.

Humans.   Humans have a central nervous system that consists of a highly developed brain and a dorsal (spinal) nerve cord that runs down the back. The central nervous system permits impulses to travel in one direction along definite pathways. There is also a peripheral nervous system that consists of an elaborate network of nerves. The peripheral nervous system carries signals between the central nervous system and all parts of the body. In addition, there are many highly developed sense organs.

Chemical Control

In both plants and animals, various aspects of their life activities are controlled by chemicals called **hormones**.

Plant Hormones.   In plants, there are no organs specialized for the production of hormones. Plant hormones are produced in greatest abundance in the cells of actively growing regions, such as the tips of roots and stems and in buds and seeds. The hormones produced in these regions affect the growth and development of cells in other parts of the plant. The effects of hormones vary with their concentration and with the type of tissue being acted on.

Animal Hormones.   Unlike plants, many animals do have organs specialized for the synthesis and secretion of hormones. These organs, called *endocrine glands,* or ductless glands, release their secretions directly into the bloodstream. Hormones are found in a wide variety of animals, both vertebrates and invertebrates. The animals' metabolic activities, as well as metamorphosis and reproduction, are controlled by various hormones.

Questions

Multiple Choice

80. Animal cells that are specialized for conducting electrochemical impulses are known as (1) nerve cells   (2) synapses   (3) nephrons   (4) neurotransmitters

81. A hawk gliding over a field suddenly dives toward a moving rabbit. The hawk's reaction to the rabbit is known as a   (1) stimulus   (2) synapse   (3) response   (4) impulse

82. The transmission of nerve impulses at synapses involves chemicals called   (1) hormones   (2) neurotransmitters   (3) enzymes   (4) nucleic acids

83. Neurotransmitters, such as acetylcholine, are initially detected by which part of a nerve cell? (1) dendrites   (2) nucleus   (3) terminal branches   (4) mitochondrion

84. The nucleus of a nerve cell is found in the (1) dendrite   (2) axon   (3) synapse   (4) cell body

85. Structures that detect stimuli are called (1) effectors (2) receptors (3) synapses (4) cell bodies

86. The secretions of endocrine glands are known as (1) enzymes (2) hormones (3) pigments (4) neurotransmitters

87. A chemical injected into a tadpole caused the tadpole to undergo rapid metamorphosis into a frog. This chemical was most probably (1) an enzyme (2) a neurotransmitter (3) a hormone (4) a blood protein

88. The two systems that directly control homeostasis in most animals are the (1) nervous and endocrine (2) endocrine and excretory (3) nervous and circulatory (4) excretory and circulatory

Short Answer
(Constructed Response)

89. In two complete sentences, distinguish between the central nervous system and the peripheral nervous system. What are the main structures and functions of each system?

90. In a complete sentence, explain why the endocrine glands are also referred to as ductless glands? How is this related to their function?

LOCOMOTION

Locomotion is the ability to move from place to place. Among many protists and animals, locomotion improves the organism's ability to survive. It increases chances of finding food and shelter, avoiding predators and other dangers, and finding a mate.

Adaptations for Locomotion

Many protists and almost all animals are capable of some form of locomotion, or **movement**. Such organisms are said to be *motile*. The hydra is generally a *sessile* organism; it tends to remain in one place, fastened to another structure. However, it does have fibers that permit some limited movements.

Protists. There are three basic forms of locomotion among protists. In the ameba, locomotion is by ameboid motion, in which the cell cytoplasm flows into the pseudopods. This causes the organism to move in the direction of the newly formed extension of its cytoplasm. In the paramecium, locomotion involves cilia, which

are short, hairlike organelles that cover the outer surface of the cell. The cilia wave back and forth in a coordinated way, moving the cell through the water. Some algae and other protozoans move by means of *flagella*, long, hairlike organelles that can pull the cell through the water (Figure 2-13).

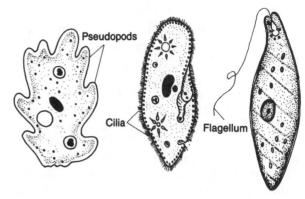

Figure 2-13. Locomotion in ameba, paramecium, and alga (euglena).

Humans. Humans have an internal skeleton, or *endoskeleton*. Locomotion is accomplished by the interaction of muscles and jointed appendages (bones and cartilage).

Questions

Multiple Choice

91. Locomotion increases an animal's opportunity to do all of the following *except* (1) obtain food (2) find a mate and reproduce (3) escape from predators (4) transmit impulses

92. Which structures are *not* associated with locomotion among protists? (1) flagella (2) cilia (3) pseudopods (4) tentacles

93. Which organism is able to move due to the interaction of its muscles and skeleton? (1) ameba (2) paramecium (3) human (4) hydra

Short Answer
(Constructed Response)

94. In a complete sentence, describe four survival advantages of locomotion.

95. Some organisms are sessile, or incapable of movement. In a complete sentence, explain how their survival might be aided in other ways.

Reading Comprehension

Base your answers to questions 96 through 99 on the information below and on your knowledge of biology. Source: *Science News* (July 1, 2000): vol. 158, no. 1, p. 11.

Darn That Diet, Anyway

Eating wisely may not be as easy as it sounds. Scientists report that some seemingly healthful foods, such as broiled chicken and baked fish, expose the diner to high concentrations of compounds that may damage the cardiovascular system—for example, by binding to blood vessel walls and making them less elastic. People with diabetes who have higher-than-normal concentrations of advanced glycation end products, or AGEs, in their blood are more likely to develop kidney and cardiovascular problems than are those with low concentrations, notes Jill P. Crandall of Mount Sinai School of Medicine in New York.

AGEs result from a complex reaction of sugars and proteins, and scientists have measured the amounts that are produced as a person digests food. AGEs are also abundant in some cooked food before it is digested, say the researchers. The team set out to see what effects diets containing foods high in AGEs might have on 11 people with diabetes.

Two weeks on a high-AGE diet increased the volunteers' average blood concentration of AGEs by 40 percent. In that time, concentrations of the AGE-linked cholesterol and the inflammatory compound tumor necrosis factor alpha (TNF-alpha) also rose significantly, notes Crandall. However, two weeks on a low-AGE diet that, for example, substituted poached chicken for broiled had the opposite effect. The diet lowered blood concentrations of AGE, AGE-linked cholesterol, and TNF-alpha.

Other researchers from Mount Sinai and the German Diabetes Research Institute in Düsseldorf have shown in laboratory tests that food-derived AGEs made blood clot more easily than normal. Such ready blood clotting can trigger strokes and heart attacks.

"You could be eating what you think is a healthy diet, but it could be bad for your diabetes," Crandall says.

96. What problems do "advanced glycation end products" (AGEs) cause for people who have diabetes?

97. How do AGEs form in the body?

98. How can AGEs trigger a heart attack or a stroke?

99. Describe one action that a person can take to reduce their risk of an AGE-induced medical problem.

Human Physiology

NUTRITION

Humans are heterotrophs—they must ingest the nutrients they need, including carbohydrates, proteins, lipids, vitamins, minerals, and water. Carbohydrates, lipids, and proteins are made up of large molecules that must be digested before they can be absorbed and used by the cells. Vitamins, minerals, and water are made up of small molecules that can be absorbed without being digested. Specific nutritional requirements of humans depend on the age, gender, and activity of the individual.

Human Digestive System

The human digestive system consists of a one-way digestive tube called the *gastrointestinal*, or GI, tract and accessory organs (Figure 3-1). Food is moved through the GI tract by rhythmic, muscular contractions called *peristalsis*. As food moves through the tract, it is broken down mechanically and chemically. The accessory organs—including the liver, gallbladder, and pancreas—secrete enzymes and other substances into the digestive tract that aid in digestion.

Oral Cavity. The mouth, or oral cavity, contains the teeth, tongue, and openings from the salivary glands. Food is ingested through the mouth, and digestion begins there. The teeth function in the mechanical breakdown of food into smaller pieces, which provides a larger surface area for the chemical action of digestive enzymes.

The *salivary glands* secrete saliva, a fluid that passes into the mouth through ducts. Saliva contains an enzyme, amylase, which begins the chemical digestion of starch. The tongue aids in chewing and in mixing saliva with the food by moving the food around in the mouth. The tongue also moves the food mass to the back of the mouth for swallowing.

Esophagus. When the food is swallowed, it passes into the esophagus, and peristalsis of the

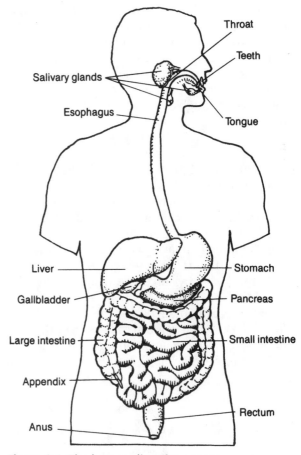

Figure 3-1. The human digestive system.

esophagus wall moves it downward to the stomach. Digestion of starch continues while the food is in the esophagus.

Stomach. Food reaching the lower end of the esophagus enters the stomach, a muscular sac in which it is mixed and liquefied (mechanical digestion). *Gastric glands* in the stomach lining secrete hydrochloric acid and the enzyme gastric protease. Hydrochloric acid provides the proper pH (acidic) required for effective functioning of gastric protease, which begins the chemical digestion of proteins.

Small Intestine. Partially digested food moves from the stomach into the *small intestine*, a long, convoluted tube in which most digestion occurs. The walls of the small intestine are lined with *intestinal glands* that secrete several different enzymes. These enzymes digest proteins, lipids, and disaccharides. The liver, gallbladder, and pancreas secrete substances into the small intestine.

The *liver* produces *bile*, which passes into the *gallbladder*, where it is stored temporarily. From the gallbladder, bile passes through ducts into the small intestine, where it acts on fats, breaking them down mechanically into tiny droplets. This process, known as *emulsification*, increases the surface area of fats for subsequent chemical digestion by enzymes. Bile also helps to neutralize the acidic food mass from the stomach.

The **pancreas** produces and secretes a juice that passes through ducts into the small intestine. Proteases, lipases, and amylase in pancreatic juice, together with the enzymes secreted by the intestinal glands, complete the chemical digestion of proteins, lipids, and carbohydrates in the small intestine.

The end products of digestion, including amino acids, fatty acids, glycerol, and glucose, are absorbed through the lining of the small intestine. The intestinal lining is specially adapted for absorption. Its surface area is greatly increased by many folds and by fingerlike projections called *villi* (singular, *villus*).

Each villus contains a lacteal and capillaries (Figure 3-2). A *lacteal* is a small vessel of the lymphatic system. Fatty acids and glycerol (the end products of fat digestion) are absorbed into the

lacteals; they are transported in the lymph, which is eventually added to the blood. Glucose and amino acids are absorbed into the blood of the capillaries and transported to the liver for temporary storage. From the liver, glucose and amino acids are distributed by the blood to all the cells, as they are needed.

When excess glucose is removed from the blood in the liver, it is converted to glycogen, an insoluble polysaccharide, and stored. When the concentration of glucose in the blood drops below a certain level, the glycogen is broken down to glucose, which is then returned to the blood. The storage of excess glucose as glycogen is an adaptation for the maintenance of a constant blood glucose level and is an example of homeostasis.

Large Intestine. Undigested and indigestible foods and water move from the small intestine into the *large intestine*, which is shorter and wider than the small intestine. Water is reabsorbed from the undigested food into the capillaries in the wall of the large intestine. This reabsorption helps the body to conserve water. The remaining wastes, called feces, are moved through the large intestine by strong peristaltic action to the rectum, where they are stored temporarily. The feces are periodically egested from the body through the anus.

Mechanism of Chemical Digestion

In digestion, large, insoluble molecules are broken down into small, soluble molecules by the process of *hydrolysis*. Each of the many hydrolytic reactions of digestion is regulated by a specific hydrolytic enzyme.

Chemically, hydrolysis is the opposite of dehydration synthesis; large molecules are split with the addition of water. In a series of reactions, polysaccharides, such as starch, are also broken down by hydrolysis into monosaccharides (simple sugars).

In the presence of water and protein-digesting enzymes (proteases), proteins are broken down into their constituent amino acids. In the hydrolysis of proteins, peptide bonds are broken.

In the presence of water and lipid-digesting enzymes (lipases), lipid molecules are broken down by hydrolysis into fatty acids and glycerol.

Nutritional Requirements

A balanced diet must contain carbohydrates, proteins, and fats, as well as vitamins, minerals, and water.

Carbohydrates. Carbohydrates serve as the major source of energy in the body. Excess carbo-

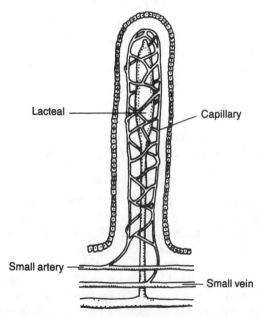

Figure 3-2. Structure of a villus.

Lacteal

Capillary

Small artery

Small vein

hydrates are converted to glycogen or fat and stored in the body as an energy reserve. *Cellulose*, a complex carbohydrate found in the cell walls of fruits, vegetables, and whole grains, provides indigestible material that serves as *roughage*. Roughage helps to move the food mass through the intestines.

Proteins. Proteins in food are broken down into their constituent amino acids, which are then used to synthesize human proteins. Twenty different amino acids are needed for the synthesis of human proteins. Twelve of these can be synthesized in the body from other amino acids; but the other eight, called the *essential amino acids*, must be obtained from the food.

All necessary amino acids must be present at the same time for protein synthesis to occur. An inadequate supply of any essential amino acid limits protein synthesis. Meat proteins generally contain all of the essential amino acids. Such foods are called complete protein foods. Vegetable proteins are generally incomplete protein foods—they lack one or more essential amino acids. However, a variety of vegetable proteins, if eaten at the same meal, can complement each other, providing all the essential amino acids.

Fats. Fats contain relatively large amounts of potential energy and serve as an energy-storage compound in organisms. Fats are also a structural component of cell membranes.

Fats are classified as saturated and unsaturated. *Saturated fats*, which are found in meats, butter, and other animal products, are solid at room temperature. Chemically, saturated fats contain the maximum number of hydrogen atoms and have no double bonds. *Unsaturated fats* contain one or more double bonds and, thus, could hold additional hydrogen atoms. An excess of saturated fats in the diet is thought to contribute to cardiovascular disease. Some forms of unsaturated fats are thought to protect against cardiovascular disease.

Disorders of the Digestive System

An *ulcer* is an open sore in the lining of the stomach or intestines. Ulcers may be caused by the presence of excess amounts of hydrochloric acid, which breaks down the lining of the digestive tract, or by bacterial infection. Ulcers are painful and sometimes cause bleeding.

Constipation is a condition marked by difficulty in eliminating feces from the large intestine. Constipation occurs when too much water is removed from the feces in the large intestine or when there is a reduction in peristaltic activity, slowing down the movement of waste through the large intestine. Insufficient roughage in the diet may also be a cause of constipation.

Diarrhea is a gastrointestinal disturbance characterized by frequent elimination of watery feces. This condition may result from decreased water absorption in the large intestine and increased peristaltic activity. Prolonged diarrhea may result in severe dehydration.

Appendicitis is an inflammation of the appendix, a small pouch located at the beginning of the large intestine. *Gallstones* are small, hardened cholesterol deposits that sometimes form in the gallbladder. When gallstones enter the bile duct and block the flow of bile, they cause severe pain.

Questions

Multiple Choice

1. Into which parts of the human digestive system are digestive enzymes secreted? (1) mouth, esophagus, stomach (2) stomach, small intestine, large intestine (3) mouth, stomach, small intestine (4) esophagus, stomach, large intestine

2. In humans, excess glucose is stored as the polysaccharide known as (1) glycogen (2) glycerol (3) maltose (4) cellulose

3. After a person's stomach was surgically removed, the chemical digestion of ingested protein would probably begin in the (1) mouth (2) small intestine (3) large intestine (4) liver

4. Which organ forms part of the human gastrointestinal tract? (1) trachea (2) esophagus (3) diaphragm (4) aorta

5. The intestinal folds and villi of the human small intestine function primarily to (1) increase the surface area for absorption of digested nutrients (2) excrete metabolic wastes (3) circulate blood (4) force the movement of food in one direction through the digestive tract

6. Lipase aids in the chemical digestion of (1) fats (2) proteins (3) enzymes (4) salts

7. In humans, which of the following is true of carbohydrate digestion? (1) It begins in the oral cavity and ends in the esophagus. (2) It begins in the oral cavity and ends in the small intestine. (3) It begins in the small intestine and ends in the large intestine. (4) It begins and ends in the small intestine.

8. Organisms are classified as heterotrophs if they derive their metabolic energy from (1) photosynthesis (2) inorganic raw materials (3) lightning (4) preformed organic compounds

9. Glands located within the digestive tube include (1) gastric glands and thyroid glands (2) gastric glands and intestinal glands (3) thyroid glands and intestinal glands (4) adrenal glands and intestinal glands

10. The small lymphatic vessels that extend into the villi are called the (1) veins (2) lacteals (3) glands (4) capillaries

11. The principal function of mechanical digestion is the (1) hydrolysis of food molecules for storage in the liver (2) production of more surface area for enzyme action (3) synthesis of enzymes necessary for food absorption (4) breakdown of large molecules to smaller ones by the addition of water

12. In which organ's walls does peristalsis occur? (1) liver (2) pancreas (3) oral cavity (4) esophagus

13. A person who consumes large amounts of saturated fats may increase his or her chances of developing (1) meningitis (2) hemophilia (3) pneumonia (4) cardiovascular disease

Base your answers to questions 14 through 18 on your knowledge of biology and on the graph below, which shows the extent to which carbohydrates, proteins, and fats are chemically digested as food passes through the human digestive tract. The letters represent sequential structures that make up the digestive tract.

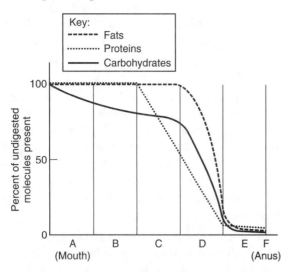

14. Proteins are digested in both (1) *A* and *B* (2) *B* and *C* (3) *C* and *D* (4) *A* and *C*

15. The organ represented by letter *C* is most probably the (1) esophagus (2) stomach (3) small intestine (4) large intestine

16. Enzymes secreted by the pancreas enter the system at (1) *E* (2) *B* (3) *C* (4) *D*

17. The final products of digestion are absorbed almost entirely in (1) *F* (2) *B* (3) *C* (4) *D*

18. Water is removed from the undigested material in (1) *A* (2) *B* (3) *E* (4) *D*

Short Answer
(Constructed Response)

19. Use your knowledge of biology to complete the following table.

Nutrient	Digestive End Products	Where Chemical Digestion Begins	End Products Absorbed by
Starches	Simple sugars		Villi capillaries
Lipids		Small intestine	
Proteins	Amino acids		

Base your answers to questions 20 and 21 on the food pyramid below, which shows the suggested daily servings of several types of food.

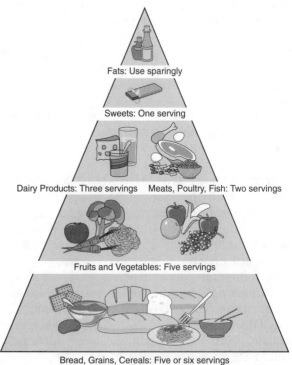

Fats: Use sparingly

Sweets: One serving

Dairy Products: Three servings   Meats, Poultry, Fish: Two servings

Fruits and Vegetables: Five servings

Bread, Grains, Cereals: Five or six servings

20. Based on the food pyramid, make up a daily meal plan for breakfast, lunch, and dinner for one person.

21. In a complete sentence, explain why people are advised to use fats sparingly.

Essay
(Extended Constructed Response)

22. Select any three organs of the human digestive system and describe the type of digestion that occurs in each.

23. Explain why most foods (nutrients) eaten by humans must be digested before they can be used by the body.

TRANSPORT

Transport includes the absorption and distribution of materials throughout the body. In humans, dissolved and suspended materials are transported in the blood, which is moved throughout the body by the circulatory system.

Blood

Blood consists of a fluid called *plasma* in which red blood cells, white blood cells, and platelets are suspended (Figure 3-3).

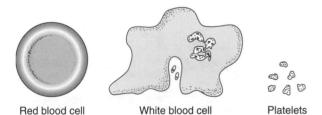

Red blood cell   White blood cell   Platelets

Figure 3-3. The three main types of blood cells.

Plasma.   Blood plasma consists mostly of water. It contains many dissolved materials, including inorganic ions, wastes, nutrients, and a variety of proteins. The proteins include antibodies, enzymes, hormones, and clotting factors.

Red Blood Cells.   The most numerous cells in the plasma are the *red blood cells*, which are produced in the marrow of certain bones. Mature red blood cells do not have a nucleus. Within red blood cells is the red, iron-containing pigment hemoglobin, which carries oxygen between the lungs and the body tissues.

White Blood Cells.   The **white blood cells** are larger than the red blood cells and contain one or more nuclei. White blood cells are produced in the bone marrow and in lymph nodes. There are several types of white blood cells, including phagocytes and lymphocytes.

Phagocytes are white blood cells that engulf and destroy bacteria at the site of an infection. By ameboid motion, phagocytes leave the capillaries and enter the body tissues, where they engulf bacteria and other foreign matter in the same way that amebas engulf food.

Lymphocytes are white blood cells that produce special protein molecules called **antibodies**. Antibodies react chemically with foreign substances or microorganisms in the blood and inactivate them. The substances that cause antibody production are called **antigens**. Most antigens are protein in nature. An antigen–antibody reaction is referred to as an *immune response*. (For more information on the immune response, see Chapter 4.)

Platelets.   The small cell fragments that are involved in the clotting of blood are called *platelets*. A platelet consists of cytoplasm surrounded by a cell membrane; it has no nucleus.

Blood Clotting.   When an injury occurs, blood vessels break and blood is released. To stop the loss of blood, a blood clot forms, blocking the wound. Clotting involves a series of enzyme-controlled reactions. All the substances required for clotting are normally present in the blood. However, the reactions leading to clot formation do not normally take place unless there is a break in a blood vessel. When such an injury occurs, blood platelets are ruptured, and they release an enzyme that initiates the clotting reactions. The plasma protein *fibrinogen* is converted to *fibrin*, which forms a meshwork of solid fibers across the wound. Blood cells become trapped in the fibers, forming the clot.

Immunity

The ability of the body to resist a specific disease is called **immunity**. Immunity, which is provided by the **immune system** and depends on the action of antibodies in the bloodstream, can develop in two ways.

Active immunity results when antibodies are produced in response to a foreign substance (antigen) in the body. When a person develops a disease, for example, chicken pox, antibodies develop against the disease-causing agent. After the illness is over, antibodies against this agent remain in the blood and protect against reinfection by the same substance or microorganism.

Active immunity is also produced by **vaccination** against a particular disease. A *vaccine* contains dead or weakened microorganisms that can stimulate antibody production but cannot cause disease.

Passive immunity develops when an individual receives antibodies from the blood of another person or from an animal. These antibodies provide temporary immunity to a particular disease. However, the "borrowed" antibodies are gradually destroyed, and the immunity they provided ends.

Allergies. In some people, exposure to certain common, foreign substances, such as dust, pollen, insect bites, foods, and medications, causes an immune response known as an *allergy*. These responses, or **allergic reactions**, are actually overreactions of the body's immune system to a foreign substance. The antibodies produced may stimulate the release of a substance called *histamine*, which causes typical allergic responses, such as sneezing, coughing, or a rash.

Blood-Typing. Knowledge of immunity has made possible the transplanting of organs and the transfusion of blood from one person to another. In both organ transplants and blood transfusions, an immune response is stimulated if the body of the recipient recognizes foreign antigens in the tissue or blood from the donor. In organ transplants, an antigen–antibody reaction against the transplanted organ is called *rejection*. Donor tissue proteins must be carefully matched to those of the recipient to avoid rejection.

Blood-typing for transfusions is based on the presence or absence of antigens on the surface of red blood cells. The most important blood group system in blood-typing is the ABO blood group system. In this system, two kinds of antigens may be found on the red blood cells: A and B. In addition, the plasma of the blood may contain antibodies: anti-A and anti-B. Table 3-1 shows the antigens and antibodies for each type of blood.

Transport Vessels

Blood circulates through the human body within the blood vessels, which include *arteries, capillaries*, and *veins*. (Refer to Figure 2-8, page 21.)

Arteries. Blood is carried from the heart to all parts of the body in arteries, which are thick-walled, muscular vessels that expand and contract to accommodate the forceful flow of blood from the heart. The rhythmic expansion and contraction of the arteries produced by the heartbeat aids the flow of blood to all parts of the body; it is called the *pulse*.

Table 3-1. Antigens and Antibodies of the ABO Blood Group System

Blood Type	Antigens on Red Cells	Antibodies in Plasma
A	A	Anti-B
B	B	Anti-A
AB	A and B	Neither Anti-A nor Anti-B
O	Neither A nor B	Anti-A and Anti-B

Capillaries. With increasing distance from the heart, arteries branch into smaller and smaller vessels, finally forming capillaries, tiny blood vessels with walls only one cell layer thick. Capillaries are the site of exchange of materials between the blood and the body tissues.

Veins. Blood flows from the capillaries into the veins, thin-walled vessels that carry the blood back to the heart. Veins contain flaps of tissue that act as valves (Figure 3-4). The valves allow the blood in the veins to flow in only one direction— back toward the heart.

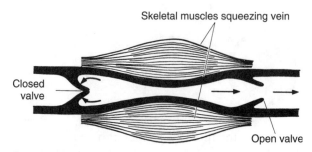

Figure 3-4. Blood flow in a vein.

Intercellular Fluid and Lymph

As blood passes through the capillaries of the body, some of the plasma is forced out of the vessels and into the surrounding tissues. This fluid, which bathes all the cells of the body, is called *intercellular fluid*, or *ICF*. Materials diffusing between the cells and the blood of the capillaries are dissolved in the ICF.

Excess intercellular fluid is drained from the tissues by vessels of the *lymphatic system*. Tiny *lymph vessels* are present in all body tissues. Excess intercellular fluid diffuses into the vessels; once inside, the fluid is called *lymph*. The lymph

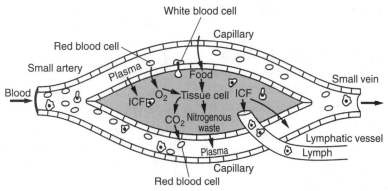

Figure 3-5. Molecules diffuse between the capillaries, intercellular fluid, and body cells.

vessels merge, forming progressively larger vessels. Eventually, all lymph flows into two large lymph ducts, which empty into veins near the heart. In this way, the fluid lost from the blood is returned to the blood (Figure 3-5).

Major lymph vessels have enlarged regions called *lymph nodes* in which phagocytic cells filter bacteria and dead cells from the lymph. Some lymph vessels contain valves that, like those in the veins, keep the lymph flowing back toward the heart.

The Heart

Blood is pumped through the blood vessels of the body by the contractions of the heart.

Structure of the Heart. The heart has four chambers (Figure 3-6). The two upper chambers, the *atria* (singular, *atrium*), receive blood returning to the heart from the rest of the body. The two lower chambers, the *ventricles*, pump blood out

of the heart into the arteries. The walls of the ventricles are thicker and more muscular than those of the atria.

Circulation Through the Heart. The deoxygenated (oxygen-poor) blood from the body is returned to the right atrium of the heart through two large veins—one from the upper part of the body and one from the lower part of the body. This deoxygenated blood flows down from the right atrium into the right ventricle; from there it is pumped out of the heart through the pulmonary arteries to the lungs. When in the lungs, the blood gives up carbon dioxide and picks up oxygen. The oxygenated (oxygen-rich) blood is then returned through the pulmonary veins to the left atrium of the heart. The blood then passes from the left atrium into the left ventricle, which pumps it through the *aorta*, the largest artery in the body.

This one-way flow of blood through the heart is controlled by valves that prevent backflow of the blood. There are valves between the atria and the ventricles, between the right ventricle and the pulmonary artery, and between the left ventricle and the aorta.

Blood Pressure. The pressure exerted by the blood on the walls of the arteries during the pumping action of the heart is referred to as *blood pressure*. During the contraction phase of the heartbeat cycle, arterial blood pressure is highest. During the relaxation phase of the heartbeat cycle, blood pressure is lowest.

Pathways of Circulation

The pathway of blood between the heart and the lungs is called the *pulmonary circulation*. The circulatory pathway between the heart and all other parts of the body except the lungs is called the *systemic circulation*. The system of blood vessels

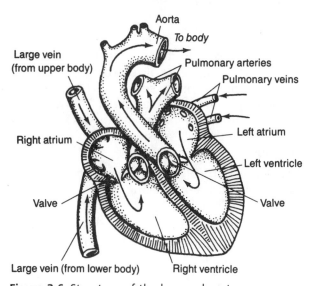

Figure 3-6. Structure of the human heart.

that supplies the heart itself is called the *coronary circulation*.

Disorders of the Transport System

Diseases of the heart and blood vessels are called *cardiovascular* diseases. The most common form of cardiovascular disease is high blood pressure, or *hypertension*, which is characterized by elevated arterial blood pressure. This condition can be caused by a number of factors, including stress, diet, heredity, cigarette smoking, and aging. High blood pressure can damage the lining of arteries and weaken the muscle of the heart.

A blockage of the coronary artery or its branches is a *coronary thrombosis*, or heart attack. As a result of the blockage, some of the muscle tissue of the heart is deprived of oxygen and is damaged.

A narrowing of the coronary arteries may cause temporary shortages of oxygen to the heart muscle, resulting in intense pain in the chest and sometimes in the left arm and shoulder. This condition is called *angina pectoris*.

Anemia is a condition in which the blood cannot carry sufficient amounts of oxygen to the body cells. Anemia may be due to inadequate amounts of hemoglobin in the red blood cells or to too few red blood cells. One form of anemia is caused by a shortage of iron in the diet.

Leukemia is a form of cancer in which the bone marrow produces abnormally large numbers of white blood cells.

Questions

Multiple Choice

24. Which is a characteristic of lymph nodes? (1) They carry blood under great pressure. (2) They move fluids by means of a muscular pump. (3) They produce new red blood cells. (4) They contain phagocytic cells.

25. The accumulation of specific antibodies in the plasma, due to the presence of an antigen, is characteristic of (1) an immune response (2) angina pectoris (3) a coronary thrombosis (4) cerebral palsy

26. An organism develops active immunity as a result of (1) manufacturing its own antigens (2) producing antibodies in response to a vaccination (3) receiving an injection of antibodies produced by another organism (4) receiving an injection of a dilute glucose solution

27. In the human body, which blood components engulf foreign bacteria? (1) red blood cells (2) white blood cells (3) antibodies (4) platelets

28. In humans, the exchange of materials between blood and intercellular fluid directly involves blood vessels known as (1) capillaries (2) arterioles (3) venules (4) arteries

29. An injury to a blood vessel may result in the formation of a blood clot when (1) bone marrow cells decrease platelet production (2) kidney tubules synthesize clotting factors (3) ruptured platelets release enzyme molecules (4) white blood cells release antibodies

30. Oxygen carried by the blood in capillaries normally enters the body cells by (1) active transport (2) osmosis (3) diffusion (4) pinocytosis

31. Which type of vessel normally contains valves that prevent the backward flow of blood? (1) artery (2) arteriole (3) capillary (4) vein

32. The blood vessels that transport deoxygenated blood to the heart are known as (1) capillaries (2) lymph vessels (3) veins (4) arteries

Base your answers to questions 33 through 37 on the diagram below, which represents the exchange of materials between capillaries and cells, and on your knowledge of biology.

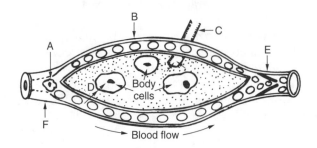

33. Blood vessel *B* has walls that are very thin, which enables this type of vessel to (1) transport hemoglobin to body cells (2) transport red blood cells into the tissue spaces (3) withstand the pressure of the blood coming in from veins (4) easily transport substances into and out of the blood

34. A function of cell *A* is to (1) carry oxygen (2) engulf disease-producing bacteria (3) transport digested food (4) produce hemoglobin

35. A substance that diffuses in the direction indicated by *D* is most likely (1) fibrin (2) oxygen (3) urea (4) bile

36. Which vessel most likely contains the greatest amount of carbon dioxide? (1) *F* (2) *B* (3) *C* (4) *E*

37. Excess intercellular fluid (ICF) is constantly drained off by lymphatic vessels. Which letter represents such a vessel? (1) *E* (2) *B* (3) *C* (4) *F*

38. The right ventricle is the chamber of the heart that contains (1) deoxygenated blood and pumps this blood to the lungs (2) deoxygenated blood and pumps this blood to the brain (3) oxygenated blood and pumps this blood to the lungs (4) oxygenated blood and pumps this blood to the brain

Base your answers to questions 39 through 42 on the diagram below and on your knowledge of biology. The diagram represents the human heart; the direction of blood flow is indicated by arrows.

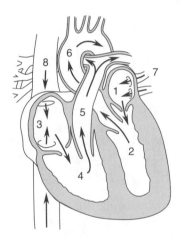

39. The aorta is represented by number (1) 1 (2) 6 (3) 8 (4) 4

40. Deoxygenated blood returns to the heart through the structure represented by number (1) 8 (2) 7 (3) 3 (4) 5

41. The chamber that pumps blood to all parts of the body except the lungs is represented by number (1) 1 (2) 2 (3) 3 (4) 4

42. Blood passes from the heart to the lungs through the structure represented by number (1) 5 (2) 6 (3) 7 (4) 8

Short Answer
(Constructed Response)

43. In a full sentence, explain what effects faulty valves would have on a human's blood flow.

44. In two or more complete sentences, describe the relationship that exists between the circulatory system and the lymphatic system.

45. The four major blood components are red blood cells, white blood cells, plasma, and platelets. In full sentences, describe one major function for each blood component listed.

46. Arteries generally contain blood that has a higher oxygen content than that of blood in the veins. In one or two complete sentences, give a scientific explanation for this observation.

47. Why are people who are anemic (have too little hemoglobin and/or too few red blood cells) often advised to take in extra iron in their diets?

Essay
(Extended Constructed Response)

48. Describe the pathway of blood flow through the heart, beginning and ending with the point at which the blood returns to the heart from the body organs.

49. Compare and contrast the structure and function of these three major types of blood vessels: arteries, veins, and capillaries.

RESPIRATION

Respiration includes cellular respiration and gas exchange. The process of cellular respiration in humans is basically the same as that in other aerobic organisms. (See Chapter 2.) Glucose is broken down completely to yield carbon dioxide and water, and ATP is formed from ADP and phosphate.

Anaerobic respiration occurs in human skeletal muscle during prolonged exercise when the amount of oxygen supplied by the circulatory system becomes inadequate for aerobic respiration. Under these circumstances, glucose is broken down in the muscle to lactic acid. The accumulation of lactic acid in skeletal muscle is thought to be responsible for muscle fatigue. When adequate oxygen is again available, the lactic acid is broken down to carbon dioxide and water.

Human Respiratory System
The human respiratory system moves respiratory gases between the external environment and the internal surfaces for gas exchange within the lungs. The respiratory system consists of a network of passageways that permit air to flow into and out of the lungs (Figure 3-7 on page 38).

Nasal Cavity. Air generally enters the respiratory system through the nostrils and passes into

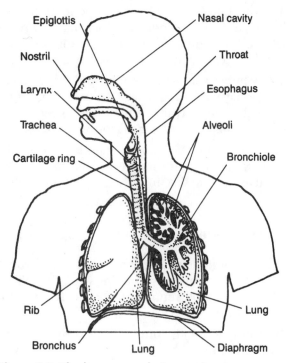

Figure 3-7. The human respiratory system.

bronchi (singular, bronchus). The bronchi, like the trachea, are lined with a mucous membrane and ringed with cartilage. Each bronchus extends into a lung, where it branches into smaller and smaller tubes called bronchioles.

The *bronchioles* are lined with a mucous membrane, but they lack cartilage rings. At the end of each bronchiole is a cluster of tiny, hollow air sacs called *alveoli*.

Alveoli. The lungs contain millions of alveoli (singular, *alveolus*). The walls of the alveoli are thin and moist and are surrounded by capillaries. The alveoli are the functional units for gas exchange in the human respiratory system. Oxygen diffuses from the alveoli into the surrounding capillaries, while carbon dioxide and water diffuse from the capillaries into the alveoli.

Lungs. Each bronchus with its bronchioles and alveoli make up a *lung*.

the *nasal cavity*. This cavity is lined with a ciliated mucous membrane that cleans, warms, and moistens the air.

Pharynx. From the nasal cavity, air passes into the *pharynx*, the area where the oral cavity and nasal cavity meet. Air passes through the pharynx on its way to the trachea.

Trachea. The *trachea*, or windpipe, is a tube through which air passes from the pharynx to the lungs. The opening (from the pharynx) to the trachea is protected by a flap of tissue called the *epiglottis*. During swallowing, the epiglottis covers the opening of the trachea so that food and liquids cannot enter the air passages. During breathing, the opening of the trachea is uncovered. In the top of the trachea is the *larynx*, or voice box, which functions in speech. The walls of the trachea contain rings of cartilage that keep the trachea open so that the passage of air remains unobstructed. The trachea is lined with a ciliated mucous membrane. Microscopic particles in the inhaled air are trapped by mucus, and the beating of the cilia sweeps the mucus upward toward the pharynx (to be expelled from the body by coughing or sneezing).

Bronchi and Bronchioles. The lower end of the trachea splits, forming two tubes called the

Breathing

Air moves into and out of the lungs during *breathing*. The lungs are highly elastic but contain no muscle tissue. They expand and contract in response to pressure changes in the chest cavity brought about by the actions of the rib cage and the diaphragm.

During *inhalation*, the ribs push upward and outward and the diaphragm moves down, enlarging the chest cavity. The enlargement of the chest cavity reduces the pressure around the lungs, which expand, and air flows into the lungs. In *exhalation*, the ribs move inward and downward and the diaphragm moves up. The chest cavity becomes smaller and air is forced out of the lungs (Figure 3-8).

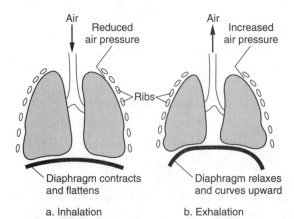

Figure 3-8. Movement of diaphragm as air goes into and out of the lungs.

Gas Exchange. The air that enters the alveoli is rich in oxygen. The blood in the capillaries surrounding the alveoli is oxygen-poor and contains the wastes of cellular respiration—carbon dioxide and water. The oxygen diffuses from the alveoli into the blood, where it enters the red blood cells and becomes loosely bound to the hemoglobin, forming a compound known as *oxyhemoglobin.*

In the capillaries of the body tissues, the oxygen and hemoglobin separate. The oxygen diffuses out of the capillaries, through the intercellular fluid, and into the body cells. Carbon dioxide and water diffuse from the cells into the blood. Carbon dioxide is carried in the blood mainly in the form of *bicarbonate ions* (HCO_3^-). When the blood returns to the lungs, these wastes diffuse into the alveoli and are expelled from the body in the exhaled air.

Breathing Rate. The rate of breathing is controlled by the breathing center in the medulla of the brain. The breathing center is sensitive to the concentration of carbon dioxide in the blood. When the carbon dioxide level is high, nerve impulses from the breathing center are sent to the rib muscles and to the diaphragm to increase the breathing rate, which speeds up the rate of excretion of carbon dioxide from the body. As the carbon dioxide level in the blood drops, the breathing rate decreases. This regulation of carbon dioxide levels is one example of the **feedback mechanisms** by which the body maintains homeostasis.

Disorders of the Respiratory System

Bronchitis is an inflammation of the linings of the bronchial tubes. As a result of such swelling, the air passages become narrowed and filled with mucus, causing breathing difficulties and coughing. *Asthma* is an allergic reaction characterized by a narrowing of the bronchial tubes, which results in difficulty in breathing. *Emphysema* is a disease in which the walls of the alveoli break down, decreasing the surface area for gas exchange. Emphysema is marked by shortness of breath, difficulty in breathing, and decreased lung capacity.

Questions

Multiple Choice

50. The alveoli in humans are structures most closely associated with (1) gas exchange (2) anaerobic respiration (3) glandular secretion (4) neural transmission

51. In humans, the center that detects and regulates the amount of carbon dioxide in the blood is situated in the (1) cerebrum (2) diaphragm (3) medulla (4) rib muscles

52. The exchange of air between the human body and the environment is a result of the rhythmic contractions of the rib cage muscles and the (1) diaphragm (2) lungs (3) trachea (4) heart

53. The breathing rate of humans is principally regulated by the concentration of (1) carbon dioxide in the blood (2) oxygen in the blood (3) platelets in the blood (4) white blood cells in the blood

Base your answers to questions 54 through 58 on the diagram below, which represents part of the human respiratory system.

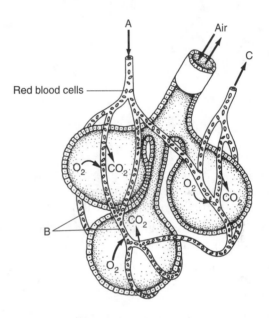

54. The blood vessels labeled *B* that are surrounding these air sacs are called (1) arteries (2) capillaries (3) veins (4) lymphatic ducts

55. These air sacs are known as (1) alveoli (2) bronchi (3) bronchioles (4) tracheae

56. The heart chamber that most directly pumps blood to the vessel network at *A* is the (1) right atrium (2) left atrium (3) right ventricle (4) left ventricle

57. The process most directly involved in the exchange of gases between these air sacs and blood vessels is called (1) active transport (2) pinocytosis (3) hydrolysis (4) diffusion

58. Compared to blood entering at *A*, blood leaving the vessel network at *C* has a lower concentration of (1) oxygen (2) hemoglobin and carbon dioxide (3) carbon dioxide (4) oxygen and hemoglobin

Short Answer
(Constructed Response)

Base your answers to questions 59 through 61 on your knowledge of biology and on the diagram below, which represents a model of the human respiratory system.

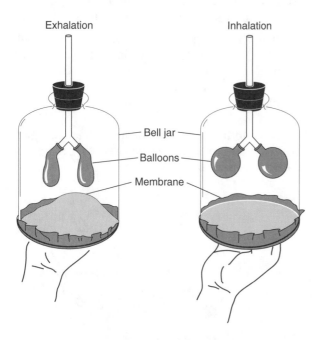

59. In a complete sentence, explain which parts of the respiratory system are represented by the Y-tube, the balloons, and the rubber membrane.

60. Describe what happens to the balloons when the rubber membrane is pulled downward.

61. Give a scientific reason for your answer to question 60. How does this process apply to humans?

62. Breathing rate is controlled by the respiratory center in the brain, which responds to carbon dioxide levels in the blood. High levels of carbon dioxide increase the breathing rate, while low levels decrease the breathing rate. In two or more complete sentences, give a scientific explanation for why a person's breathing rate increases during and after vigorous exercise.

Essay
(Extended Constructed Response)

63. Discuss how the alveoli in our lungs satisfy the conditions needed in a good respiratory surface. Include at least three conditions that allow gas exchange to take place.

64. Describe the pathway that air follows during breathing in a human, beginning with the taking in of air from the environment. Include, in the correct sequence, the parts of the respiratory system through which the air must pass.

EXCRETION

The metabolic wastes of humans include carbon dioxide, water, salts, and urea. Excretory wastes pass from the cells into the blood and are carried to the excretory organs that expel them from the body. The excretory organs include the lungs, liver, sweat glands, and kidneys.

Lungs. The *lungs* function in the excretion of carbon dioxide and water vapor, which are the wastes of cellular respiration.

Liver. The *liver* is a large organ that performs many functions essential to human survival. One of the excretory functions of the liver is to get rid of excess amino acids. The amino groups are removed and converted into *urea*, which is excreted by the kidneys. The remainder of the amino acid molecules are broken down by cellular respiration. The liver is also responsible for the breakdown of red blood cells.

Sweat Glands. The *sweat glands* of the skin excrete wastes, including water, salts, and a small amount of urea. These wastes pass by diffusion from capillaries into the sweat glands and then through ducts to pores on the surface of the skin (Figure 3-9). The mixture of wastes and water excreted by the sweat glands is called sweat, or *perspiration*.

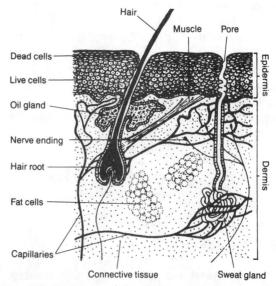

Figure 3-9. Structure of the skin.

Perspiration functions primarily in the regulation of body temperature. The evaporation of sweat from the surface of the skin occurs when heat is absorbed from skin cells, and it serves to lower the body temperature. This method of temperature regulation is another example of homeostasis.

Urinary System

The human urinary system consists of the kidneys, ureters, urinary bladder, and urethra (Figure 3-10).

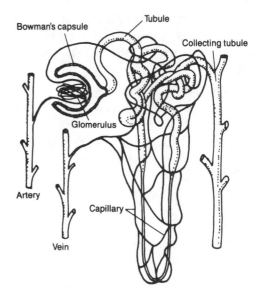

Figure 3-11. Structure of a nephron.

and salts, and is called *urine*. Urine passes from the small tubule of the nephron into larger tubules and then to a ureter.

Ureters and Urinary Bladder. Urine flows from each kidney into a large tubule called the *ureter*. The ureters carry the urine to the urinary bladder, a muscular organ in which urine is stored temporarily.

Urethra. Urine is periodically expelled from the bladder into a tube called the *urethra*. This tube leads to the outside of the body.

Diseases of the Urinary System

Diseases of the kidneys affect the body's ability to eliminate normal amounts of metabolic wastes. *Gout* is a condition that produces symptoms similar to arthritis and is caused by deposits of uric acid in the joints. Victims of gout suffer from severe pain and stiffness in the joints. Diets that are extremely high in protein result in the production of large amounts of urea, which the kidneys must remove from the blood. The extra strain on the kidneys in eliminating these wastes may result in a kidney disorder, or **malfunction**.

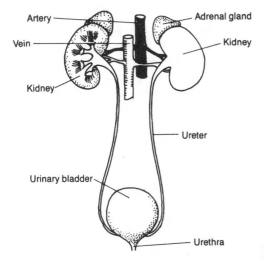

Figure 3-10. Structure of the human urinary system.

Kidneys. Human *kidneys* perform two major functions: they remove urea from the blood, and they regulate the concentrations of most of the substances in the body fluids. Blood is carried to each kidney by a large artery. Within the kidney, the artery divides and subdivides into smaller and smaller arteries and then into balls of capillaries called *glomeruli* (singular, *glomerulus*). Each glomerulus is part of a *nephron*, the functional unit of the kidney (Figure 3-11). There are about one million nephrons in each kidney.

A nephron consists of a glomerulus surrounded by a cup-shaped structure called the *Bowman's capsule*. Extending from the capsule is a long, coiled tubule that is surrounded by capillaries. As blood flows through the glomerulus, water, salts, urea, glucose, and some amino acids diffuse out of the blood into Bowman's capsule. This process is called *filtration*. As these substances—referred to as the *filtrate*—pass through the long, coiled tubule of the nephron, glucose, water, amino acids, and some of the salts are reabsorbed by active transport into the blood in the capillaries surrounding the tubule. The fluid that remains in the tubules consists of water, urea,

Questions

Multiple Choice

65. Which human body system includes the lungs, liver, skin, and kidneys? (1) respiratory (2) digestive (3) transport (4) excretory

66. In humans, the filtrate produced by the nephrons is temporarily stored in the (1) glomerulus (2) alveolus (3) gallbladder (4) urinary bladder

67. What is the principal nitrogenous waste in humans? (1) salt (2) urea (3) uric acid (4) carbon dioxide

68. In humans, the organ that breaks down red blood cells and deaminates amino acids is the (1) kidney (2) liver (3) gallbladder (4) small intestine

69. In addition to water, the principal components of urine are (1) amino acids and fatty acids (2) urea and salts (3) ammonia and bile (4) hydrochloric acid and bases

70. Nitrogenous wastes are produced as a result of the metabolism of (1) glucose (2) glycogen (3) fatty acids (4) amino acids

71. In humans, urine is eliminated from the bladder through the (1) urethra (2) ureter (3) nephron (4) collecting tubule

72. The basic structural and functional excretory units of the human kidney are known as (1) nephridia (2) nephrons (3) alveoli (4) ureters

73. The excretory organ associated with the storage of glycogen is the (1) stomach (2) lung (3) kidney (4) liver

Base your answers to questions 74 through 76 on your knowledge of biology and on the diagram below, which illustrates a nephron and its capillaries.

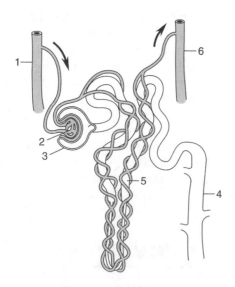

74. Into which structure does the filtrate first pass? (1) 5 (2) 6 (3) 3 (4) 4

75. In which area is water being reabsorbed? (1) 5 (2) 2 (3) 3 (4) 4

76. In which area does urine collect? (1) 1 (2) 2 (3) 6 (4) 4

Short Answer
(Constructed Response)

77. In two or more full sentences, compare the structure of a sweat gland with that of a nephron. Be sure to note their similarities and differences.

78. In complete sentences, describe how each of the following functions as an excretory organ: the liver; the skin; the lungs.

Base your answers to questions 79 through 82 on the diagram and information presented below. The diagram represents a nephron from which samples of fluid were extracted. The samples were recovered from the areas labeled *A* and *B* in the diagram. The concentrations of five substances in the fluid extracted from both sites were compared and the results are listed in the table below.

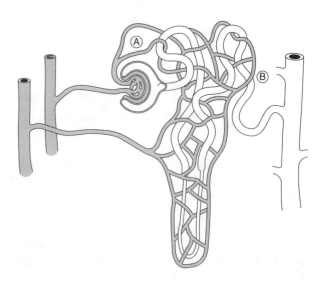

Substance	Concentration at A	Concentration at B
Water	High	Low
Urea	Moderate	High
Glucose	High	High
Amino acids	High	Zero
Salts	Low	High

79. Explain the change in the concentration of water and urea from area *A* to area *B*.

80. Why are there no amino acids present in the fluid extracted from area *B*, yet the concentration at area *A* was high?

81. What process occurs at area *A*? What process occurs at area *B*?

82. Examine the data for glucose concentration. Based on the data, from what disease might this person be suffering?

NERVOUS SYSTEM

Regulation in humans involves the interaction of the nervous and endocrine systems. The two systems are similar in that they both secrete chemicals and both play a major role in the maintenance of homeostasis. In general, they differ in that the responses of the nervous system are more rapid and of shorter duration than those of the endocrine system.

Nerve Cells

The nervous system is made up of nerve cells, or *neurons*, which are adapted for the transmission of impulses. (See Chapter 2.) The nervous system contains three different types of nerve cells, which differ both in structure and function; these are the sensory neurons, motor neurons, and interneurons.

Sensory neurons transmit impulses from the sense organs, or receptors, to the brain and the spinal cord. Sense organs include the eyes, ears, tongue, nose, and skin.

Motor neurons transmit impulses from the brain and spinal cord to the *effectors*, that is, to the muscles and the glands.

Interneurons are found in the spinal cord and brain; they transmit nerve impulses from sensory neurons to motor neurons.

Nerves

The nerve cells, or parts of nerve cells, are bound together in bundles called *nerves*. There are three kinds of nerves: *sensory nerves*, which contain only sensory neurons; *motor nerves*, which contain only motor neurons; and *mixed nerves*, which contain both sensory and motor neurons.

Central Nervous System

The two main divisions of the human nervous system are the *central nervous system,* which includes the brain and spinal cord, and the *peripheral nervous system*, which includes all the nerves outside the central nervous system.

The Brain. The *brain* is a large mass of nerve cells located in the cranial cavity. It is surrounded and protected by the bones of the skull. The three major parts of the brain are the cerebrum, the

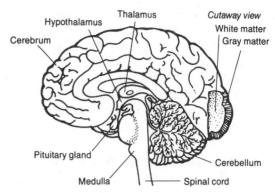

Figure 3-12. Structure of the human brain.

cerebellum, and the medulla (Figure 3-12). Each controls different functions of the body.

In humans, the *cerebrum* is the largest part of the brain. It is the center for thought, memory, and learning; it receives and interprets messages from the sense organs; and it initiates all voluntary, or conscious, movements.

The *cerebellum* is located below and behind the cerebrum. It coordinates all motor activities and is involved in maintaining the body's balance.

The *medulla* is located at the base of the brain and connects the brain and the spinal cord. The medulla controls many important involuntary activities in the body, including breathing, heartbeat, blood pressure, and peristalsis.

The Spinal Cord. The medulla of the brain is continuous with the *spinal cord*, which is surrounded and protected by the vertebrae of the backbone, or spinal column. The spinal cord coordinates activities between the brain and other body structures. Impulses from sense receptors throughout the body are transmitted by sensory neurons to the spinal cord. In the spinal cord, impulses are transmitted by interneurons to the brain. Impulses from the brain are carried by motor neurons through the spinal cord and then to the appropriate effectors.

Peripheral Nervous System

The peripheral nervous system includes all neurons, both sensory and motor, outside the central nervous system; these nerve cells carry impulses between the central nervous system and the rest of the body. The two main divisions of the peripheral nervous system are the somatic nervous system and the autonomic nervous system.

The *somatic nervous system* includes all the nerves that control the movements of the voluntary muscles of the body, as well as the sensory neurons that transmit impulses from sense receptors to the central nervous system.

The *autonomic nervous system* consists of the nerves that control the activities of smooth muscle, cardiac muscle, and glands. The activities of this system, which are not under voluntary control, include regulation of the heartbeat and circulation, respiration, and peristalsis.

Behavior and the Nervous System

All animals, including humans, have behaviors that help them maintain homeostasis and aid their survival. These behaviors are controlled by the nervous system. Some behaviors are inborn, while others are learned.

Habits. A *habit* is a kind of learned behavior that becomes automatic through repetition. The repetition establishes pathways for nerve impulse transmission that permit a rapid, automatic response to a particular stimulus.

Reflexes. An automatic, inborn response to a particular stimulus is called a *reflex.* In a reflex response, impulses follow a set pathway called a *reflex arc* (Figure 3-13). In this pathway, impulses pass from a receptor to a sensory neuron to an interneuron (in the spinal cord) to a motor neuron to an effector. Although impulses may also pass from an interneuron to the brain, the reflex response is controlled by the spinal cord and occurs without the involvement of the brain. Reflexes are generally protective in nature, allowing a rapid response to a potentially dangerous stimulus.

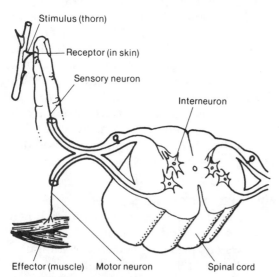

Stimulus (thorn)

Receptor (in skin)

Sensory neuron

Interneuron

Effector (muscle)   Motor neuron   Spinal cord

Figure 3-13. A typical reflex arc.

Disorders of the Nervous System

Cerebral palsy is a group of diseases caused by damage to the parts of the brain that control vol-untary movement. This damage occurs during embryonic development. *Meningitis* is an inflammation of the membranes that surround the brain and spinal cord. Meningitis may be caused by viral or bacterial infections, and symptoms include headache, muscle stiffness, fever, and chills. A *stroke* is a disorder in which the brain is damaged as a result of a *cerebral hemorrhage* (a broken blood vessel) or a blood clot (in a blood vessel) in the brain. *Polio* is a disease that is caused by a virus that affects the central nervous system, and which may result in paralysis. Polio can be prevented by immunization.

Questions

Multiple Choice

83. The major function of a motor neuron is to (1) transmit impulses from the spinal cord to the brain   (2) act as a receptor for environment stimuli   (3) transmit impulses from sense organs to the central nervous system   (4) transmit impulses from the central nervous system to muscles or glands

84. Nerves are composed of bundles of   (1) muscle cells   (2) neurons   (3) phagocytes   (4) bone cells

85. Which part of the human central nervous system is involved primarily with sensory interpretation and thinking?   (1) spinal cord   (2) medulla   (3) cerebrum   (4) cerebellum

86. The somatic nervous system contains nerves that run from the central nervous system to the (1) muscles of the skeleton   (2) heart   (3) smooth muscles of the gastrointestinal tract   (4) endocrine glands

87. If the cerebellum of a human were damaged, which of the following would probably result? (1) inability to reason   (2) difficulty in breathing (3) loss of sight   (4) loss of balance

88. Which is the correct route of an impulse in a reflex arc?
(1) receptor → sensory neuron → interneuron → motor neuron → effector
(2) effector → receptor → motor neuron → sensory neuron → interneuron
(3) sensory neuron → effector → motor neuron → receptor → interneuron
(4) motor neuron → sensory neuron → interneuron → effector

Base your answers to questions 89 through 92 on the following diagram of the human brain.

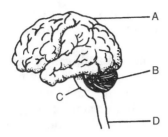

89. Injury to which part would most likely result in loss of memory?   (1) *A*   (2) *B*   (3) *C*   (4) *D*

90. Which part of the brain controls the involuntary movements of the digestive system?   (1) *A*   (2) *B*   (3) *C*   (4) *D*

91. Which part of the brain is involved with balance and the coordination of body movements?   (1) *A*   (2) *B*   (3) *C*   (4) *D*

92. Sight and hearing are functions of the structure labeled   (1) *A*   (2) *B*   (3) *C*   (4) *D*

93. The brain and the spinal cord make up the (1) autonomic nervous system   (2) peripheral nervous system   (3) central nervous system (4) somatic nervous system

94. Impulses are transmitted from receptors to the central nervous system by   (1) receptor neurons   (2) sensory neurons   (3) interneurons (4) motor neurons

Short Answer
(Constructed Response)

95. Use the following terms to complete the chart below, which outlines the organization of the human nervous system: somatic nervous system, brain, cerebrum, cerebellum, autonomic nervous system, medulla, spinal cord.

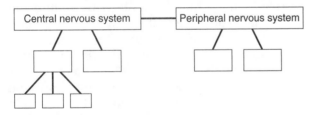

96. The brain is divided into three major regions: the cerebrum, cerebellum, and medulla. In full sentences, describe the role that each part plays in the human nervous system.

Essay
(Extended Constructed Response)

97. Explain how a reflex arc works to protect the human body from a potentially dangerous stimulus. Provide an example.

98. The human nervous system is one of the most (if not *the* most) complex of all in the entire animal kingdom. Discuss three ways that our nervous system has allowed us (for better or worse) to make such "advanced" accomplishments in relation to the rest of the natural world.

ENDOCRINE SYSTEM

The human endocrine system is made up of the endocrine glands, which secrete hormones directly into the blood. The hormones are transported by the circulatory system to the organs and tissues on which they act.

Endocrine Glands.
The glands of the human endocrine system are the hypothalamus, pituitary, thyroid, parathyroids, adrenals, islets of Langerhans, and gonads (ovaries and testes) (Figure 3-14).

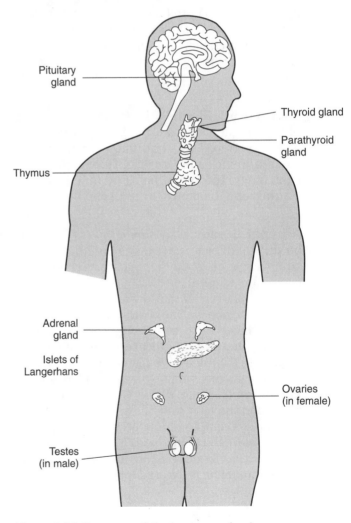

Figure 3-14. Structure of the human endocrine system.

Hypothalamus. Hormone-secreting cells are present in a small part of the brain called the *hypothalamus*. The hormones of the hypothalamus influence the activities of the pituitary gland.

Pituitary Gland. Many hormones are secreted by the *pituitary gland*, which is located at the base of the brain. Some pituitary hormones regulate the activities of other endocrine glands.

Growth-stimulating hormone is a pituitary hormone that has widespread effects in the body in addition to stimulating the growth of long bones.

Thyroid-stimulating hormone (TSH) is a pituitary hormone that stimulates the secretion of the thyroid hormone thyroxin.

Follicle-stimulating hormone (FSH) is a pituitary hormone that stimulates the development of follicles in the ovaries of females. In males, it influences sperm production.

Thyroid Gland. The iodine-containing hormone *thyroxin* is produced by the *thyroid gland*, which is located in the neck. Thyroxin regulates the rate of metabolism in the body cells and is essential for normal physical and mental development.

Parathyroid Glands. Embedded in the back of the thyroid gland are the *parathyroid glands*, which secrete the hormone *parathormone*. Parathormone controls calcium metabolism. Calcium is required for normal nerve function, blood clotting, and the growth of teeth and bones.

Adrenal Glands. An *adrenal gland* is located on the top of each kidney. The outer layer of the adrenal glands is the adrenal cortex; the inner layer is the adrenal medulla.

The *adrenal cortex* secretes two types of steroid hormones. One type stimulates the conversion of fats and proteins to glucose, thereby increasing the level of glucose in the blood. The other type stimulates the reabsorption of sodium from the kidney tubules into the bloodstream. The concentration of sodium in the blood affects blood pressure and water balance.

The *adrenal medulla* secretes the hormone *adrenaline*, which increases the blood glucose level and accelerates the heartbeat and breathing rates. Adrenaline is released in times of stress and heavy exercise.

Islets of Langerhans. The small groups of endocrine cells that are found throughout the pancreas are called the *islets of Langerhans*. These endocrine cells secrete the hormones insulin and glucagon.

The hormone **insulin** promotes the absorption of glucose from the blood into the body cells, thereby lowering the blood glucose level. It also stimulates the conversion of glucose to glycogen in the liver and in skeletal muscle.

The hormone *glucagon* increases the blood glucose level by promoting the conversion of glycogen to glucose in the liver and skeletal muscle. The glucose then passes from the organs back into the blood. Through their opposite effects, insulin and glucagon function to help the body maintain homeostasis by keeping the blood glucose level within certain limits.

The Gonads. The male and female *gonads*—the testes and ovaries—both function as endocrine glands. The **testes** (singular, *testis*) secrete the male sex hormone **testosterone**, which stimulates the development of the male reproductive organs and secondary sex characteristics; it also stimulates the production of **sperm**. The **ovaries** secrete the female sex hormones **estrogen** and **progesterone**. Estrogen influences the development of the female reproductive organs and secondary sex characteristics; it also stimulates the production of **egg** cells. Progesterone stimulates the thickening of the uterine lining in preparation for the implantation of an **embryo** (the fertilized egg cell).

Negative Feedback

The secretion of hormones by the endocrine glands is regulated by a mechanism known as *negative feedback*. In many cases, the level of one hormone in the blood stimulates or inhibits the production of a second hormone. The blood level of the second hormone in turn stimulates or inhibits the production of the first hormone. For example, the relationship between the pituitary's secretion of thyroid-stimulating hormone (TSH) and the thyroid's secretion of the hormone thyroxin is a classic type of *negative feedback mechanism*.

When the concentration of thyroxin in the blood drops below a certain level, the pituitary is stimulated to secrete TSH. This hormone, in turn, then stimulates the secretion of thyroxin by the thyroid. When the blood thyroxin concentration reaches a certain level, the further secretion of TSH by the pituitary is inhibited. In this way, the body can regulate thyroxin levels—just as it regulates carbon dioxide levels—in order to maintain **stability**, or homeostasis.

Disorders of the Endocrine System

A *goiter* is an enlargement of the thyroid gland that is most commonly caused by a lack of iodine in the diet. *Diabetes* is a disorder in which the islets of Langerhans do not secrete adequate amounts of insulin into the bloodstream and, as a result, the blood glucose level is elevated.

Questions

Multiple Choice

99. Which of the following is *not* an endocrine gland?   (1) thyroid   (2) salivary gland   (3) pancreas   (4) testis

100. The part of the brain that is most directly related to the endocrine system is the   (1) cerebrum   (2) medulla   (3) hypothalamus   (4) cerebellum

101. Which structure secretes the substance it produces directly into the bloodstream?   (1) gallbladder   (2) salivary gland   (3) adrenal gland   (4) skin

102. The hormones insulin and glucagon are produced by the   (1) thyroid   (2) pituitary   (3) pancreas   (4) liver

103. Which hormone lowers blood sugar levels by increasing the rate of absorption of glucose by the body cells?   (1) follicle-stimulating hormone   (2) insulin   (3) parathormone   (4) adrenalin

104. A person was admitted to the hospital with abnormally high blood sugar level and a very high sugar content in his urine. Which gland most likely caused this condition by secreting lower than normal amounts of its hormone?   (1) pancreas   (2) parathyroid   (3) salivary   (4) thyroid

105. Which hormone stimulates activity in the ovaries?   (1) testosterone   (2) thyroid stimulating hormone   (3) insulin   (4) follicle stimulating hormone

106. A person's rate of metabolism is regulated by a hormone secreted by the   (1) parathyroids   (2) thyroid   (3) pancreas   (4) adrenals

107. Estrogen, which influences the development of secondary sex characteristics, is secreted by the   (1) pituitary   (2) adrenals   (3) parathyroids   (4) ovaries

108. In humans, the level of calcium in the blood is regulated by the   (1) pancreas   (2) thyroid   (3) adrenals   (4) parathyroids

109. The mechanism that regulates the secretion of hormones by endocrine glands is called (1) peristalsis   (2) active transport   (3) negative feedback   (4) filtration

110. Insufficient iodine in the diet may cause goiter, a disorder of the   (1) adrenal glands   (2) pancreas   (3) pituitary gland   (4) thyroid gland

Short Answer
(Constructed Response)

Base your answers to questions 111 through 114 on the graph below, which shows the levels of glucose and insulin present in a person's blood after eating a meal.

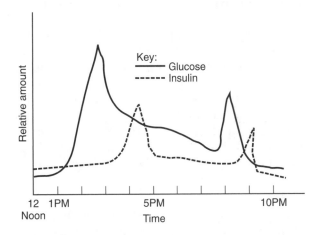

111. At approximately what times did the glucose level spike in this person?

112. What effect does insulin seem to have on the blood glucose level?

113. Describe the apparent relationship between the levels of glucose and the levels of insulin.

114. What is the most probable reason for the time lag between the spikes in glucose level and the spikes in insulin level?

Essay
(Extended Constructed Response)

115. Explain how a negative feedback mechanism works by describing how the pituitary gland and thyroid gland affect each other. How does this feedback mechanism help in the maintenance of homeostasis? (Be sure to mention the hormones produced by each gland.)

LOCOMOTION

Locomotion, or movement, in humans involves the interaction of bones, cartilage, muscles, tendons, and ligaments.

Bones

The human skeleton is made up mainly of bones of various shapes and sizes. All bones are made of *bone tissue*, which is quite hard and rigid. Bones provide support and protection for the soft parts of the body; they are the sites of attachment for muscles; and, at joints, bones act as levers, enabling the body to move when the attached muscles contract. The production of new red blood cells and white blood cells occurs in the marrow of certain long bones.

Cartilage

In addition to bone, the human skeleton contains *cartilage*, a type of flexible, fibrous, elastic connective tissue. In embryos, most of the skeleton is made of cartilage. After birth, a child's cartilage is gradually replaced by bone, so that in adults, almost all of the cartilage has been replaced. In adults, cartilage is found at the ends of ribs, between vertebrae, at the ends of bones, and in the nose, ears, and trachea. Cartilage provides cushioning and flexibility at joints, and support and pliability in structures such as the nose and ears.

Joints

The places in the skeleton where the bones are connected to each other are called *joints*. Joints make movement of the skeleton possible. There are several kinds of movable joints in the human body. *Hinge joints*, which can move back and forth, are in the elbow and knee. *Ball-and-socket joints*, which are capable of circular movements, are found in the shoulder and hip. The neck has a *pivot joint*, which can move in a half circle. The bones of the skull are joined in *immovable joints*.

Muscles

Unlike other body tissues, muscle tissue has the capacity to contract, or shorten. All movement in the body involves muscle tissue. There are three types of muscle tissue in the human body: skeletal muscle, smooth muscle, and cardiac muscle (Figure 3-15).

Skeletal Muscle. The voluntary muscles attached to the bones of the skeleton are made of *skeletal muscle* tissue. Muscle tissue of this type appears striated, or striped, when viewed with a microscope, and is also known as *striated muscle*. The contraction of skeletal muscle is controlled by the nervous system, which makes coordinated movements possible.

Skeletal muscles generally operate in antagonistic pairs; the contraction of one muscle of the pair extends the limb, while contraction of the

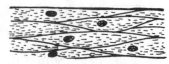

Smooth muscle

Cardiac muscle

Skeletal muscle

Figure 3-15. Smooth, cardiac, and skeletal muscle.

other muscle flexes the limb. Figure 3-16 shows the muscles of the upper arm. The triceps is the extensor, while the biceps is the flexor. When the biceps contracts, the triceps relaxes, and the arm flexes, bending at the elbow. When the triceps contracts, the biceps relaxes, and the arm is extended.

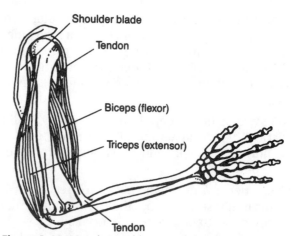

Figure 3-16. Muscles and bones of the upper arm.

Smooth Muscle. When viewed with a microscope, *smooth muscle* tissue does not appear striated. This type of muscle, which is also called *visceral muscle*, is found in the walls of the digestive organs and arteries, as well as in other internal organs. Smooth muscles are not under voluntary control.

Cardiac Muscle. The *cardiac muscle* tissue is found only in the heart. Although it appears striated when viewed with a microscope, cardiac muscle tissue is not under voluntary control, and its structure is different from that of skeletal muscle tissue.

Tendons and Ligaments

Muscles are attached to bones by tough, inelastic, fibrous cords of connective tissue called *tendons.* Bones are connected together at movable joints by *ligaments,* which are composed of tough, elastic connective tissue.

Disorders of Locomotion

Arthritis is an inflammation of the joints, which can be very painful and make movement difficult. *Tendonitis* is an inflammation of a tendon, usually where it is attached to a bone. This condition occurs most commonly in athletes.

Questions

Multiple Choice

116. Which type of muscle tissue found in the walls of the human stomach is most closely associated with the process of peristalsis? (1) striated (2) cardiac (3) voluntary (4) smooth

117. Bones are attached to each other at movable joints by (1) elastic ligaments (2) cartilaginous tissues (3) smooth muscles (4) skeletal muscles

118. Which is *not* a major function of cartilage tissues in a human adult? (1) giving pliable support to body structures (2) cushioning joint areas (3) adding flexibility to joints (4) providing skeletal levers

119. Which type of connective tissue makes up the greatest proportion of the skeleton of a human embryo? (1) ligaments (2) cartilage (3) tendons (4) bone

120. Which structure contains pairs of opposing skeletal muscles? (1) stomach (2) small intestine (3) heart (4) hand

121. Which statement most accurately describes human skeletal muscle tissue? (1) It is involuntary and striated. (2) It is involuntary and lacks striations. (3) It is voluntary and striated. (4) It is voluntary and lacks striations.

122. In the human elbow joint, the bone of the upper arm is connected to the bones of the lower arm by flexible connective tissue called (1) tendons (2) ligaments (3) muscles (4) neurons

For each phrase in questions 123 through 127, select the human body structure in the list below that is best described by that phrase.

Human Body Structures
A. Bones
B. Cartilage tissues
C. Ligaments
D. Smooth muscles
E. Tendons
F. Voluntary muscles

123. Cause peristalsis in the digestive tract (1) *B* (2) *C* (3) *D* (4) *F*

124. Serve as extensors and flexors (1) *A* (2) *D* (3) *E* (4) *F*

125. Serve as levers for body movements (1) *A* (2) *B* (3) *C* (4) *E*

126. Bind the ends of bones together (1) *B* (2) *C* (3) *D* (4) *E*

127. Attach the muscles to bones (1) *B* (2) *C* (3) *D* (4) *E*

Short Answer
(Constructed Response)

128. In complete sentences, briefly compare and contrast the following pairs of structures found in the human skeletal and muscular (locomotion) systems:
a) Skeletal and smooth muscle
b) Tendon and ligament
c) Bone and cartilage

Refer to Figure 3-16, which shows the human arm with its bones and (upper arm) muscles, to answer questions 129 through 132. Be sure to phrase your answers in complete sentences.

129. Describe what happens to the arm when the biceps contracts.

130. What happens to the arm when the triceps contracts?

131. Why are the biceps and triceps considered an antagonistic pair?

132. What do you think is the origin of the phrase "flex your muscles"?

Essay
(Extended Constructed Response)

133. Describe the roles that muscles, tendons, bones, and joints play in locomotion.

134. How do the skeletal and muscular systems interact to produce locomotion?

135. Discuss four advantages that locomotion gives to an organism.

Reading Comprehension

Base your answers to questions 136 through 140 on the information below and on your knowledge of biology. Source: *Science News* (June 10, 2000): vol. 157, no. 24, p. 381.

Bypass Surgery in Elderly Works Fine

People over age 75 fare nearly as well during the years immediately after coronary artery bypass surgery as people roughly 15 years younger do, researchers in Japan reported in May.

The researchers tracked the postoperative progress of 190 patients over 75 years old and 1,380 others under 75 years. The average age of people in the older group was 77 and in the other group, 62. People in both groups had sought care for various heart problems. All underwent coronary artery bypass surgery at Shin-Tokyo Hospital in Chiba.

Patients in the other group were more likely than those in the younger group to have complications from surgery—27 percent versus 14 percent. The older patients also were more prone to congestive heart failure during the follow-up period, which averaged 3 years, the researchers report.

However, the incidence of heart-related deaths in the two groups was similar. The researchers also found that the overall frequency of cardiac problems 1, 3, or 5 years after surgery didn't differ significantly between the groups. Indeed, at least 88 percent of the older patients had no new cardiac problems during the follow-up period.

Many elderly cardiac patients and their spouses "are very anxious about the fate of patients after [bypass] surgery," says study coauthor Hitoshi Hirose, a physician at Shin-Tokyo Hospital. Because of the new results, he says, "I believe more elderly people may go for the surgery."

In bypass surgery, physicians typically use a vein taken from another part of the body and surgically attach it to the heart to reroute blood around a clogged coronary artery. How much blood can pass through the grafted vessel is a measure of the success of such operations. This measure didn't differ significantly between the two groups in the study.

136. What two problems do the elderly seem to experience more frequently (than younger patients do) just after coronary bypass surgery?

137. How does the frequency of cardiac problems compare in the younger and older groups one, three, and five years after surgery?

138. How might these new results affect the decision of the elderly to undergo surgery for heart problems?

139. In one complete sentence, explain how a bypass surgery is typically done.

140. How is the success of a bypass surgery measured?

CHAPTER 4

Maintaining Homeostasis

A DYNAMIC EQUILIBRIUM

Under normal circumstances, an organism is able to maintain stability, or homeostasis, in relation to both its internal and external environments. This maintaining of a **dynamic equilibrium** means that despite the fact that environmental conditions may change, an organism responds by taking corrective actions that restore healthy conditions within its body.

For example, to maintain its normal temperature of about 37° Celsius, the human body can make simple adjustments to keep its temperature within a safe range. If the body is too cold, small blood vessels in the skin may constrict in order to direct blood flow to the vital, internal organs. In addition, the body may shiver to generate more heat. If the body is overheated, blood vessels near the skin surface can dilate (open wider) to promote blood flow to the skin in order to lose heat to the surrounding air. The skin may also produce perspiration (sweat) as a means of lowering the body temperature.

Feedback Mechanisms

Many homeostatic adjustments in organisms involve interactions called *negative feedback mechanisms*, or feedback loops. An initial change in one part of the loop (in response to some changing condition) stimulates a reaction in another part of the system. When the condition has been corrected, the second part of the loop feeds back information to the first part, shutting it off. This, in turn, shuts off the response (that it initially caused) in the second part. Homeostasis is maintained. If conditions in the body change, the feedback system is triggered into action again.

A very common negative feedback loop involves the pituitary gland, the thyroid gland, and their hormones. If the level of thyroxin (a thyroid hormone that regulates metabolism) is too low, the pituitary gland secretes thyroid-stimulating hormone (TSH). This causes the thyroid to in-

crease its production of thyroxin. As the levels of thyroxin in the blood increase, the pituitary gland stops secreting TSH. Without the TSH, the thyroid slows down its secretion of thyroxin. In this way, the levels of thyroxin are maintained within normal limits (Figure 4-1).

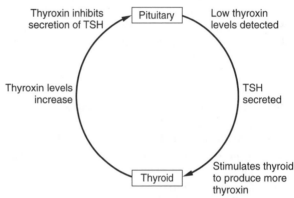

Figure 4-1. A negative feedback loop, involving the pituitary and thyroid glands.

WHEN HOMEOSTASIS FAILS: ILLNESS AND DISEASE

Causes of Disease

Any breakdown in an organism's ability to maintain or restore equilibrium can result in illness, disease, or even death. The causes of disease are many and varied. Diseases that are caused by factors inside the body are usually inherited and due to defective genetic traits. Diseases that are caused by factors outside the body, and that can be passed from one person to another, are called *infectious* diseases. Factors that cause such diseases include microorganisms, or **microbes**, that are harmful. These disease-causing microbes, called **pathogens**, may include bacteria, fungi, protozoa, and worms, as well as nonliving particles of protein and *nucleic acid*, called viruses.

Sometimes, unhealthful habits or risky behaviors can jeopardize health and lead to illness. Poor nutrition, cigarette smoking, and abuse of alcohol and drugs can all result in serious illness and a breakdown of homeostasis. For example, excessive consumption of alcoholic beverages can cause cirrhosis of the liver, a fatal disease.

Cancer. Disease may also occur when certain cells in the body behave abnormally due to a genetic mutation. Such cells can divide uncontrollably and result in the growth of *tumors*. Tumors may be benign (not spreading) or malignant (spreading). Uncontrolled growth, or *metastasis*, of malignant cells is known as **cancer**. When cancer cells spread throughout the body, they interfere with the functioning of normal cells. In such cases, the cancer can become life threatening. Although cancer may occur spontaneously, certain factors are known to increase the risk of developing it. Tobacco smoking, unhealthful diet, genetic factors, and exposure to **radiation** and certain chemicals called *carcinogens* are all thought to play a part in causing cancer.

Symptoms of Disease. Some diseases show their symptoms as soon as they begin to develop or soon after they are triggered by a pathogen. An example is influenza (the "flu"), which is caused by viruses. Other diseases may take several days, weeks, or even years before their symptoms appear. **AIDS** (*a*cquired *i*mmuno*d*eficiency *s*yndrome) and cancer are examples of diseases that may develop in the body for years before their symptoms appear.

Questions

Multiple Choice

1. The term that describes a body's overall ability to maintain homeostasis is (1) negative loop system (2) low maintenance (3) dynamic equilibrium (4) infectious

2. Which of the following items has been linked to the development of cancer? (1) cigarette smoking (2) genetic factors (3) exposure to radiation (4) all of the above

3. Pathogens may include all of the following *except* (1) fungi (2) protozoa (3) bacteria (4) plants

4. Viruses differ from other pathogens in that *only* viruses (1) contain a true nucleus (2) reproduce on their own every 20 minutes

(3) consist only of protein and nucleic acid
(4) are able to infect healthy cells

5. Which of the following represents a correct cause-and-effect sequence? (1) cirrhosis of the liver → excessive alcohol consumption (2) low thyroxin levels → increase in TSH secretion (3) symptoms of disease → exposure to pathogen (4) dilation of blood vessels in skin → overheating of the body

Short Answer (Constructed Response)

6. Select three of the following risk factors and, for each one selected, write one or two complete sentences in which you explain how that risk factor can interfere with the proper functioning of the immune system: drug abuse; poor nutrition; stress; smoking; radiation; genetic factors.

Base your answers to questions 7 through 9 on the diagram of the negative feedback loop, shown below, and on the following data: structure *A* releases a substance, *X*, that can stimulate structure *B* to release its substance, *Y*.

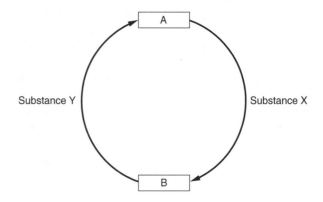

7. Under what conditions would structure *A* probably release substance *X*?

8. Explain what happens when the levels of substance *Y* get too high.

9. What type of substances are *X* and *Y* most likely to be?

THE IMMUNE SYSTEM: PROTECTION AGAINST DISEASE

The human body is well protected against invading pathogens. The first line of defense prevents harmful microorganisms from getting into the body by blocking their entry. The skin, when unbroken, provides an effective physical barrier to nearly all pathogenic organisms. Secretions such as tears, saliva, and mucus provide an effective physical and chemical barrier; they contain enzymes that destroy pathogens or help trap and flush them out of the body.

Nevertheless, some pathogens manage to elude the first line of defense and gain entry. They may do so through breaks in the skin (cuts and scrapes) or through the eyes and natural openings in the body, such as the mouth and nostrils. Once inside, these invaders are confronted by the *immune system*, the body's primary defense mechanism. Invaders may be destroyed by being engulfed by special cells or by being chemically marked for destruction and elimination.

Functions of the Immune System

How does the immune system function? All cells have very specific proteins on their plasma membrane surfaces. The immune system is able to recognize proteins on cells that are foreign and to distinguish them from its own body's proteins. These invading foreign proteins are referred to as *antigens*.

Specialized Blood Cells. The human immune system consists of specialized white blood cells and lymphatic organs such as the spleen, thymus, and tonsils. The system also has a number of *lymph nodes* that participate in defense mechanisms. Some white blood cells, called *macrophages*, engulf and digest pathogens. After destroying the pathogens, these white cells often die, too.

White blood cells called *T cells* are specialized to kill pathogens or mark them for destruction. Other white blood cells, called *B cells*, produce very specific *antibodies* against the pathogens. Antibodies have a chemical structure that precisely matches the shape of the antigen with which they react. Once the match has been made, the pathogen is destroyed. Some of the antibody-producing blood cells remain in the body's immune system as "memory cells." These specialized cells can quickly mount an attack if the body is invaded again by the same pathogen (Figure 4-2).

Vaccinations

A *vaccine* is a weakened pathogen or its antigen that is injected into a person. *Vaccinations* are given to people to provide *immunity* against particular pathogens. Once recognized by the immune system, antibodies specific to that antigen are made. The cells that produce the antibodies remain as memory cells in the person. If the actual pathogen invades the body at a later time,

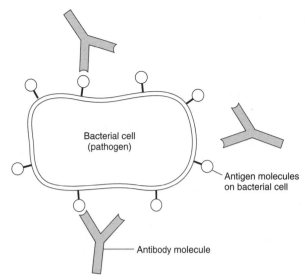

Figure 4-2. The immune system produces antibodies that are specific to the invading foreign antigens.

these memory cells can launch an immediate response and attack the invaders, often before they have a chance to cause any disease symptoms. Some examples of vaccines that are given to people include those for the flu, MMR (measles, mumps, rubella), and hepatitis. In most states, children must be vaccinated for several diseases before they are even permitted to attend school.

PROBLEMS IN THE IMMUNE SYSTEM

Overreactions of the Immune System

In some individuals, the immune system overreacts to certain stimuli or antigens that are harmless to most other people. Unfortunately, these severe reactions cause, rather than prevent, suffering and illness for the person.

Allergic Reactions. An *allergic reaction* is a strong response to allergens in pollen, animal fur, mold, insect stings, foods, and so on. The sufferer may experience sneezing, watery and itchy eyes, a runny nose, hives, coughing, and/or swelling. These uncomfortable symptoms are triggered by the immune system's release of substances called *histamines*. Although these allergy symptoms are inconvenient, they are responses made by the body in an attempt to expel the invading antigen. In some cases, the swelling may be so severe in the sinuses or throat that it interferes with breathing. An extreme type of allergic reaction, known as anaphylactic shock, occurs in some people in response to bee or wasp stings. This condition causes severe swelling and can be truly life threatening.

Autoimmune Diseases.

In very rare cases, the immune system accidentally targets some of the body's own cell proteins as antigens. Once the immune system has identified an antigen as foreign, the cells bearing that protein are attacked as if they were invading foreign pathogens. This reaction produces a condition known as an *autoimmune disease* (*auto* meaning "self"). Examples of such serious diseases include rheumatoid arthritis (which causes inflammation and pain in the joint membranes) and lupus erythematosus (which causes painful swelling of the skin and joints, fever, rash, hair loss, fatigue, and sensitivity to light).

Immune Response to Transplants.

People who receive transplanted organs, such as a heart, liver, or kidney (due to a *malfunction* of their own organ), may also experience problems with their immune response. Because the organ is recognized as foreign, the immune system may launch an attack against it, causing the body to reject the new organ. Physicians attempt to match the chemistry of the organ donor as closely as possible with that of the recipient, in order to minimize the risk of organ rejection. In addition, *immunosuppressant* drugs may be used to lessen the immune response. However, use of these medications can leave the transplant recipient quite vulnerable to infection by various microbes.

A Damaged or Weakened Immune System

HIV (*h*uman *i*mmunodeficiency *v*irus), the agent that causes AIDS, damages the immune system by destroying specific T cells known as *helper T cells*. This leaves the affected person with a severely limited immune response. For that reason, AIDS is called an *immunodeficiency disease*. In fact, AIDS sufferers are prone to and frequently die from a variety of diseases that a healthy person's immune system could probably conquer (especially with the use of medicine), rather than from the virus itself.

Finally, as a person gets older, his or her immune system gradually weakens in its ability to respond to pathogens or cancerous cells. Consequently, older adults may be more prone than younger individuals to becoming ill or developing (malignant) tumors. Fatigue, stress, substance abuse, and poor nutrition can also contribute to a weakened immune response.

Questions

Multiple Choice

10. Which cells are important components of the human immune system? (1) red blood cells (2) liver cells (3) white blood cells (4) nerve cells

11. A blood test showed that a person had increased levels of antibodies. This may indicate that the person has (1) an infection (2) diabetes (3) low blood pressure (4) an enlarged thyroid

12. Antibodies are produced by (1) T cells (2) lymph node cells (3) B cells (4) liver cells

13. Substances that trigger a defensive response by the immune system are called (1) antibodies (2) antigens (3) lymph nodes (4) macrophages

14. A similarity between antibodies and enzymes is that both (1) are lipids (2) are produced by liver cells (3) can make blood vessels dilate (4) have very specific shapes and functions

15. Vaccines are given to people in order to (1) upset their homeostasis (2) immunize them against certain diseases (3) inject T cells and B cells into them (4) test if they can destroy the pathogen

16. A person's sneezing, coughing, and watery eyes right after exposure to cat hair are all indications of (1) an autoimmune disease (2) an infection caused by the cat (3) an allergic reaction (4) early warning signs of cancer

Short Answer
(Constructed Response)

Base your answers to questions 17 through 19 on the graph below, which shows the relationship between exposure to an antigen and the antibody response that followed. Be sure to use complete sentences to answer all questions.

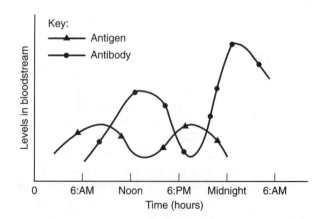

17. At what times did the antigen reach maximum levels in the bloodstream?

18. What relationship exists between the antigen levels and antibody levels in this graph?

19. The second peak of the antibody level is much greater than the first peak. Explain why.

Essay
(Extended Constructed Response)

20. A pharmaceutical company is proposing that its new product, Immunoblast, can help strengthen a person's immune system. Design an experiment in which you could test the effectiveness of this new product. Include the following steps: (a) state the problem you are investigating; (b) propose a suitable hypothesis; and (c) write out clearly the procedure you would follow to carry out your experiment.

21. Each year, before the start of the flu season, older adults are advised to get a flu shot, or vaccination, to protect them. In a brief essay, answer the following questions: (a) Why is the flu shot recommended more for older adults than for younger ones? (b) How is the vaccine intended to protect people from the flu? (c) Why do some people who receive the flu shot actually get the flu from it? (d) Why is a new vaccination needed every year?

22. Describe two ways that the risk of organ rejection can be minimized in a transplant patient. Discuss one problem that is associated with one of the methods you have described.

Reading Comprehension

Base your answers to questions 23 through 26 on the information below and on your knowledge of biology. Source: *Science News* (July 15, 2000): vol. 158, no. 3, p. 40.

Hormone Treats Autoimmune Disease

A medication combining the drug prasterone and the hormone dehydroepiandrosterone, or DHEA, stabilizes or improves symptoms of the autoimmune disease lupus, according to a study from a company in California.

People with systemic lupus erythematosus suffer severe immune responses against their own body. Symptoms include skin rashes, arthritis, muscle pain, and sometimes organ damage.

Among 265 women with mild to moderate lupus, 132 receiving the drug combo, called GL701, reported fewer flare-ups of their disease than 133 women receiving a placebo, says Kenneth E. Schwartz of Genelabs Technologies in Redwood City, Calif.

After 60 days of treatment, 66 percent of the women taking GL701 showed improvement in disease severity and self-reported quality of life, compared with 49 percent of the women taking a placebo, says Schwartz. "The therapeutic effect was most apparent in patients with more severe disease," he says.

As a possible drawback to GL701, women had lower blood concentrations of high-density lipoproteins, which make up so-called good cholesterol, after taking the drug than before. Genelabs is currently seeking FDA approval for GL701. If approved, it would be the first new treatment for lupus in about 40 years.

23. What is lupus erythematosus? Name three of its symptoms.

24. How is the medication called GL701 prepared (that is, what is it made up of)?

25. According to the article, what scientific evidence supports the efficacy of the drug GL 701?

26. Describe a possible drawback to the use of this new medication.

Base your answers to questions 27 through 30 on the following information and on your knowledge of biology. Source: *Science News* (July 22, 2000): vol. 158, no. 4, p. 63.

Man-made Thymus Churns out Immune Cells

In the thymus, so-called T cells mature into full-fledged immune system sentinels. Seeking better ways to grow these white blood cells in the laboratory, David T. Scadden of Massachusetts General Hospital in Boston and his colleagues have built an artificial thymus by seeding a three-dimensional carbon matrix with tissue from the immune organ.

When precursor T cells are added to this matrix, mature cells emerge within 2 weeks, the investigators report in the July NATURE BIOTECHNOLOGY. This artificial thymus "has the potential to generate not only normal T cells to replace cells lost as a result of infection, chemotherapy, radiotherapy or aging, but also cells that can be manipulated to treat a number of diseases," David L. Porter and Stephen G. Emerson, both of the University of Pennsylvania in Philadelphia, say in an accompanying commentary.

27. What role does the thymus gland play in immunity?

28. How did scientists produce the artificial thymus?

29. According to the article, what evidence is there that the artificial thymus actually functions like a real thymus?

30. As children mature, their thymus gland gradually shrinks so that, by the time they are adults, the gland has stopped working and totally disappeared. Predict how the artificial thymus might be used one day to treat children and adults who suffer from AIDS.

Base your answers to questions 31 to 34 on the information below and on your knowledge of biology. Use one or more complete sentences to answer each question.

Anthrax: Causes and Cures

A health issue that has been prominent in the news recently is an infectious disease called anthrax. Although normally restricted to grazing animals and the people who work closely with them, anthrax has become an issue of wider concern because of its use as an agent of germ warfare, or bioterrorism. Anthrax is caused by bacteria, called *Bacillus anthracis,* which form spores that can remain dormant in the soil for decades. The spores can find their way into a host, such as a cow or human, by being breathed in, swallowed, or through a break in the skin. These three routes of anthrax infection are called inhalation, intestinal, and cutaneous. Once inside the host's body, the spores are engulfed by scavenger cells of the body's immune system. The spores then become active, releasing anthrax bacteria that divide and replicate. The bacteria release a toxin that, while not very deadly itself, triggers an overreaction by the immune system so that it turns against itself. This can lead to the death of the host.

The symptoms of anthrax differ according to the method of infection. A cutaneous anthrax infection begins at the point of entry on the skin as a small bump resembling an insect bite. The bump quickly develops into a sore or lesion with a black area in the center. About 20 percent of cutaneous anthrax cases will result in death if left untreated. Symptoms of intestinal anthrax include vomiting, fever, and severe diarrhea. About 25 to 60 percent of intestinal anthrax cases lead to death. For inhalation anthrax, the initial symptoms are similar to those of a cold or flu. After several days, however, the symptoms progress to severe breathing problems, shock, and organ failure. This form of anthrax is usually fatal.

Because anthrax is caused by a type of bacterium, the disease generally responds well to antibiotics, if treatment begins soon after infection. The antibiotic most often prescribed for anthrax is called *Cipro* (or ciprofloxacin), but other antibiotics are effective against anthrax as well, including doxycycline, tetracycline, and penicillin. Many people in areas where anthrax cases have been reported want to start taking antibiotics right away, even if there is little or no risk that they have been exposed. However, doctors are reluctant to encourage unnecessary use of antibiotics, because such overuse can lead to the development of drug-resistant bacteria. There is also a vaccine that can provide protection against anthrax infection. Use of the vaccine is generally restricted to laboratory technicians and members of the armed forces, but the list of people eligible for the vaccine may be expanded in light of recent events.

31. What are the three methods by which an individual can become infected by anthrax?

32. People who work with wool clothing or blankets seem to be at higher risk of contracting anthrax. What might explain this?

33. Which type of anthrax infection is the most deadly?

34. Why do doctors caution against people needlessly taking antibiotics?

Reproduction and Development

The survival of a species depends on reproduction, that is, the production of new individuals. There are two ways that organisms can reproduce: **asexually** and **sexually**. In *asexual reproduction*, only one parent is involved, and the new organism develops from a cell or cells of the parent organism. In *sexual reproduction,* there are usually two parents, and each one contributes a specialized **sex cell** to the new organism. The two sex cells, one from each parent, fuse to form the first cell of the new generation.

MITOSIS

All cells arise from other cells by cell division, during which the nucleus duplicates, or **replicates**, and the cytoplasm divides in two, forming two cells. The process of **mitosis** (a nuclear process) is the orderly series of changes that results in the duplication of the complete set of chromosomes and the formation of two new nuclei that are identical to each other and to the nucleus of the original parent cell. The division of the cytoplasm occurs either during or after mitosis, and it results in the formation of two new, identical daughter cells. The effect of this is that all the cells that come from a single cell are genetically identical to it and to each other; they are all *clones.*

Events of Mitosis

During the period between cell divisions, the chromosome material is dispersed in the nucleus in the form of *chromatin*. At the beginning of mitosis, before the chromosomes become visible as distinct units, the chromatin replicates. It then contracts, forming a visible set of double-stranded chromosomes. Each double-stranded chromosome consists of two identical strands, or *chromatids*, joined by a *centromere* (Figure 5-1).

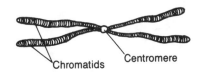

Figure 5-1. A double-stranded chromosome.

During the early stages of mitosis, the nuclear membrane disintegrates and disappears, while a network of fibers called the *spindle apparatus* forms. In animal cells, two small organelles called *centrioles* move to the opposite ends, or *poles*, of the cell, where they are involved in the formation of the spindle apparatus. Plant cells generally lack centrioles, but the spindle apparatus forms without them, and the movement of chromosomes is similar to that in animal cells.

The double-stranded chromosomes become attached to the spindle apparatus and line up along the cell's center, or equator. The two chromatids of each double-stranded chromosome separate and move to opposite poles of the cell. A nuclear membrane forms around each of the two sets of single-stranded chromosomes, forming two daughter nuclei—identical to each other and to the original nucleus (Figure 5-2, page 58).

Division of the Cytoplasm

In animal cells, the cytoplasm is divided when the cell membrane "pinches in" at the cell's center, separating the two nuclei and dividing the cytoplasm into approximately equal halves.

In plant cells, the cytoplasm is divided when a *cell plate* forms across the center of the cell. The cell plate then forms the new cell walls.

Uncontrolled Cell Division

In multicellular organisms, cells sometimes undergo abnormal and rapid divisions, resulting in growths called tumors, which invade surrounding

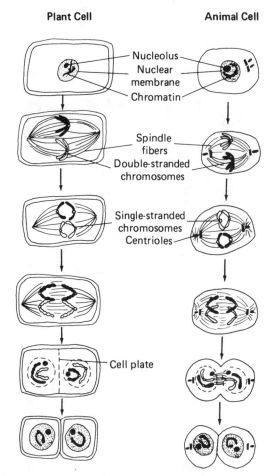

Plant Cell   Animal Cell

Nucleolus
Nuclear membrane
Chromatin

Spindle fibers
Double-stranded chromosomes

Single-stranded chromosomes
Centrioles

Cell plate

Figure 5-2. Stages of mitosis.

tissues and organs and interfere with their normal activities. Such tumors are linked to a group of diseases known, collectively, as *cancer.* (For more information, refer to Chapter 4).

Questions

Multiple Choice

1. Each of the two daughter cells that results from the normal mitotic division of the original parent cell contains   (1) the same number of chromosomes but has genes different from those of the parent cell   (2) the same number of chromosomes and has genes identical to those of the parent cell   (3) one-half the number of chromosomes but has genes different from those of the parent cell   (4) one-half the number of chromosomes and has genes identical to those of the parent cell

2. The following list describes some of the events associated with normal cell division.
A. nuclear membrane formation around each set of newly formed chromosomes

B. pinching in of cell membrane to separate daughter nuclei and divide cytoplasm
C. replication of each chromosome to form sets of double-stranded chromosomes
D. movement of single-stranded chromosomes to opposite ends of the spindle fibers
What is the normal sequence in which these events occur?   (1) $A \rightarrow B \rightarrow C \rightarrow D$ (2) $C \rightarrow B \rightarrow D \rightarrow A$ (3) $C \rightarrow D \rightarrow A \rightarrow B$ (4) $D \rightarrow C \rightarrow B \rightarrow A$

3. What is the result of normal chromosome replication?   (1) Lost or worn-out chromosomes are replaced.   (2) Each daughter cell is provided with twice as many chromosomes as the parent cell.   (3) The exact number of centrioles is produced for spindle fiber attachment.   (4) Two identical sets of chromosomes are produced.

4. Normally, a complete set of chromosomes is passed on to each daughter cell as a result of   (1) reduction division   (2) mitotic cell division   (3) meiotic cell division   (4) nondisjunction

5. In nondividing cells, the chromosome material is in the form of   (1) chromatids   (2) centrioles   (3) spindle fibers   (4) chromatin

6. Organelles that play a role in mitotic division in animal cells but not in plant cells are   (1) centrioles   (2) chromatids   (3) cell plates   (4) chromosomes

Short Answer
(Constructed Response)

7. Colchicine is a drug that prevents chromosomes from separating during cell division. In a full sentence, describe how colchicine might affect daughter cells produced by a cell during mitosis.

8. Red blood cells lose their nuclei when they become fully mature. How does this explain the fact that red blood cells cannot undergo mitosis? Be sure to answer in a complete sentence.

Essay
(Extended Constructed Response)

9. Compare and contrast the process of mitosis in a plant cell and in an animal cell.

10. Research how a tumor forms. What role does mitosis play in the formation of a tumor?

TYPES OF ASEXUAL REPRODUCTION

Asexual reproduction is the production of new organisms without the joining of nuclei from two specialized sex cells. In asexual reproduction, the new organism develops by mitotic cell divisions, and the offspring are genetically identical to the parent.

Binary Fission

The form of asexual reproduction that occurs most commonly in one-celled organisms, such as the ameba and paramecium, is *binary fission* (Figure 5-3). In this type of reproduction, the nucleus divides by mitosis, and the cytoplasm divides, forming two daughter cells of equal size. These newly formed cells are smaller than the parent cell, but they contain the same number of chromosomes.

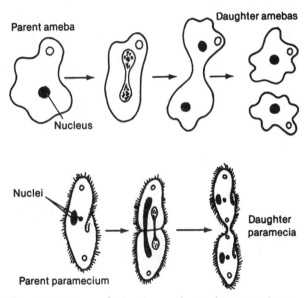

Figure 5-3. Binary fission in ameba and paramecium.

Budding

Yeasts and some other simple organisms carry on a form of asexual reproduction called *budding*, which is basically similar to binary fission. However, in budding, the division of the cytoplasm is unequal, so that one of the daughter cells is larger than the other. The daughter cells may separate, or they may remain attached, forming a colony (Figure 5-4).

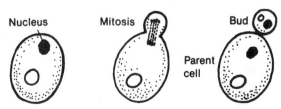

Figure 5-4. Budding in yeast.

In multicellular organisms such as the hydra, budding refers to the production of a multicellular growth, or *bud*, from the body of the parent (Figure 5-5). The bud is produced by mitotic cell division, and it develops into a new organism. The new organism may detach from the parent, or it may remain attached, forming a colony.

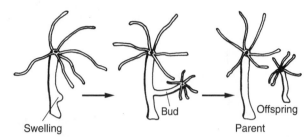

Figure 5-5. Budding in hydra.

Sporulation

In some multicellular organisms, such as bread mold, specialized cells called *spores* are produced in large numbers by mitosis. This process is called *sporulation*. Spores are generally surrounded by a tough coat, which enables them to survive harsh environmental conditions. Each spore may then develop into a new organism when environmental conditions become favorable.

Regeneration

The process of *regeneration* refers to the replacement, or regrowth, of lost or damaged body parts. For example, a lobster may regenerate a lost claw. In some cases, an entire new animal can develop from a part of the parent organism. A new sea star can develop from one arm and part of the central disk of an existing sea star (which then regenerates the missing arm). In this case, regeneration is a type of asexual reproduction.

Invertebrates generally show a greater capacity for regeneration than vertebrates do, probably because they have many more unspecialized cells and parts than vertebrates do.

Vegetative Propagation

In plants, *vegetative propagation* involves various forms of asexual reproduction in which new plants develop from the roots, stems, or leaves of the parent plant. Examples include new plant growth from bulbs, tubers, cuttings, and runners (Figure 5-6 on page 60).

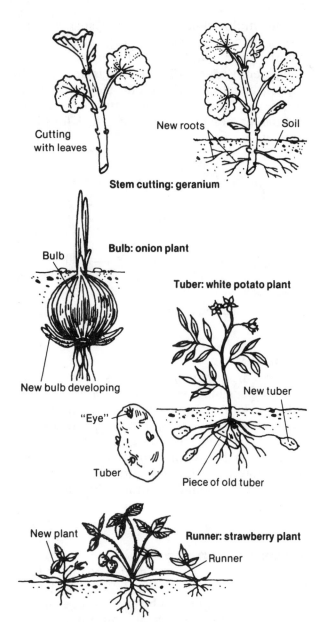

Stem cutting: geranium

Bulb: onion plant

Tuber: white potato plant

Runner: strawberry plant

Figure 5-6. Forms of vegetative propagation.

Questions

Multiple Choice

11. Compared to the parent cell, a daughter cell produced as a result of binary fission (1) has one-half as many chromosomes (2) has twice as many chromosomes (3) is the same size, but has fewer chromosomes (4) is smaller but has the same number of chromosomes

12. A form of asexual reproduction that occurs in yeast is (1) binary fission (2) budding (3) vegetative propagation (4) spore formation

13. What is a type of asexual reproduction that commonly occurs in many species of unicellular protists? (1) external fertilization (2) tissue regeneration (3) binary fission (4) vegetative propagation

14. A type of asexual reproduction in which new plants develop from the roots, stems, or leaves of an existing plant is called (1) binary fission (2) sporulation (3) regeneration (4) vegetative propagation

15. A form of asexual reproduction found in bread mold involves the production of large numbers of specialized cells, each surrounded by a tough coat. This process is called (1) binary fission (2) budding (3) sporulation (4) regeneration

16. Compared to vertebrates, invertebrate animals exhibit a higher degree of regenerative ability because they (1) produce larger numbers of sex cells (2) produce larger numbers of spindle fibers (3) possess more chromosomes in their nuclei (4) possess more undifferentiated cells

17. What specific type of reproduction is shown below in the diagrams of an ameba? (1) vegetative propagation (2) binary fission (3) budding (4) meiosis

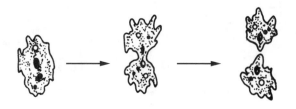

Short Answer (Constructed Response)

18. The ameba is a one-celled organism that reproduces asexually by mitosis. In one sentence, explain why all the offspring of a single ameba can be considered clones.

19. A scientist noted that a paramecium culture he had in his laboratory reproduced more rapidly than average when kept in a sunny corner of the room. Other paramecium cultures kept in darker parts of the room reproduced more slowly. Use your knowledge of biology to complete parts *a* through *c* below.
a) Write a testable question this observation might lead the scientist to ask.
b) State one plausible hypothesis to explain the scientist's observations.
c) Write an experimental procedure that the scientist could use to test the hypothesis.

20. What role does mitosis play in asexual reproduction?

21. In what ways are regeneration and vegetative propagation similar? Why are the offspring identical to the parent in both processes?

MEIOSIS AND SEXUAL REPRODUCTION

In organisms that reproduce sexually, specialized sex cells, or **gametes**, are produced by *meiosis,* a special kind of cell division. One type of gamete, the *sperm cell,* is produced by the male parent, while the other type of gamete, the *egg cell,* is produced by the female parent. The fusion of the nuclei of the sperm cell and the egg cell is called **fertilization**. The resulting cell, which is called the **zygote**, undergoes repeated mitotic cell divisions to form the *embryo.*

Chromosome Number

All members of a given species have a characteristic number of chromosomes in each of their body cells. This *diploid,* or *2n, chromosome number* normally remains constant from generation to generation. For example, all human body cells have 46 chromosomes, fruit flies have 8, and garden peas have 14.

The chromosomes of a body cell are actually in the form of *homologous pairs.* The two chromosomes of each homologous pair are similar in size and shape, and control the same traits. Thus, in human body cells there are 23 pairs of homologous chromosomes (23 from the mother and 23 from the father), in fruit flies there are 4 pairs, and in garden peas there are 7 pairs.

Mature sperm and egg cells contain half the diploid number of chromosomes—they contain one member of each homologous pair. Half the diploid chromosome number is called the *monoploid,* or *1n, chromosome number.* Mature sex cells (gametes) contain the monoploid (also called *haploid*) number of chromosomes; every other cell in the body contains the diploid number.

In sexually mature individuals, monoploid egg cells and sperm cells are formed in the gonads (ovaries and testes) by the process of **meiosis,** or *reduction division.*

Meiosis

Meiosis occurs only in maturing sex cells and consists of two nuclear and cytoplasmic divisions but only one chromosome replication. The first meiotic division produces two cells, each containing the monoploid number of double-stranded chromosomes. The second meiotic division results in the formation of four cells, each containing the monoploid number of single-stranded chromosomes.

As a result of meiosis, a single primary sex cell with the diploid chromosome number gives rise to four cells, each with the monoploid (*n*) chromosome number. These cells mature into gametes—either sperm cells or egg cells.

Meiosis is a source of genetic variations because it provides new combinations of chromosomes for the resulting gametes. A gamete receives only one member of each pair of homologous chromosomes from the 2*n* primary sex cells. The sorting of these chromosomes during formation of the gametes is random.

Gametogenesis

The process by which sperm and eggs are produced is called *gametogenesis.* It involves meiotic cell division and cell maturation. Gametogenesis occurs in specialized paired sex organs, or *gonads.* The male gonads are the testes; the female gonads are the ovaries. In most animals, the sexes are separate, that is, each individual has either testes or ovaries. However, some animals, such as the hydra and the earthworm, have both male and female gonads. Such animals are called *hermaphrodites.*

Spermatogenesis. The production of sperm is called *spermatogenesis* (Figure 5-7 on page 62). The process begins with meiosis in primary sperm cells, which are diploid. As a result of meiosis, each primary sperm cell develops into four monoploid cells of equal size. As they mature, these cells lose most of their cytoplasm and develop a long, whiplike flagellum that is used for locomotion.

Oogenesis. Egg cells are produced by *oogenesis* (Figure 5-8 on page 62). In oogenesis, a primary egg cell undergoes meiosis. The chromosomal changes are the same as those that occur in spermatogenesis (from 2*n* to *n*). However, in oogenesis, division of the cytoplasm is unequal. The first meiotic division produces one large cell and one small one called a *polar body.* The larger cell then undergoes the second meiotic division, forming an egg cell and another polar body. The first polar body may also undergo a second meiotic division, forming two polar bodies. Oogenesis results in the production of one large, monoploid egg cell and three small polar bodies.

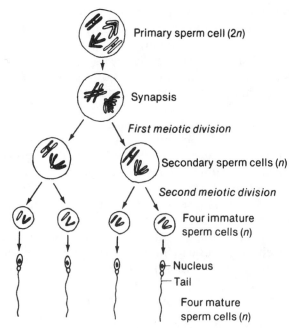

Figure 5-7. Spermatogenesis: the production of mature sperm cells.

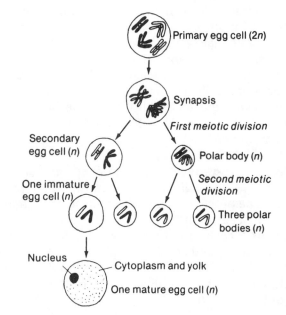

Figure 5-8. Oogenesis: the production of one mature egg cell.

The polar bodies disintegrate. The advantage of the unequal cytoplasmic division is that the egg cell is provided with a large supply of stored nutrients in the form of yolk.

Comparison of Mitosis and Meiosis

The daughter cells produced by mitotic cell division have the same number and kinds of chromosomes as the original parent cell. (A cell with the 2n chromosome number produces daughter cells with the 2n chromosome number.) Mitosis produces extra body cells for growth and repair of tissues. It is also associated with asexual reproduction.

In contrast, as a result of meiotic cell division, the daughter cells have one-half the number of chromosomes of the original cell. (A cell with the 2n chromosome number produces daughter cells with the n chromosome number.) Meiosis occurs only in the gonads during the production of gametes.

Questions

Multiple Choice

22. Monoploid gametes are produced in animals as a result of (1) meiosis (2) mitosis (3) fertilization (4) fission

23. In human males, the maximum number of functional sperm cells that is normally produced from each primary sex cell is (1) one (2) two (3) three (4) four

24. Sexually reproducing species show greater variation than asexually reproducing species due to (1) lower rates of mutation (2) higher rates of reproduction (3) environmental changes (4) sorting of chromosomes during gametogenesis

25. In animals, polar bodies are formed as a result of (1) meiotic cell division in females (2) meiotic cell division in males (3) mitotic cell division in females (4) mitotic cell division in males

26. During the normal meiotic division of a diploid cell, the change in chromosome number that occurs is represented as (1) $4n \rightarrow n$ (2) $2n \rightarrow 4n$ (3) $2n \rightarrow 1n$ (4) $1n \rightarrow \frac{1}{2}n$

27. In a species of corn, the diploid number of chromosomes is 20. What would be the number of chromosomes found in each of the normal egg cells produced by this species? (1) 5 (2) 10 (3) 20 (4) 40

28. A human zygote is produced from two gametes that are identical in (1) size (2) method of locomotion (3) genetic composition (4) chromosome number

29. Organisms that contain both functional male and female gonads are known as (1) hybrids (2) hermaphrodites (3) protists (4) parasites

Short Answer
(Constructed Response)

Base your answers to questions 30 through 33 on your knowledge of biology and on the diagram below, which represents a diploid cell about to undergo meiosis. The shapes inside the cell represent homologous chromosomes.

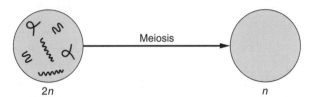

2n   Meiosis   n

30. Copy the diagram into your notebook. In the empty circle, draw one of the resulting daughter cells produced by the diploid cell at the end of meiosis.

31. What is the diploid chromosome number of the original cell?

32. What will be the chromosome number of a daughter cell produced by this cell?

33. Name an organ in which this cell might be found. Explain your answer.

34. The diagrams below represent the sequence of events in a cell undergoing normal meiotic cell division.

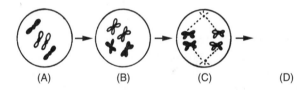

(A)   (B)   (C)   (D)

Which diagram most likely represents stage *D* of this sequence?   (1) 1   (2) 2   (3) 3   (4) 4

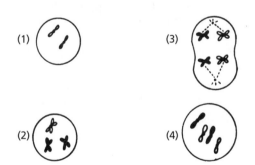

Essay
(Extended Constructed Response)

35. Briefly compare the processes of mitosis and meiosis. What is the function of each process?

36. Compare and contrast the processes of sperm and egg production in terms of (a) where

each process occurs and (b) the relative numbers of gametes produced by each process.

37. Discuss why, in sexual reproduction, it is necessary for the gametes to have the monoploid number of chromosomes rather than the diploid number. How does the process of meiosis ensure that the gametes will be monoploid?

38. Explain how the daughter cells produced during meiosis may be genetically different from one another even though they result from the same original diploid cell. Why is this variation important? Why are cells produced by mitosis *not* genetically different from one another?

FERTILIZATION AND DEVELOPMENT

Fertilization is the union of a monoploid (*n*) sperm nucleus with a monoploid (*n*) egg nucleus to form a diploid (2*n*) cell, the *zygote*, which is the first cell of the new organism. Fertilization restores the diploid species number of chromosomes.

External Fertilization

The union of a sperm and an egg outside the body of the female is called *external fertilization*. External fertilization generally occurs in a watery environment and is characteristic of reproduction in frogs, most fish, and many other aquatic vertebrates.

In external fertilization, large numbers of eggs and sperm are released into the water at the same time to increase the chances that fertilization will take place and to help ensure that at least some of the fertilized eggs will develop, avoid being eaten, and survive to adulthood.

Internal Fertilization

The union of a sperm and an egg inside the moist reproductive tract of the female is called **internal fertilization**. Reproduction in most terrestrial, or land-dwelling, vertebrates, including birds and mammals, is characterized by internal fertilization.

In internal fertilization, relatively few eggs are produced at one time, since the chances that fertilization will occur are much greater with internal fertilization than with external fertilization.

Stages of Development

The early stages of embryonic development are similar in all animals. The process known as **development** begins when the zygote undergoes a rapid series of mitotic cell divisions called *cleavage*.

Cleavage. During cleavage, there is no increase in the size of the embryo—just an increase in the number of cells it contains (Figure 5-9). Cell growth and specialization begin after cleavage.

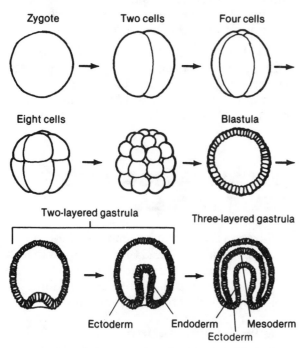

Figure 5-9. Early stages of embryonic development.

Blastula Formation. The mitotic divisions of cleavage result in the formation of the *blastula*, a hollow ball made up of a single layer of cells.

Gastrulation. As mitotic divisions continue, one side of the blastula pushes inward, or indents, in a process called *gastrulation*. The resulting embryonic stage, called a *gastrula*, consists of an inner layer, or *endoderm*, and an outer layer, or *ectoderm*. A third layer, called the *mesoderm*, forms between the endoderm and ectoderm. The endoderm, mesoderm, and ectoderm are called the *germ layers*.

Differentiation and Growth. The germ layers undergo changes, or **differentiation**, to form the various tissues, organs, and **organ systems** of the developing animal (see Table 5-1).

Embryonic development involves growth as well as differentiation. *Growth* includes both an increase in the size of the embryonic cells and an increase in the number of cells.

External Development
Embryonic development may occur outside or inside the body of the female. Growth of the embryo outside the female's body is called *external development*.

Table 5-1. Tissues and Organs Formed From The Embryonic Germ Layers

Embryonic Layer	Organs and Organ Systems
Ectoderm	Nervous system; skin
Mesoderm	Muscles; circulatory, skeletal, excretory, and reproductive systems
Endoderm	Lining of digestive and respiratory tracts; liver; pancreas

The eggs of many fish and amphibians are fertilized externally and develop externally in an aquatic environment. The eggs of birds and many reptiles (and even a few mammals) are fertilized internally but develop externally, encased in tough, protective shells to prevent their drying out.

Internal Development
Growth of the embryo inside the female's body is called **internal development**. In most mammals, both fertilization and development are internal. The eggs of mammals have little yolk and are very small compared with the eggs of reptiles and birds. In all mammals, the young are nourished after birth by milk from the mother's mammary glands.

Placental Mammals. Most mammals are placental mammals in which the embryo develops in the **uterus**, or womb, of the female and receives food and oxygen and gets rid of wastes through the placenta.

The **placenta** is a temporary organ that forms within the uterus from embryonic and maternal tissues; it is rich in both embryonic and maternal blood vessels. Dissolved materials pass between the mother and the embryo through the blood vessels in the placenta—food and oxygen pass from the mother to the embryo, while wastes pass from the embryo to the mother. The blood of the mother and the embryo never mix.

Questions

Multiple Choice

39. In the early development of a zygote, the number of cells increases, without leading to an increase in size, in the process of (1) ovulation (2) cleavage (3) germination (4) metamorphosis

40. In a developing embryo, the process most closely associated with the differentiation of cells is called (1) gastrulation (2) menstruation (3) ovulation (4) fertilization

41. In most species of fish, the female produces large numbers of eggs during the reproductive cycle. This would indicate that reproduction in fish is most probably characterized by (1) internal fertilization and internal development (2) internal fertilization and external development (3) external fertilization and internal development (4) external fertilization and external development.

42. Which type of fertilization and development do birds and most reptiles have? (1) internal fertilization and internal development (2) internal fertilization and external development (3) external fertilization and internal development (4) external fertilization and external development

43. The embryos of some mammals, such as the kangaroo and the opossum, complete their development externally. What is the source of nutrition for their last stage of development? (1) milk from maternal mammary glands (2) diffusion of nutrients through the uterine wall (3) food stored in the egg yolk (4) solid foods gathered and fed to them by the mother

44. In mammals, the placenta is essential to the embryo for (1) nutrition, reproduction, growth (2) nutrition, respiration, excretion (3) locomotion, respiration, excretion (4) nutrition, excretion, reproduction

45. Which characteristic of sexual reproduction specifically favors the survival of terrestrial animals? (1) fertilization within the body of the female (2) male gametes that may be carried by the wind (3) fusion of gametes in the outside environment (4) fertilization of eggs in the water

Base your answers to questions 46 through 49 on your knowledge of biology and on the diagram below, which represents early stages of embryonic development.

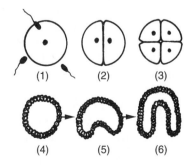

46. The structures labeled *2* and *3* are formed as a direct result of (1) meiosis (2) gastrulation (3) cleavage (4) differentiation

47. The structure in stage *4* represents a (1) zygote (2) blastula (3) gastrula (4) follicle

48. The cells of the outer layer give rise to the (1) digestive system and liver (2) excretory system and muscles (3) circulatory system and gonads (4) nervous system and skin

49. Which cells are *not* represented in any of the diagrams? (1) endoderm (2) mesoderm (3) ectoderm (4) gastrula

Short Answer (Constructed Response)

Refer to the following four terms, which describe the early stages of embryonic development, to answer questions 50 through 52: *gastrula, cleavage, zygote, blastula.*

50. List these terms in the correct order, from earliest to latest stage of embryonic development.

51. For each term listed, draw a simple sketch to illustrate that stage of embryonic development.

52. In complete sentences, briefly describe what occurs during each of these embryonic stages.

Essay (Extended Constructed Response)

53. Animals that are characterized by external fertilization produce many times more gametes (sperm and eggs) than do animals that have internal fertilization. Discuss two reasons for this observation.

HUMAN REPRODUCTION AND DEVELOPMENT

Male Reproductive System

The male reproductive system functions in the production of sperm cells, male sex hormones, and in the placement of sperm into the female reproductive system.

Sperm Production. The sperm-producing organs, the *testes*, are located in an outpocketing of the body wall called the *scrotum* (Figure 5-10, page 66). The temperature in the scrotum, which is 1°C to 2°C cooler than normal body temperature, is best suited for the production and storage of sperm.

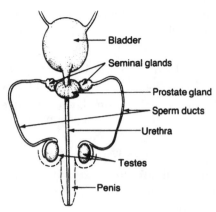

Figure 5-10. The human male reproductive system.

From the testes, the sperm pass through a series of ducts into which liquid is secreted by various glands. The liquid serves as a transport medium for the sperm cells and is an adaptation for life on land. The liquid and sperm together are called *semen*. Semen passes to the outside of the body through the urethra, a tube through the penis. The *penis* is used to deposit the semen in the female reproductive tract.

Hormone Production. The testes produce the male sex hormone testosterone, which regulates the maturation of sperm cells. Testosterone also regulates the development of male secondary sex characteristics, including body form, beard development, and deepening of the voice.

Female Reproductive System
The female reproductive system functions in the production of egg cells and female sex hormones.

Egg Production. The female reproductive organs, the *ovaries*, are located within the lower portion of the body cavity (Figure 5-11). In the ovaries, each egg cell is present in a tiny sac called a *follicle*. About once a month, a follicle matures and bursts, and the egg within it is released from the surface of the ovary, a process called *ovulation*. The egg cell then passes into the *oviduct*, or

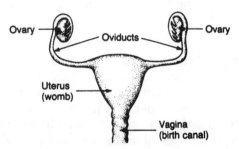

Figure 5-11. The human female reproductive system.

fallopian tube, which leads to the *uterus*. If sperm are present, fertilization may occur. If the egg is fertilized, it passes into the uterus, where embryonic development may occur. If the egg is not fertilized, it degenerates.

The lower end of the uterus, the *cervix*, opens to a muscular tube called the *vagina*, or *birth canal*. When embryonic development is complete, the baby leaves the body of the mother through the vagina.

Hormone Production. The ovaries produce the female sex hormones estrogen and progesterone. These hormones regulate the maturation of egg cells, as well as the development of secondary sex characteristics, including the development of the mammary glands and the broadening of the pelvis. Estrogen and progesterone are also involved in the menstrual cycle and **pregnancy**.

The Menstrual Cycle
The series of events that prepares the uterus for pregnancy is called the *menstrual cycle*. The cycle begins with the thickening of the lining of the uterine wall. The lining also becomes vascularized (filled with blood vessels). If fertilization does not occur, the thickened uterine lining breaks down and the material is expelled from the body during menstruation. The cycle then begins again.

The menstrual cycle begins at *puberty*, the stage at which the individual becomes capable of reproducing. It is temporarily interrupted by pregnancy and sometimes by illness, and ceases permanently at *menopause*. The cycle is regulated by the interaction of hormones, and lasts approximately 28 days.

The menstrual cycle consists of four stages (Figure 5-12).

a) During the follicle stage, an egg matures and the follicle secretes estrogen, which stimulates the thickening of the uterine lining. This stage lasts about 14 days.

b) About midway in the cycle, ovulation occurs. The egg is released from the ovary and enters the oviduct.

c) Following ovulation, the *corpus luteum* forms from the ruptured follicle. The corpus luteum secretes progesterone, which continues the vascularization of the uterine lining started by estrogen. This stage lasts about 12 days.

d) If fertilization does not occur, the egg cell and the thickened uterine lining break down, and the extra tissue, together with some blood and mucus, pass out of the

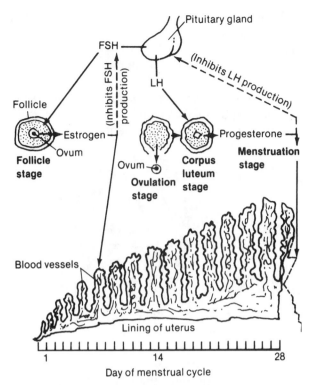

Figure 5-12. Stages of the menstrual cycle.

body through the vagina. The shedding of the uterine lining is called *menstruation*. This stage lasts from two to four days.

Hormones of the Menstrual Cycle

The menstrual cycle is controlled by hormones that are released by the hypothalamus, pituitary gland, and ovaries.

During the follicle stage, the pituitary gland, under the influence of hormones from the hypothalamus, secretes FSH (follicle-stimulating hormone), which in turn stimulates the follicle to secrete estrogen. Estrogen stimulates ovulation and initiates vascularization of the uterine lining.

Increased blood estrogen levels inhibit the production of FSH by the pituitary, and the secretion of LH (luteinizing hormone) by the pituitary increases. Ovulation occurs at about this time in the cycle. After ovulation, LH stimulates the formation of the corpus luteum from the ruptured follicle. The corpus luteum secretes progesterone, which enhances the vascularization of the uterine lining.

If fertilization does not occur, the high levels of progesterone in the blood inhibit the production of LH by the pituitary. The drop in LH level causes a drop in the progesterone level. The lining of the uterus thins out, and at about the twenty-eighth day of the cycle, the shedding of the uterine lining, or menstruation, begins. The

blood flow of menstruation is caused by the breakage of many small blood vessels.

The relationship between the ovarian hormones estrogen and progesterone and the pituitary hormones FSH and LH is an example of a *negative feedback mechanism*.

Fertilization and Development

If fertilization does occur in the oviduct, the zygote undergoes cleavage to form a blastula. Six to ten days later, the blastula becomes implanted in the uterine lining. Gastrulation usually occurs after implantation. The germ layers of the gastrula begin to differentiate and grow, resulting in the formation of specialized tissues and organs. The placenta and umbilical cord form, enabling the embryo to obtain nutrients and oxygen and to dispose of metabolic wastes. An amnion (membrane-enclosed sac) filled with fluid provides a watery environment for the embryo and protects it from shocks.

In Vitro Fertilization

Fertilization that occurs outside the body of the female is known as *in vitro* fertilization. After fertilization, the early embryo is implanted into the uterus, where development is completed.

Multiple Births

Sometimes two or more embryos develop in the uterus simultaneously. Fraternal twins develop when two eggs are released from the ovary at the same time and both are fertilized. The two eggs are fertilized by two different sperm cells. Fraternal twins may be of the same sex or opposite sexes. Identical twins develop when a zygote separates into two equal halves early in cleavage. Each half develops into an offspring. Since identical twins develop from the same zygote, they have identical genetic makeups and are always of the same sex.

Birth and Development

The time between fertilization and birth is referred to as the *gestation period*. In humans, the gestation period is about nine months. After the first three months of gestation, the embryo is referred to as a **fetus**. At the end of the gestation period, the secretion of progesterone decreases and another hormone from the pituitary causes strong muscular contractions of the uterus. The amnion bursts, and the baby is pushed out of the mother's body through the vagina.

During *postnatal development* (development after birth), humans pass through different stages, including childhood, puberty, adulthood, and old age. Puberty begins at early adolescence. In males, puberty usually occurs between the ages of 12 and 18; in females, it usually occurs between the ages of 10 and 14.

Aging is a series of complex structural and functional changes in the body that occur naturally with the passage of time. The causes of aging are not fully understood. However, it now appears that aging may result from an interaction of both genetic and environmental factors. The aging process ends in death, which may be described as an irreversible cessation of brain function.

Questions

Multiple Choice

54. Which of the following structures *least* affects the human female menstrual cycle? (1) pituitary (2) ovary (3) pancreas (4) corpus luteum

55. A woman gave birth to twins, one girl and one boy. The number of egg cells involved was (1) 1 (2) 2 (3) 3 (4) 4

56. Which structure is the membrane that serves as the protective, fluid-filled sac in which an embryo is suspended? (1) pituitary (2) placenta (3) corpus luteum (4) amnion

Base your answers to questions 57 through 59 on the diagram below, which represents a cross section of a part of the human female reproductive system, and on your knowledge of biology.

57. Which structure is prepared for the implantation of a fertilized egg as a result of the action of reproductive hormones? (1) *A* (2) *B* (3) *C* (4) *D*

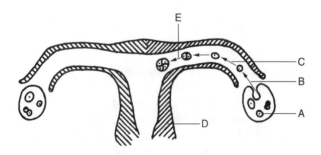

58. Within which structure does fertilization normally occur? (1) *A* (2) *B* (3) *C* (4) *D*

59. Which step represents the process of ovulation? (1) *A* (2) *B* (3) *C* (4) *D*

60. The technique of uniting a sperm cell and an egg cell within a test tube is called (1) *in vitro* fertilization (2) internal fertilization (3) gametogenesis (4) artificial ovulation

Base your answers to questions 61 through 63 on the diagram below, which represents a stage in human embryonic development.

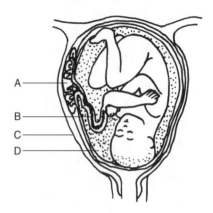

61. The exchange of oxygen, food, and wastes between the mother and the fetus occurs at structure (1) *A* (2) *B* (3) *C* (4) *D*

62. What is the function of the fluid labeled *D*? (1) nourishment (2) protection (3) excretion (4) respiration

63. The structure labeled *C*, within which embryonic development occurs, is known as the (1) oviduct (2) birth canal (3) uterus (4) placenta

For each of the processes described in questions 64 through 66, choose from the list below the correct stage of the human menstrual cycle during which that process occurs.

Human Menstrual Cycle Stages
A. Ovulation
B. Follicle stage
C. Menstruation
D. Corpus luteum stage

64. The lining of the uterus is shed. (1) *A* (2) *B* (3) *C* (4) *D*

65. An egg is released from an ovary. (1) *A* (2) *B* (3) *C* (4) *D*

66. An egg matures in an ovary. (1) *A* (2) *B* (3) *C* (4) *D*

67. Which of the following hormones is *not* involved in the regulation of the human menstrual cycle? (1) progesterone (2) estrogen (3) FSH (4) testosterone

68. Fraternal twins develop from (1) one egg and two sperm (2) two eggs and one sperm (3) two eggs and two sperm (4) one egg and one sperm

69. Identical twins develop from (1) one egg and two sperm (2) two eggs and one sperm (3) two eggs and two sperm (4) one egg and one sperm

Short Answer
(Constructed Response)

Base your answers to questions 70 through 73 on the graph below, which shows a woman's changing hormone levels for FSH and estrogen over a period of 21 days, and on your knowledge of human reproductive biology. Be sure to write your answers in complete sentences.

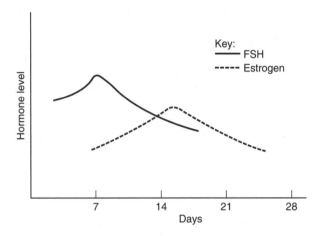

70. Describe the relationship depicted in the graph between FSH and estrogen.

71. Why does the level of estrogen begin rising *after* the FSH level rises?

72. Why do the FSH levels begin to fall after the seventh day?

73. On approximately what day are the woman's estrogen levels highest?

Essay
(Extended Constructed Response)

74. List the four major hormones that play a role in the menstrual cycle and discuss how they interact during the cycle.

75. Mr. and Mrs. W have been trying to conceive their first child for over one year, with no success. They decide to visit their doctors for medical tests. Blood tests on Mrs. W reveal that her FSH levels are abnormally low. Discuss how this finding might explain the couple's inability to conceive. What medical treatment(s) might help Mrs. W become pregnant?

76. Briefly discuss the function of the following structures in the development of the human embryo: placenta, umbilical cord, amnion.

SEXUAL REPRODUCTION IN FLOWERING PLANTS

Flowers are the reproductive organs of the *angiosperms*, or flowering plants.

Structure of Flowers

Flowers may contain the following structures: sepals, petals, stamens, and pistils (Figure 5-13).

Sepals are leaflike structures at the base of a flower that enclose and protect the flower bud. In some species the sepals are green, while in others the sepals are white or brightly colored.

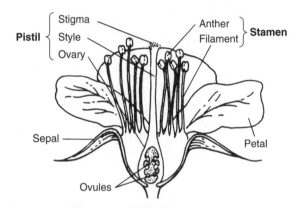

Figure 5-13. Structure of a flower.

Petals are leaflike structures inside the sepals that surround the reproductive organs of the flower. Petals may be brightly colored or white and often have a sweet fragrance.

Stamens are the male reproductive organs of a flower. Each stamen consists of an oval-shaped *anther* supported by a stalk, or *filament. Pollen grains*, which contain monoploid sperm nuclei, are produced by meiosis by the diploid cells of the anther. The thick wall that encloses the pollen grain prevents the contents from drying out. This is an adaptation for life on land.

Pistils are the female reproductive organs of a flower. A pistil consists of a stigma, style, and ovary. The *stigma*, which is a knoblike, sticky structure, is adapted for receiving pollen grains. The stigma is supported by the *style*, a slender stalk that connects the stigma to the *ovary*, which is at the base of the pistil. In the ovary, monoploid egg cells are produced by meiosis in structures called *ovules*.

The flowers of some species contain both stamens and pistils. In other species, some flowers contain only stamens, while others contain only pistils. The flowers of some species have both sepals and petals, while the flowers of other species lack one or the other.

Pollination and Fertilization

The transfer of pollen grains from an anther to a stigma is called *pollination*. The transfer of pollen from an anther to a stigma of the same flower or to a stigma of another flower on the same plant is called *self-pollination*. The transfer of pollen from an anther of one flower to the stigma of a flower on another plant is *cross-pollination*. Cross-pollination increases the chances of genetic variation in the offspring.

Pollination may be carried out by wind, insects, or birds. Brightly colored petals and the scent of nectar attract insects and birds. Pollen grains from a flower adhere to their bodies and are carried to another flower, where they rub off on the sticky surface of a stigma.

When a pollen grain reaches a stigma, it *germinates*, or sprouts (Figure 5-14). A pollen tube grows from the pollen grain down through the stigma and style to an ovule within the ovary. The growth of the pollen tube is controlled by the tube nucleus. Two sperm nuclei and the tube nucleus pass down through the pollen tube. The sperm nuclei enter an ovule, where one sperm nucleus fertilizes the egg nucleus to form a diploid (2n) zygote. The other sperm nucleus fuses with two *polar nuclei* in the ovule to form a triploid (3n) *endosperm nucleus*, which divides to form a food storage tissue. The zygote undergoes repeated mitotic divisions to form a multicellular plant embryo. After fertilization, the ovule ripens to form a *seed*, while the ovary develops into a *fruit*. The seeds of flowering plants are found inside the fruits.

Structure of a Seed

A seed consists of a seed coat and a plant embryo with one or two cotyledons (Figure 5-15). The *seed coat*, which develops from the outer coverings of the ovule, surrounds and protects the embryo. The plant embryo consists of the epicotyl, hypocotyl, and cotyledon. The *epicotyl* is the upper portion of the embryo; it develops into the leaves and upper portion of the stem. The *hypocotyl* is the lower portion of the embryo; it develops into the roots and, in some species, the lower portion of the stem. The *cotyledons* contain endosperm, the stored food that provides nutrients for the developing plant.

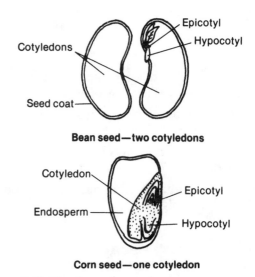

Bean seed—two cotyledons

Corn seed—one cotyledon

Figure 5-15. Structure of a seed.

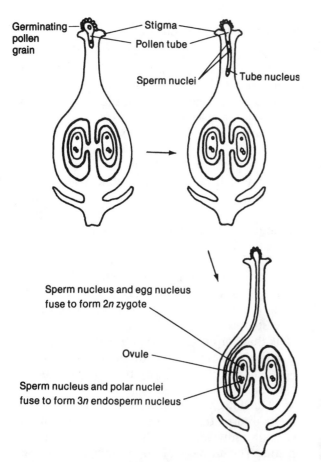

Figure 5-14. Fertilization in flowering plants.

Fruits

The fruits of flowering plants are structures that are specialized for seed dispersal. Fruits carry the seeds away from the parent plant, which helps to prevent overcrowding. The fruits of dandelions and maples, for example, are dispersed by wind; coconuts are dispersed by water; and cockleburs are fruits that become attached to the fur of animals and are carried away as they move. Fleshy fruits are eaten by animals, and their seeds are later deposited with the animal's wastes.

Seed Germination

When conditions of moisture, oxygen, and temperature are favorable, seeds germinate. The embryo plant develops leaves and roots, and begins to produce its own food by photosynthesis. The development of a mature plant from an embryo involves cell division, cell differentiation, and growth.

Plant Growth

In flowering plants, only certain regions, called *meristems*, are able to undergo cell division. There are two types of meristem regions: apical meristems are found in the tips of roots and stems, and cell division there brings about an increase in length; lateral meristems, or *cambiums*, are found between the xylem and phloem, and cell division there brings about an increase in the diameter of roots and stems. The undifferentiated cells of the meristem regions divide actively and then undergo elongation and differentiation, forming the different kinds of plant tissues.

Questions

Multiple Choice

77. Which reproductive structures are produced within the ovaries of plants? (1) pollen grains (2) sperm nuclei (3) egg nuclei (4) pollen tubes

78. In a flowering plant, the ovule develops within a part of the (1) style (2) anther (3) pistil (4) stigma

79. Which embryonic structure supplies nutrients to a germinating bean plant? (1) pollen tube (2) hypocotyl (3) epicotyl (4) cotyledon

80. Heavy use of insecticides in springtime may lead to a decrease in apple production in the fall, which is most probably due to interference with the process of (1) pollination (2) cleavage (3) absorption (4) transpiration

Base your answers to questions 81 through 83 on the diagram below and on your knowledge of biology.

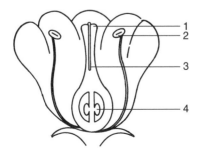

81. In this diagram, the stigma and the anther are (1) 1 and 2 (2) 1 and 4 (3) 2 and 4 (4) 2 and 3

82. Which process has occurred in this flower? (1) pollen germination (2) seed formation (3) zygote formation (4) fruit production

83. In which part would fertilization occur? (1) 1 (2) 2 (3) 3 (4) 4

84. In a bean seed, the part of the embryo that develops into the leaves and upper portion of the stem is known as the (1) seed coat (2) epicotyl (3) hypocotyl (4) cotyledon

85. A condition necessary for the germination of most seeds is favorable (1) light (2) chlorophyll concentration (3) temperature (4) nitrate concentration

86. In flowering plants, the entire female reproductive organ is called the (1) filament (2) anther (3) style (4) pistil

87. In flowering plants, pollen grains are formed in the (1) style (2) anther (3) sepal (4) stigma

88. The seeds of a flowering plant develop from the ripened (1) fruits (2) cotyledons (3) ovules (4) endosperm

89. The endosperm of a bean seed is contained within its (1) cotyledons (2) ovules (3) stamen (4) petals

90. The fruits of a flowering plant develop from the ripened (1) seeds (2) ovules (3) ovaries (4) pollen tubes

91. Which of the following is *not* part of a plant embryo? (1) epicotyl (2) seed coat (3) hypocotyl (4) cotyledon

92. Which portion of a bean seed would contain the greatest percentage of starch? (1) seed coat (2) epicotyl (3) cotyledon (4) hypocotyl

Base your answers to questions 93 and 94 on the diagram below, which shows the internal structure of a bean seed, and on your knowledge of biology.

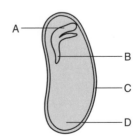

93. In which structure would most of the stored food for the embryo be found? (1) A (2) B (3) C (4) D

94. The epicotyl and the hypocotyl are represented by   (1) *A* and *C*   (2) *B* and *D*   (3) *A* and *B*   (4) *C* and *D*

Short Answer
(Constructed Response)

95. In two complete sentences, explain why cross-pollination increases the chances of genetic variation in the offspring of flowering plants.

96. In two or more full sentences, compare sexual reproduction in mammals and flowering plants. In what way is the process similar in these two types of organisms?

Reading Comprehension

Base your answers to questions 97 through 100 on the information below and on your knowledge of biology. Source: *Science News* (February 5, 2000): vol. 157, no. 6, p. 95.

Lung Cancer Gene Has Gender Bias

Of all cancers, lung cancer causes the most deaths in the United States. Smoking leads to almost 90 percent of cases, but researchers have been unable to explain why among smokers, women seem to be 2 to 3 times as susceptible to the disease as men are.

A new study may help explain this gender bender. A gene for a protein that promotes lung cancer growth is more likely to be active in women than in men, says Sharon P. Shriver of Pennsylvania State University in State College.

Known as *gastrin-releasing peptide receptor*, or *GRPR*, the gene is not typically active in the lungs of nonsmokers, Shriver says. Tests of lung cancer cells, however, show that nicotine turns the gene on, she and her colleagues at the University of Pittsburgh report in the Jan. 5 JOURNAL OF THE NATIONAL CANCER INSTITUTE. The gene resides on the X chromosome. Therefore, women have twice as many copies of *GRPR* as men do and so are probably more susceptible to smoking's carcinogenic effects.

Shriver and her colleagues looked at normal lung tissue that had been removed from 38 women and 40 men during surgery related to lung cancer or another lung disease. Among the nonsmokers, 55 percent of the women and none of the men had active copies of the gene. Among people who had smoked less than the equivalent of a pack of cigarettes a day over 25 years, 75 percent of the women and 20 percent of the men had active *GRPR* copies, she says. In those who smoked more, about 70 percent of both men and women had an active *GRPR* in their lungs.

The incidence of lung cancer was 12 times higher for women with an active *GRPR* gene than for women with inactive genes. It was only 2.4 times higher for men with the active gene than for men without it, Shriver says. If further work bears out her findings, she says, *GRPR* activity might predict which people are most likely to develop cancer. "This kind of early marker for lung cancer is something we don't have right now," she says. Lung cancer is deadly because doctors don't usually detect it until late in its course.

97. How is cigarette smoking related to the incidence of lung cancer?

98. Why do women seem to develop lung cancer more frequently than men do?

99. How does nicotine (in cigarettes) affect activity of the *GRPR* gene?

100. How might these findings be used to predict or detect early lung cancer development?

CHAPTER 6

Transmission of Traits

FOUNDATIONS OF GENETICS

Genetics is the branch of biology that deals with patterns of **inheritance**, or heredity. *Heredity* is the biological process by which parents pass on genetic information to their offspring through their gametes. The science of genetics originated with the work of an Austrian monk, *Gregor Mendel*, who performed a series of experiments on pea plants between 1856 and 1868.

Principles of Mendelian Genetics

In his breeding experiments, Mendel (who, like everyone else at that time, had no knowledge of genes or chromosomes) made careful observations of the inheritance patterns of specific contrasting traits found in pea plants. Through a mathematical analysis of the traits found in the large numbers of offspring from his experimental crosses, Mendel developed his principles of *dominance*, *segregation*, and *independent assortment*. Mendel also concluded that the traits he observed were controlled by pairs of inherited "factors," with one member of each pair coming from each parent organism. Thus, in organisms that reproduce sexually, half of the offspring's genetic material is contributed by the female parent and half by the male parent. As a result, the offspring has traits from both parents, and is never identical to either one of them.

Gene-Chromosome Theory

The importance of Mendel's work was not recognized until the early 1900s, when the development of better microscopes enabled biologists to observe chromosome behavior during meiotic cell division. Biologists then linked the separation of homologous chromosome pairs during meiosis and their **recombination** at fertilization with the inheritance of Mendel's factors. Breeding experiments carried out by T. H. Morgan with the fruit fly, *Drosophila*, provided supporting evidence for Mendel's principles of inheritance.

Mendel's inherited, or **hereditary**, factors—now known as **genes**—are arranged in a linear fashion on the chromosomes. Each gene has a definite position, or *locus* (plural, *loci*), on the chromosome. The two alternate genes that control each trait are called *alleles*, and they are located in the same position on homologous chromosomes. This *gene–chromosome theory* explains the hereditary patterns observed by Mendel.

Gene Expression

Every organism has at least two alleles that govern every trait. As mentioned, these two genes are passed on—one from the mother and one from the father—to the offspring. The genes encode information that is expressed as the traits of the organism, a phenomenon called **gene expression**. A single gene (that is, one set of alleles) may control one or several traits. Alternatively, some traits are determined by more than one gene (that is, by more than one set of alleles).

Although all the body cells in an organism contain the same genetic instructions, the cells may differ considerably from one another in structure and function. The reason is that, in any given cell, only some of the genes are expressed, while all other genes are inactivated. For example, in liver cells, it is mainly the genes that pertain to liver functions that are active, while the other genes are inactive. The same is true of all other cells in a body. You can think of the genes on a cell's chromosomes as recipes in a cookbook: the book may contain hundreds of recipes, but if you are making a chocolate cake, you will read only the instructions for making that item. Likewise, the cell reads only the instructions for making its specific products.

Genes that are "on" are expressed, while those that are "off" are not expressed. There are many mechanisms that can switch genes on and off, including intracellular chemicals, enzymes, regulatory proteins, and the cell's environment. In addition, a particular gene may alternately be expressed or inactivated, depending on the cell's needs at the time.

SOME MAJOR CONCEPTS IN GENETICS

Dominance

In his experiments, Mendel crossed plants that were pure for contrasting traits. For example, he crossed pure tall plants with pure short plants. All the offspring of such crosses showed only one of the two contrasting traits. In the cross of tall plants and short plants, all the offspring were tall. In this type of inheritance, the allele that is expressed in the offspring is said to be *dominant*; the allele that is present but not expressed is said to be *recessive*. This pattern illustrates Mendel's principle of dominance.

By convention, the dominant allele is represented by a capital letter, while the recessive allele is represented by the lowercase form of the same letter. For example, the allele for tallness, which is dominant, is shown as T, while the allele for shortness, which is recessive, is shown as t.

If, in an organism, the two genes of a pair of alleles are the same, for example, TT or tt, the organism is said to be *homozygous,* or pure, for that trait. The genetic makeup of the organism, which is its *genotype*, is either homozygous dominant (TT) or homozygous recessive (tt). If the two genes of a pair of alleles are different, for example, Tt, the organism is said to be *heterozygous*, or *hybrid*, for that trait.

The physical appearance of an organism that results from its genetic makeup is called its *phenotype*. For example, a pea plant that is heterozygous for height has the genotype Tt and the phenotype of being tall. When an organism that is homozygous for the dominant trait is crossed with an organism that is homozygous for the recessive trait ($TT \times tt$), the phenotype of the offspring is like that of the dominant parent. Thus, the heterozygous offspring (Tt) is tall.

In studies involving genetic crosses, the organisms that are used to begin the studies are called the *parent generation*. The offspring produced by crossing members of the parent generation are called the *first filial*, or F_1, *generation*. The offspring of a cross between members of the F_1 generation make up the *second filial*, or F_2, *generation*.

Questions

Multiple Choice

1. When a strain of fruit flies homozygous for light body color is crossed with a strain of fruit flies homozygous for dark body color, all of the offspring have light body color. This illustrates Mendel's principle of (1) segregation (2) dominance (3) incomplete dominance (4) independent assortment

2. Two genes located in corresponding positions on a pair of homologous chromosomes and associated with the same characteristic are known as (1) gametes (2) zygotes (3) chromatids (4) alleles

3. For a given trait, the two genes of an allelic pair are not alike. An individual possessing this gene combination is said to be (1) homozygous for that trait (2) heterozygous for that trait (3) recessive for that trait (4) pure for that trait

4. In pea plants, flowers located along the stem (*axial*) are dominant to flowers located at the end of the stem (*terminal*). Let A represent the allele for axial flowers and a represent the allele for terminal flowers. When plants with axial flowers are crossed with plants having terminal flowers, all of the offspring have axial flowers. The genotypes of the parent plants are most likely (1) $aa \times aa$ (2) $Aa \times Aa$ (3) $aa \times Aa$ (4) $AA \times aa$

5. Curly hair in humans, white fur in guinea pigs, and needlelike spines in cacti all partly describe each organism's (1) alleles (2) autosomes (3) chromosomes (4) phenotype

6. The appearance of a recessive trait in offspring of animals most probably indicates that (1) both parents carried at least one recessive gene for that trait (2) one parent was homozygous dominant and the other parent was homozygous recessive for that trait (3) neither parent carried a recessive gene for that trait (4) one parent was homozygous dominant and the other parent was hybrid for that trait

7. Which statement describes how two organisms may show the same trait yet have different genotypes for that phenotype? (1) One is homozygous dominant and the other is heterozygous. (2) Both are heterozygous for the dominant trait. (3) One is homozygous dominant and the other is homozygous recessive. (4) Both are homozygous for the dominant trait.

8. In cabbage butterflies, white color (W) is dominant and yellow color (w) is recessive. If a pure white cabbage butterfly mates with a yellow cabbage butterfly, all the resulting (F_1) butterflies are heterozygous white. Which cross represents the genotypes of the parent generation? (1) $Ww \times ww$ (2) $WW \times Ww$ (3) $WW \times ww$ (4) $Ww \times Ww$

Short Answer
(Constructed Response)

9. In two or more complete sentences, explain how two organisms can have the same phenotype but different genotypes.

10. To illustrate your answer to question 9, pick a trait (real or imagined), use a letter to represent it, and write the genotypes of the parents and F_1 generations for each organism.

Essay
(Extended Constructed Response)

11. Why do the offspring of sexually reproducing organisms resemble both parents? Why are they not identical to either one of the parents?

12. Explain why the body cells of an organism can differ in structure and function, even though they all contain the same genetic information.

Segregation and Recombination

When gametes are formed during meiosis, the two chromosomes of each homologous pair separate, or *segregate*, randomly. Each gamete contains only one allele for each trait. After the gametes fuse during fertilization, the resulting (zygote) cell contains pairs of homologous chromosomes, but new combinations of alleles may be present. This process is described by Mendel's principle of segregation.

Figure 6-1 illustrates segregation and recombination in a cross between two individuals that are heterozygous for tallness. In a large number of such crosses, with a large number of offspring, two types of numerical ratios can be observed. In terms of genotype, the ratio is 1 homozygous dominant (*TT*) : 2 heterozygous (*Tt*) : 1 homozygous recessive (*tt*). In terms of phenotype, the ratio is 3 tall : 1 short. These genotype and phenotype ratios are typical for all crosses between organisms that are hybrid for one trait.

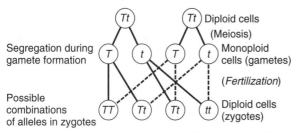

Figure 6-1. Segregation and recombination of alleles.

The Testcross

To determine the genotype of an organism that shows the dominant phenotype, a testcross is performed. In a *testcross*, the organism in question is crossed with a homozygous recessive organism (Figure 6-2). If the test organism is homozygous dominant, all the offspring will be heterozygous and show the dominant phenotype. If any offspring show the recessive phenotype, the individual being tested would have to be heterozygous.

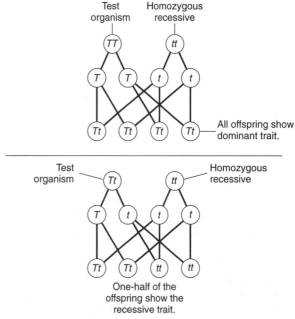

Figure 6-2. Use of a testcross to determine an organism's genotype.

Punnett Squares

The possible offspring of a genetic cross are often shown with diagrams called *Punnett squares*. We can use a Punnett square to show the possible offspring of a cross between a heterozygous tall pea plant (*Tt*) and a homozygous short pea plant (*tt*).

The first step in using a Punnett square is to determine the possible genotypes of the gametes of each parent. In this example, the heterozygous tall plant (*Tt*) produces two types of gametes: half will contain the dominant gene for height, *T*, and half will contain the recessive gene, *t*. The gametes of the homozygous short plant (*tt*) will each contain the recessive gene for height, *t*.

As shown in Figure 6-3 on page 76, the letters that represent the trait carried by the gametes of one parent are written next to the boxes on the left side of the square; the letters for the gametes of the other parent are written above the boxes on top of the square. The letters are combined to show offspring genotypes as follows: letters on top of the square are written in the boxes below them, and letters on the side are written in the boxes to the right of them. The dominant gene, when present, is written first. The pairs of letters in the four boxes represent the possible combinations of genes in the offspring of the cross. Of the possible offspring of this cross, half would be heterozygous tall (*Tt*) and half would be homozygous (recessive) short (*tt*).

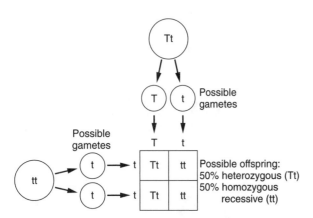

Figure 6-3. Use of a Punnett square to determine possible genotypes of offspring.

Linkage

Mendel's observation of the independent inheritance of different traits was the basis for his principle of independent assortment. When the events of meiosis were discovered, it became clear that traits are inherited independently of one another only when their genes are on non-homologous chromosomes. However, when the genes for two different traits are located on the same pair of homologous chromosomes, they tend to be inherited together. Such genes are said to be *linked*. The patterns of inheritance and phenotype ratios for linked traits are different from those of nonlinked traits (the kind observed by Mendel).

Crossing-Over

During *synapsis* in the first meiotic division, the chromatids of a pair of homologous chromosomes often twist around each other, break, exchange segments, and rejoin (Figure 6-4). This exchange of segments, called *crossing-over*, results in a rearrangement of linked genes and produces variations in offspring. Crossing-over is an important source of genetic variation in sexual reproduction.

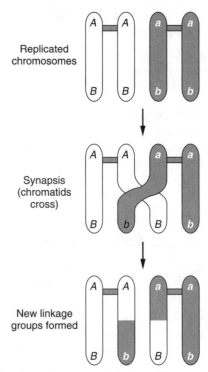

Figure 6-4. Crossing-over of chromatids.

Questions

Multiple Choice

13. Polydactyly is a characteristic in which a person has six fingers per hand. Polydactyly is dominant over the trait for five fingers. If a man who is heterozygous for this trait marries a woman with the normal number of fingers, what are the chances that their child would be polydactyl? (1) 0%   (2) 50%   (3) 75%   (4) 100%

14. A cross between two pea plants that are hybrid for a single trait produces 60 offspring. Approximately how many of the offspring would be expected to exhibit the recessive trait?   (1) 15   (2) 45   (3) 30   (4) 60

15. Which principle states that during meiosis chromosomes are distributed to gametes in a random fashion?   (1) dominance   (2) linkage   (3) segregation   (4) mutation

16. In guinea pigs, black coat color is dominant over white coat color. The offspring of a mating between two heterozygous black guinea pigs would probably show a phenotype ratio of (1) two black to two white   (2) one black to three white   (3) three black to one white   (4) four black to zero white

17. The offspring of a mating between two heterozygous black guinea pigs would probably show a genotype ratio of   (1) 1 *BB* : 2 *Bb* : 1 *bb* (2) 3 *Bb* :1 *bb*   (3) 2 *BB* : 2 *bb*   (4) 2 *BB* : 1 *Bb* : 1 *bb*

18. If a breeder wanted to discover whether a black guinea pig was homozygous (*BB*) or heterozygous (*Bb*) for coat color, the animal in question would have to be crossed with an individual that has the genotype   (1) *BB* (2) *bb* (3) *Bb* (4) *BbBb*

19. In horses, black coat color is dominant over chestnut coat color. Two black horses produce both a black- and a chestnut-colored offspring. If coat color is controlled by a single pair of genes, it can be assumed that   (1) in horses, genes for coat color frequently mutate   (2) one of the parent horses is homozygous dominant and the other is heterozygous for coat color   (3) both parent horses are homozygous for coat color   (4) both parent horses are heterozygous for coat color

20. Mendel's principle of independent assortment applies to traits whose genes are found on (1) homologous chromosomes   (2) sex chromosomes   (3) the same chromosome   (4) nonhomologous chromosomes

21. The process in which the chromatids of pairs of homologous chromosomes exchange segments is called   (1) linkage   (2) crossing-over   (3) independent assortment   (4) intermediate inheritance

Short Answer
(Constructed Response)

22. Based on your answer to question 19, explain how two black horses could produce a chestnut-colored offspring. Be sure to write your answer in full sentences.

23. When is a testcross used? In two or more complete sentences, explain how it works.

Base your answers to questions 24 through 26 on the diagram below, which represents a pair of homologous chromosomes at the beginning of meiosis. The letters *A, B, C, a, b,* and *c* represent pairs of alleles located on the chromosomes.

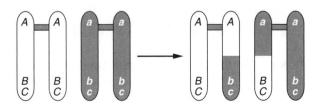

24. Compare the sets of chromosomes on the left with those on the right. Explain what has happened.

25. What process (not shown) is responsible for the observed results?

26. How does this process lead to variations among offspring?

Essay
(Extended Constructed Response)

27. Explain the following statement: Traits are inherited independently of one another only if their genes are on nonhomologous chromosomes. You may use diagrams to support your explanation.

Sex Determination

The diploid cells of many organisms contain two types of chromosomes: *autosomes* and *sex chromosomes*. There is generally one pair of sex chromosomes, and all the other chromosomes are autosomes. In human body cells there are 22 pairs of autosomes and one pair of sex chromosomes. The sex chromosomes are called the *X* and *Y* chromosomes. Females have two *X* chromosomes, and males have one *X* and one *Y* chromosome.

During meiotic cell division, the sex chromosomes, like all other chromosome pairs, are separated (Figure 6-5). The resulting gametes contain only one sex chromosome. Since females have two *X* chromosomes, each female gamete receives an *X* chromosome. Since the genotype of males is *XY*, sperm cells may receive either an *X* or a *Y* chromosome. The sex of the offspring is determined at fertilization and depends on whether the egg is fertilized by a sperm with an *X* or a sperm with a *Y* chromosome. If the sperm has an *X* chromosome, the resulting zygote will be female (*XX*). If the sperm has a *Y* chromosome, the resulting zygote will be male (*XY*).

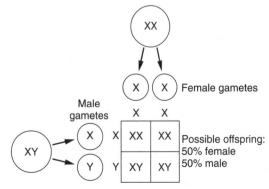

Figure 6-5. Sex determination of offspring.

Sex-Linked Traits

T. H. Morgan, in his experiments with fruit flies, found that some rare, abnormal recessive traits appear with greater frequency in males than in females. From his observations, Morgan concluded that the genes for these traits are present on the *X* chromosome and that there are no corresponding alleles for these traits on the *Y* chromosome. Genes found on the *X* chromosome are called *sex-linked genes*. Recessive sex-linked traits appear more frequently in males than in females because in females there is usually a normal, dominant allele on the other *X* chromosome, so that the phenotype is normal. In males, there is no second allele, so the presence of one recessive gene produces a recessive phenotype.

Both *hemophilia* and *color blindness* are sex-linked disorders; they occur more frequently in males than in females. Hemophilia is a condition in which the blood does not clot properly, while color blindness is an inability to distinguish certain colors. The genes for normal blood clotting and normal color vision are dominant; the genes for hemophilia and color blindness are recessive. For a female to show either of these disorders, she must have recessive genes (alleles) on both of her *X* chromosomes. Females with one normal, dominant gene and one recessive gene for these disorders are called *carriers*. They can pass the disorder to their offspring but do not themselves show symptoms of the disorder. Figure 6-6 shows the possible genotypes of children of a normal male and a female carrier of color blindness.

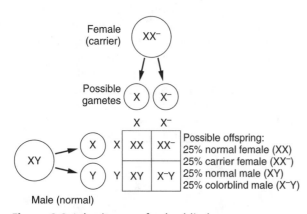

Figure 6-6. Inheritance of color blindness.

Questions

Multiple Choice

28. If a color-blind man marries a woman who is a carrier for color blindness, it is most probable that (1) all of their sons will have normal color vision (2) half of their sons will be color-blind (3) all of their sons will be color-blind (4) none of their children will have normal color vision

29. A color-blind man marries a woman with normal vision. Her mother was color-blind. They have one child. What is the chance that this child will be color-blind? (1) 0% (2) 25% (3) 50% (4) 100%

30. A color-blind woman marries a man who has normal color vision. What are their chances of having a color-blind daughter? (1) 0% (2) 25% (3) 75% (4) 100%

31. Which parental pair could produce a color-blind female? (1) homozygous normal-vision mother and color-blind father (2) color-blind mother and normal-vision father (3) heterozygous normal-vision mother and normal-vision father (4) heterozygous normal-vision mother and color-blind father

32. Which statement correctly describes the normal number and type of chromosomes present in human body cells of a particular sex? (1) Males have 22 pairs of autosomes and 1 pair of *XX* sex chromosomes. (2) Females have 23 pairs of autosomes. (3) Males have 22 pairs of autosomes and 1 pair of *XY* sex chromosomes. (4) Males have 23 pairs of autosomes.

33. Based on the pattern of inheritance known as sex linkage, if a male is a hemophiliac, how many genes for this trait are present on the sex chromosomes in each of his diploid cells? (1) 1 (2) 2 (3) 3 (4) 4

34. Traits controlled by genes on the *X* chromosome are said to be (1) sex-linked (2) mutagenic (3) incompletely dominant (4) homozygous

Short Answer
(Constructed Response)

35. Use a diagram to show why, for each pregnancy, the chances of giving birth to either a boy or a girl is 50-50. In a complete sentence, explain the results shown in your diagram.

36. Explain why hemophilia occurs more often in males than in females. Use a diagram to illustrate your answer.

GENETIC MUTATIONS

Changes in the genetic material are called **mutations**. Mutations in body cells can be passed on to new cells of the individual as a result of mitosis, but they cannot be transmitted to offspring by sexual reproduction. However, mutations in sex cells *can* be transmitted to the next generation. Mutations may involve alterations in chromosomes or alterations in the chemical makeup of genes.

Chromosomal Alterations

Chromosomal alterations involve a change in the structure or number of chromosomes. The effects of chromosomal alterations are often seen in the phenotype of an organism because each chromosome contains many genes.

Nondisjunction. During meiosis, the two chromosomes of each homologous pair separate from each other; each gamete produced by the division receives only one member of each homologous pair. The separation of homologous chromosomes is called disjunction. *Nondisjunction* is a type of chromosomal alteration in which one or more pairs of homologous chromosomes fail to separate normally during meiotic cell division (Figure 6-7).

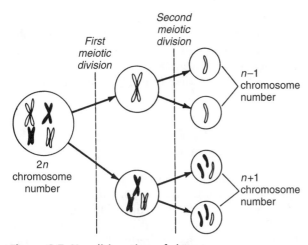

Figure 6-7. Nondisjunction of chromosomes.

As a result of nondisjunction, one of the gametes produced contains both members of the homologous pair, while another gamete contains neither chromosome. Nondisjunction results in the production of some gametes with more chromosomes than normal and some gametes with fewer chromosomes than normal. If one of these abnormal gametes is involved in fertilization, the resulting zygote will have either more than or less than the normal (2*n*) number of chromosomes.

Down syndrome in humans is caused by the presence of an extra chromosome number 21. Nondisjunction during gamete production in one of the parents produces a gamete with an extra chromosome 21. As a result of fertilization, this extra chromosome is transmitted to the offspring.

Polyploidy. Occasionally during gamete formation, a complete set of chromosomes fails to undergo disjunction, and a gamete is produced that contains the diploid (2*n*) chromosome number. If a diploid gamete unites with a normal (*n*) gamete during fertilization, the resulting zygote will have a 3*n* chromosome number. If two 2*n* gametes fuse, a 4*n* zygote results. The inheritance of one or more complete extra sets of chromosomes is called *polyploidy*. This condition is common in plants but rare in animals. In plants, polyploid individuals are usually larger or more vigorous than the normal, diploid varieties. Certain strains of wheat, potatoes, alfalfa, apples, tobacco, and zinnias are polyploid. Some polyploid plants produce seedless fruit and are sterile.

Changes in Chromosome Structure. Changes in the makeup of chromosomes may result from random breakage and recombination of chromosome parts. *Translocation* occurs when a segment of one chromosome breaks off and reattaches to a nonhomologous chromosome. *Addition* occurs when a segment breaks off one chromosome and reattaches to the homologous chromosome. *Inversion* occurs when a segment breaks off and reattaches in reverse on the same chromosome. *Deletion* occurs when a segment breaks off and does not reattach to any other chromosome.

Gene Mutations

A random change in the chemical makeup of the DNA (genetic material) is a *gene mutation*. The effects of some gene mutations, such as albinism, are noticeable, but other gene mutations may not produce noticeable effects.

Inheritable gene mutations tend to be harmful to the individual. For example, sickle-cell anemia and Tay-Sachs disease are caused by gene mutations. Fortunately, most gene mutations are recessive and are hidden by the normal, dominant allele. However, if both parents carry the same recessive mutant gene, there is a chance that their offspring will be homozygous recessive and show the harmful trait.

Occasionally, random gene mutations produce changes that make an individual better adapted to the environment. Over time, such helpful mutant genes tend to increase in frequency within a population.

Mutagenic Agents

Although mutations occur spontaneously, the rate of mutation can be increased by exposure to certain chemicals and forms of **radiation** that act as *mutagenic agents*. For example, forms of mutagenic radiation include X rays, ultraviolet rays, radioactive substances, and cosmic rays. Mutagenic chemicals include formaldehyde, benzene, and asbestos fibers.

Questions

Multiple Choice

37. Which phrase best describes most mutations? (1) dominant and disadvantageous to the organism (2) recessive and disadvantageous to the organism (3) recessive and advantageous to the organism (4) dominant and advantageous to the organism

38. The failure of a pair of homologous chromosomes to separate during meiotic cell division is called (1) nondisjunction (2) translocation (3) addition (4) deletion

39. The condition in which a gamete contains the $2n$ or $3n$ number of chromosomes is called (1) translocation (2) a gene mutation (3) polydactyly (4) polyploidy

40. The presence of only one X chromosome in each body cell of a human female produces a condition known as Turner syndrome. This condition most probably results from the process called (1) polyploidy (2) crossing-over (3) nondisjunction (4) hybridization

41. A random change in the chemical structure of DNA produces (1) polyploidy (2) a translocation (3) nondisjunction (4) a gene mutation

42. Down syndrome in humans is characterized by the presence of an extra chromosome 21 in all cells of the body. The number of chromosomes present in the body cells of individuals with this condition is (1) $n + 1$ (2) $3n$ (3) $2n + 1$ (4) $4n$

43. Ultraviolet rays, X rays, and certain other forms of radiation can increase the rate of gene mutation. These forms of radiation are said to act as (1) mutagenic agents (2) catalysts (3) enzymes (4) indicators

44. The large size and exceptional vigor of certain varieties of wheat, alfalfa, apples, and zinnias are due to the possession of extra sets of chromosomes, which result from (1) incomplete dominance (2) gene mutations (3) nondisjunction of complete sets of chromosomes (4) nondisjunction of chromosome number 21 only

45. The graph below shows the relationship between maternal age and the number of cases of children born with Down syndrome per 1000 births.

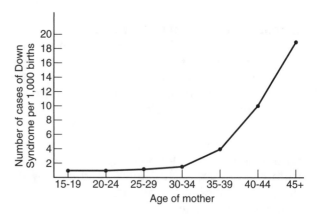

According to the graph, the incidence of Down syndrome (1) generally decreases as maternal age increases (2) is about nine times greater at age 45 than at age 30 (3) stabilized at 2 per 1000 births after age 35 (4) is greater at age 15 than at age 35

46. A type of chromosomal alteration in which a segment of chromosome breaks off and does not reattach to any chromosome is called (1) addition (2) inversion (3) deletion (4) translocation

Short Answer
(Constructed Response)

Base your answers to questions 47 through 50 on the following information about an experiment and on your knowledge of biology.

Two groups of 100 lima beans each were used. Group A was exposed to natural light for a period of 24 hours and then planted. Group B was exposed to microwave energy for 24 hours and then planted under the same conditions as Group A. When the seeds germinated, the plants were observed for growth over a period of two weeks. The results are summarized in the table below.

Group	Number of Plants	
	Normal Growth	Stunted and/or Pale
A	83	17
B	54	46

47. What hypothesis was most likely being tested in this experiment?

48. In a complete sentence, describe the results of the experiment.

49. Based on the data, propose a conclusion for the experiment.

50. What are some of the implications of the data?

Essay
(Extended Constructed Response)

51. Explain how it is possible for an individual to inherit an extra chromosome. List two or more human genetic disorders caused by the inheritance of an abnormal number of chromosomes.

52. Mutagens are agents that increase the rate of gene mutations in cells. Identify three types of mutagenic agents and briefly explain how each one causes mutations. Describe how people may reduce their chances of being harmed by these particular agents.

HEREDITY AND THE ENVIRONMENT

The development and expression of inherited traits can be influenced by environmental factors such as nutrients, temperature, sunlight, and so on. The relationship between gene action and environmental influence can be seen in the following examples.

Temperature affects fur color in the Himalayan rabbit. Under normal circumstances, these rabbits are white with black ears, nose, tail, and feet. (The black fur helps the rabbit absorb more heat in its extremities.) However, when some of the white fur on a Himalayan rabbit's back is shaved off and the area kept covered with an ice pack, the new hairs grow in black. The artificial change in temperature produces a change in fur color.

Experiments have shown that the production of chlorophyll requires exposure to sunlight. When parts of a leaf are covered with dark paper, chlorophyll production stops in the area that is covered. Only the exposed part produces chlorophyll, is green, and performs photosynthesis.

Stress and nutrition can affect gene expression. For example, someone who has a tall genotype may not develop a tall phenotype if his or her growth is stunted by malnutrition.

PLANT AND ANIMAL BREEDING

Using the principles of genetics, plant and animal breeders have been able to produce, improve, and maintain new varieties of plants and animals. Methods of **selective breeding** used by such people include artificial selection, inbreeding, and hybridization.

In *artificial selection*, individuals with the most desirable traits (for example, sheep with thick, soft wool) are crossed or allowed to mate in the hopes that their offspring will show the desired traits.

The offspring of selected organisms may be mated with one another to produce more individuals with the desirable traits. This technique, called *inbreeding*, involves the mating of closely related organisms. (Of course, the risk of inbreeding is that harmful recessive genes are more likely to be inherited and cause disorders in the offspring.)

Two varieties of a species may have different desirable traits. In a technique called *hybridization*, breeders cross two such varieties in the hope of producing hybrid offspring that show the desirable traits of both varieties. For example, if one variety of rose has very large petals and another variety has a very sweet scent, their hybrid might show both desirable traits.

Questions

Multiple Choice

53. If bean plant seedlings are germinated in the dark, the seedlings will lack green color. The best explanation for this condition is that (1) bean plants are heterotrophic organisms (2) bean seedlings lack nitrogen compounds in their cotyledons (3) the absence of an environmental factor limits the expression of a genotype (4) bean plants cannot break down carbon dioxide to produce oxygen in the dark

54. In many humans, exposing the skin to sunlight over prolonged periods of time results in the production of more pigment by the skin cells (tanning). This change in skin color provides evidence that (1) ultraviolet light can cause mutations (2) gene action can be influenced by the environment (3) the inheritance of skin color is an acquired characteristic (4) albinism is a recessive characteristic

55. Identical twins were separated at birth and brought together after 13 years. They varied in height by 5 centimeters and in weight by 10 kilograms. The most probable explanation for these differences is that (1) their environments affected the expression of their traits (2) their cells did not divide by mitotic cell division (3) they developed from two different zygotes (4) they differed in their genotypes

56. A normal bean seedling that had the ability to produce chlorophyll did not produce any chlorophyll when grown in soil that was totally deficient in magnesium salts. Which statement concerning this plant's inability to produce chlorophyll is true? (1) The lack of magnesium prevented the plant's roots from absorbing water. (2) The production of chlorophyll was controlled solely by heredity. (3) The lack of magnesium caused a mutation of the gene that controlled chlorophyll production. (4) The production of chlorophyll was influenced by environmental conditions.

57. To ensure the maintenance of a desirable trait in a particular variety of plant, a farmer would use (1) binary fission (2) mutagenic agents (3) artificial selection (4) natural selection

58. The mating of very closely related organisms in order to produce the most desirable traits is known as (1) inbreeding (2) hybridization (3) karyotyping (4) crossing-over

59. Plant and animal breeders usually sell or get rid of undesirable specimens and use only the desirable ones for breeding. This practice is referred to as (1) vegetative propagation (2) artificial selection (3) natural breeding (4) random mating

Short Answer
(Constructed Response)

60. Identify three environmental factors that can influence phenotype. Give an example of each.

61. In a complete sentence, describe some steps a breeder would take to produce an organism that has desirable traits.

HUMAN HEREDITY

The principles of genetics apply to all organisms. However, specific studies of human genetics are limited because humans are not suitable subjects for experimentation: human generation time is too long; there are only a small number of offspring per generation in a human family; and it is unethical to perform such experiments on humans. Knowledge of human heredity has been gathered indirectly through studies of human pedigree charts and materials obtained in the course of genetics counseling.

Human Pedigree Charts

The patterns of inheritance of certain traits can be traced in families for a number of generations. These patterns can be illustrated in *pedigree charts* that show the presence or absence of certain genetic traits in each generation. The use of a pedigree chart may also make it possible to identify carriers of recessive genes.

Human Genetic Disorders

Some diseases caused by genetic abnormalities are sickle-cell anemia, Tay-Sachs disease, and phenylketonuria. These disorders are caused by gene mutations.

Sickle-cell anemia is a blood disorder found most commonly in individuals of African descent. The disorder is caused by a gene mutation that results in the production of abnormal hemoglobin molecules and red blood cells. The abnormal hemoglobin and sickle-shaped cells do not carry oxygen efficiently, resulting in anemia. The sickle-shaped red cells also tend to obstruct blood vessels, causing severe pain. Sickle-cell anemia occurs in individuals homozygous for the trait. Both homozygous and heterozygous individuals can be detected by blood tests.

Tay-Sachs disease is a recessive genetic disorder in which nerve tissue in the brain deteriorates because of an accumulation of fatty material. The disorder is a result of the body's inability to synthesize a particular enzyme. Tay-Sachs disease, which is fatal, occurs most commonly among Jewish people of Central European descent.

Phenylketonuria (PKU) is a disorder in which the body cannot synthesize an enzyme necessary for the normal metabolism of the amino acid phenylalanine. The disease, which occurs in homozygous recessive individuals, is characterized by the development of mental retardation. Analysis of the urine of newborn infants can detect PKU. If PKU is detected, mental retardation can be prevented by maintaining a diet free of phenylalanine.

Detection of Genetic Disorders

Some human genetic disorders can be detected either before or after birth by the use of one or more of the following techniques.

Advances in genetic research have resulted in the development of simple blood and urine tests that can determine if an individual has certain genetic disorders. Carriers of sickle-cell anemia and Tay-Sachs disease can be identified by these screening techniques.

Karyotyping is a technique in which a greatly enlarged photograph of the chromosomes of a cell is prepared. The homologous pairs of chromosomes are matched together, and the chromosomes are examined to see if there are any abnormalities in number or structure.

Amniocentesis is a technique in which a small sample of amniotic fluid is withdrawn from the amniotic sac of a pregnant woman. The fluid contains fetal cells, which can be used for karyotyping or for chemical analysis. Amniocentesis is used in the identification of sickle-cell anemia, Tay-Sachs disease, and Down syndrome in fetuses.

Genetic Counseling

The various techniques described above are used by *genetics counselors* to inform concerned parents about the possible occurrence of genetic defects in their children. For couples whose families show the presence of a particular genetic disorder, a pedigree chart may be developed to predict the probability of their children's having the disorder. Amniocentesis, followed by karyotyping and chemical tests, may be performed once pregnancy is established.

Questions

Multiple Choice

62. An inherited metabolic disorder known as phenylketonuria (PKU) is characterized by severe mental retardation. This condition results from the inability to synthesize a single   (1) enzyme   (2) hormone   (3) vitamin   (4) carbohydrate

63. Which statement best describes amniocentesis?   (1) Blood cells of an adult are checked for anemia.   (2) Saliva of a child is analyzed for the amino acids.   (3) Urine of a newborn baby is analyzed for the amino acid phenylalanine.   (4) Fluid surrounding a fetus is removed for chemical and genetic analysis.

64. Which is a genetic disorder in which abnormal hemoglobin leads to fragile red blood cells and obstructed blood vessels?   (1) phenylketonuria   (2) sickle-cell anemia   (3) leukemia   (4) Down syndrome

65. Human disorders such as PKU and sickle-cell anemia, which are defects in the synthesis of individual proteins, are most likely the result of   (1) gene mutations   (2) nondisjunction   (3) crossing-over   (4) polyploidy

66. Which technique can be used to examine the chromosomes of a fetus for possible genetic defects?   (1) pedigree analysis   (2) analysis of fetal urine   (3) karyotyping   (4) blood cell tests

Short Answer
(Constructed Response)

67. In a complete sentence, give three reasons why a direct study of the inheritance of human traits is difficult to carry out.

68. In two full sentences, briefly describe the two ways that information about patterns of human heredity is usually obtained.

MODERN GENETICS

Biochemists have learned that the DNA of the chromosomes is the genetic material that is passed from generation to generation. Genes are sections of DNA (deoxyribonucleic acid) molecules. DNA controls cellular activities by controlling the production of enzymes.

DNA Structure

DNA molecules are very large; each is made up of thousands of repeating units called **nucleotides**. A DNA nucleotide is composed of three parts: a *phosphate group;* a molecule of the 5-carbon sugar *deoxyribose;* and a *nitrogenous base* (Figure 6-8).

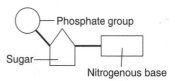

Figure 6-8. Structure of a DNA nucleotide unit.

There are four different nitrogenous bases found in DNA nucleotides: *adenine, cytosine, guanine,* and *thymine.* Therefore, there are four different kinds of nucleotides, depending on which nitrogenous base is present.

Watson-Crick Model.   In the model of DNA developed by James Watson and Francis Crick, the DNA molecule consists of two connected chains of nucleotides forming a ladderlike structure (Figure 6-9, on page 84). The sides of the "ladder" are composed of alternating phosphate and deoxyribose (sugar) molecules. Each rung of the ladder consists of a pair of nitrogenous bases bonded together by hydrogen bonds. The two chains of the DNA molecule are twisted to form a spiral, or *double helix.*

The four nitrogenous bases of DNA nucleotides bond together in only one way: adenine (A) pairs with thymine (T), and cytosine (C) pairs with guanine (G). Because the bases pair together

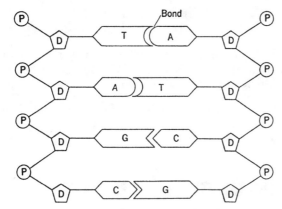

Figure 6-9. Structure of the DNA molecule.

in only one way, the two strands of a DNA molecule are always *complementary*. Where there is an adenine nucleotide on one strand, there is a thymine nucleotide on the other; where there is a cytosine on one strand, there is a guanine on the other. If you know the order of bases on one strand, then you also know the order on the second strand.

DNA Replication

DNA, unlike any other chemical compound, can make exact copies of itself—that is, DNA can **replicate**. This process, called DNA *replication*, is a necessary part of the chromosome replication that occurs during mitosis and meiosis.

In replication, the double-stranded DNA helix unwinds; the two strands then separate, or unzip, by breaking the hydrogen bonds between the nitrogenous base pairs. Free nucleotides from the cytoplasm then enter the nucleus, where they bond to their complementary bases on the DNA strands (Figure 6-10). Replication produces two

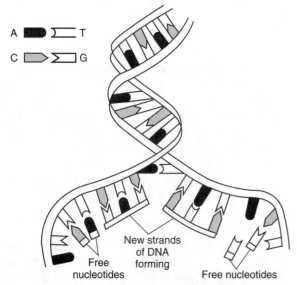

Figure 6-10. Replication of DNA strands.

identical DNA molecules that are exact copies of the original molecule. The process of DNA replication is actually carried out by a team of several important, specific enzymes.

Gene Control of Cellular Activities

The unique qualities of an organism are determined by the DNA of its genes. The genes control enzyme synthesis, and the enzymes control cell activities. For example, a dominant gene enables people to produce the enzyme lactase, which digests milk sugar (lactose). People who lack an active copy of this gene cannot digest milk sugar and, thus, are lactose intolerant.

The hereditary information is in the sequence of the nucleotides in DNA molecules. The DNA nucleotide sequence determines the sequence of amino acids in enzymes and other proteins. The genetic control of protein synthesis involves RNA as well as DNA.

RNA

Molecules of *ribonucleic acid*, or *RNA*, are similar to DNA in that they are also made up of nucleotide units. However, in RNA nucleotides, the 5-carbon sugar *ribose* is substituted for deoxyribose, and the nitrogenous base *uracil* (U) is substituted for thymine. RNA molecules consist of one strand of nucleotides, while DNA molecules have two. There are three kinds of RNA molecules in cells: *messenger RNA* (mRNA), *transfer RNA* (tRNA), and *ribosomal RNA* (rRNA).

Messenger RNA is synthesized in the cell nucleus. Portions of a DNA molecule unwind, and the two strands separate. The RNA nucleotides pair with complementary bases on a DNA strand, forming a strand of messenger RNA that is complementary to the DNA strand. The DNA strand serves as a **template**, or pattern, for the synthesis of messenger RNA. In this way, the hereditary information in the nucleotide sequence of DNA is copied in complementary form into the nucleotide sequence of messenger RNA.

The sequence of nucleotides in messenger RNA contains the genetic code, which determines the amino acid sequence of proteins. The genetic code for each amino acid is a specific sequence of three nucleotides. The three-nucleotide sequence in messenger RNA that specifies a particular amino acid is called a *codon*.

Transfer RNA molecules are found in the cytoplasm. Their function is to carry amino acid molecules to the *ribosomes*, the sites of protein synthesis. Ribosomes are made up of rRNA and proteins. There are 20 different kinds of amino acids in cells, and there is a different form of transfer RNA for each amino acid. Each kind of transfer RNA has a three-nucleotide sequence, called an *anticodon*, which is complementary to a codon on the messenger RNA.

Protein Synthesis

Protein synthesis begins with the synthesis of messenger RNA molecules, which then move from the nucleus into the cytoplasm. In the cytoplasm, the strand of messenger RNA becomes associated with ribosomes (Figure 6-11). Amino acids are carried to the ribosomes and messenger RNA by the transfer RNAs. The anticodons of the transfer RNAs align with the codons of the messenger RNA. The amino acids carried by the transfer RNAs bond together in a sequence determined by the base sequence of the messenger RNA. The resulting chain of amino acids is a polypeptide. Some proteins consist of a single polypeptide chain, while others include two or more.

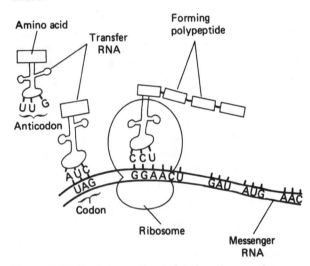

Figure 6-11. Protein synthesis (at the ribosome).

One Gene–One Polypeptide Hypothesis

According to the *one gene–one polypeptide hypothesis*, each gene controls the synthesis of a single polypeptide. A modern definition of the gene is the sequence of nucleotides in a DNA molecule necessary to synthesize one polypeptide.

Gene Mutations

Any change in the sequence of nucleotides in a DNA molecule is a gene mutation. If the mutation occurs in the DNA of the sex cells, it may be inherited. Gene mutations may involve the *addition* or *deletion* of bases, or the *substitution* of one base for another. Sickle-cell anemia is caused by the substitution of one incorrect nitrogenous base in a gene that controls hemoglobin synthesis. The incorrect base results in the insertion of one incorrect amino acid, which in turn affects the structure and function of the hemoglobin protein.

Cloning

The process by which a group of genetically identical offspring are produced from the cells of an organism is called **cloning**. The cloning of plants shows great promise for agriculture, where plants with desirable qualities can be produced rapidly from the cells of a single plant. The cloning of animals has been achieved in frogs, mice, sheep, goats, cows, and monkeys.

Genetic Engineering

Gene splicing, or **genetic engineering**, involves the transfer of genetic material from one organism to another. This **recombining** of genes results in the formation of *recombinant* DNA. Using gene-splicing techniques, genes from one organism can be inserted into the DNA of another organism. Human genes that control the synthesis of insulin, interferon, and growth hormone have been introduced into bacterial cells, where they function as part of the bacterial DNA. In this way, bacterial cells are being used to synthesize certain substances needed by humans. Genetic engineering may eventually be able to correct some genetic defects and produce commercially desirable plants and animals.

Techniques of Genetic Engineering. The technique of making recombinant DNA (rDNA) molecules involves three important components.

First, a specific enzyme is needed to cut the DNA from the donor genes at a specific site. This enzyme is called a *restriction enzyme*. The enzyme is used to cut out a piece of DNA that contains one or more desired genes from the donor's DNA.

Next, a *vector* is needed to receive the donor DNA. Most frequently, a naturally occurring circular piece of bacterial DNA, called a *plasmid*, is used for this purpose.

Finally, an enzyme is used to "stitch" the donor DNA into the plasmid vector. This enzyme is called *ligase*, and it creates permanent bonds between the donor DNA and the plasmid DNA. The result is that the donor DNA is incorporated into the bacterial plasmid, forming the recombinant DNA (rDNA).

It is important that the donor and the plasmid DNA be cut with the same restriction enzyme. Since each enzyme cuts DNA only at a specific site, the two different DNAs will have matching cut ends known as "sticky ends." The nitrogenous bases exposed at these cut sites can then match up according to the base-pairing rules, A to T and G to C (Figure 6-12).

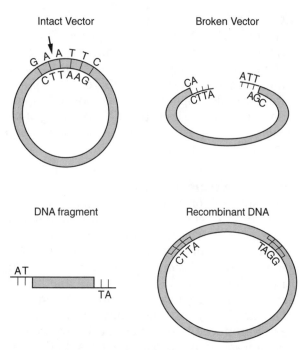

Figure 6-12. Use of a restriction enzyme and vector to form recombinant DNA.

The rDNA is then inserted into bacteria. When these bacteria reproduce, they copy the rDNA plasmid along with their own DNA. The plasmid is copied thousands of times, forming a clone (a colony having identical genetic material).

In addition to copying the plasmid along with their other DNA, the bacteria *express* the genes that the plasmid carries, including the donor genes. As they reproduce, the bacteria continue to code for production of the desired protein. In this way, the bacteria can produce human proteins because they carry the genes with the instructions. This technique has made it possible to produce many chemicals that are needed by people who cannot produce them, due to genetic disorders. Two human proteins that have been successfully synthesized by rDNA techniques are the hormone insulin and human growth hormone.

Questions

Multiple Choice

69. Which diagram illustrates the correct structure of a segment of a DNA molecule? (1) 1 (2) 2 (3) 3 (4) 4

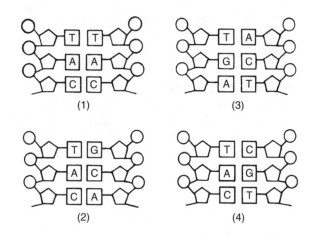

70. DNA and RNA molecules are similar in that they both contain (1) nucleotides (2) a double helix (3) deoxyribose sugars (4) thymine

71. Which series is arranged in correct order according to *decreasing* size of structures? (1) DNA, nucleus, chromosome, nucleotide, nitrogenous base (2) nucleotide, chromosome, nitrogenous base, nucleus, DNA (3) nucleus, chromosome, DNA, nucleotide, nitrogenous base (4) chromosome, nucleus, nitrogenous base, nucleotide, DNA

72. Which substances are components of a DNA nucleotide? (1) phosphate, deoxyribose, and uracil (2) phosphate, ribose, and adenine (3) thymine, deoxyribose, and phosphate (4) ribose, phosphate, and uracil

73. Which two bases are present in equal amounts in a double-stranded DNA molecule? (1) cytosine and thymine (2) adenine and thymine (3) adenine and uracil (4) cytosine and uracil

74. By which process can a group of genetically identical plants be rapidly produced from the cells of a single plant? (1) screening (2) karyotyping (3) gene splicing (4) cloning

To answer questions 75 through 78, select from the list below the type of nucleic acid that is best described by the phrase. (Note that there are only three choices.)

A. DNA
B. Messenger RNA
C. Transfer RNA

75. Genetic material responsible for the traits of an organism, that is passed from parent to offspring (1) A (2) B (3) C

76. Carries genetic information from the cell nucleus out to the ribosomes (1) A (2) B (3) C

77. Contains thymine instead of uracil   (1) A
(2) B   (3) C

78. Carries amino acid molecules to the ribosomes in the cytoplasm   (1) A   (2) B   (3) C

79. In humans, a gene mutation results from a change in the   (1) sequence of the nitrogenous bases in DNA   (2) chromosome number in a sperm cell   (3) chromosome number in an egg cell   (4) sequence of the sugars and phosphates in DNA

80. The genetic code for one amino acid molecule consists of   (1) five sugar molecules   (2) two phosphates   (3) three nucleotides   (4) four hydrogen bonds

81. During the replication of a DNA molecule, separation of the DNA molecule will normally occur when hydrogen bonds are broken between (1) thymine and thymine   (2) guanine and uracil (3) adenine and cytosine   (4) cytosine and guanine

82. In the diagram, what substance is represented by the letter x?   (1) ribose   (2) deoxyribose   (3) phosphate   (4) adenine

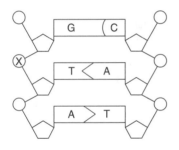

83. Which terms describe gene activities that ensure homeostatic control of life processes and continuity of hereditary material?   (1) oxidation and hydrolysis   (2) enzyme synthesis and DNA replication   (3) oxygen transport and cyclosis (4) pinocytosis and dehydration synthesis

84. The formation of recombinant DNA results from the   (1) addition of messenger RNA molecules to an organism   (2) transfer of genes from one organism to another   (3) substitution of a ribose sugar for a deoxyribose sugar   (4) production of a polyploid condition by a mutagenic agent

85. The replication of a double-stranded DNA molecule begins when the strands "unzip" at the (1) phosphate bonds   (2) ribose molecules   (3) deoxyribose molecules   (4) hydrogen bonds

Base your answers to questions 86 though 90 on the following diagram, which represents the process of protein synthesis in a typical cell.

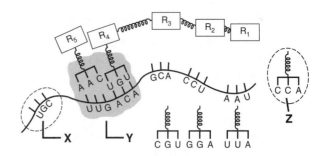

86. The original template for this process is a molecule of   (1) DNA   (2) messenger RNA (3) transfer RNA   (4) ribosomal RNA

87. The units labeled R_1, R_2, and R_3 represent (1) nucleotides   (2) RNA molecules   (3) DNA molecules   (4) amino acids

88. The organelle labeled Y, on which this process occurs, is the   (1) nucleus   (2) ribosome (3) chloroplast   (4) mitochondria

89. The circled portion labeled X is known as (1) an amino acid   (2) a codon   (3) an anticodon (4) a single nucleotide

90. The circled portion labeled Z represents a molecule of   (1) DNA   (2) messenger RNA (3) transfer RNA   (4) ribosomal RNA

Short Answer
(Constructed Response)

91. In two or more complete sentences, describe the two important functions of DNA.

92. Why is DNA replication critical to the survival of organisms?

93. The following is a scrambled list of the techniques used in making recombinant DNA. Write these steps in the correct sequence and, for each step, explain why it is placed in that order.

Steps
Cut open plasmid with restriction enzyme
Obtain synthesized protein from the bacteria
Clone bacterial cells with rDNA plasmids
Insert donor DNA into the open plasmid
Cut out donor DNA with restriction enzyme
Add ligase to bond donor DNA and plasmid

Essay
(Extended Constructed Response)

94. Explain the role of each of the following items in making recombinant DNA: restriction enzymes; plasmids; ligase.

95. How are the techniques of genetic engineering making it possible to treat some diseases caused by genetic disorders? Provide an example.

Reading Comprehension

Base your answers to questions 96 through 100 on the information below and on your knowledge of biology.

Gene Splicing, Bacteria, and Insulin

Recent advances in cell technology and gene transplanting have allowed scientists to perform some interesting experiments. These experiments include splicing a human gene into the genetic material of bacteria. The altered bacteria express the added genetic material.

Bacteria reproduce rapidly under certain conditions. This means that bacteria with the gene for human insulin could multiply rapidly, resulting in a large bacterial population that could produce large quantities of human insulin.

The traditional source of insulin is the pancreases of slaughtered farm animals. Continued use of this type of insulin can trigger allergic reactions in some humans. The new bacteria-produced insulin does not appear to produce these side effects.

The bacteria used for these experiments are *E. coli*, bacteria common to the digestive systems of many humans. Some scientists question these experiments and are concerned that the altered *E. coli* may accidentally get into water supplies.

96. Transplanting genetic material into bacteria is a simple task. (1) true (2) false (3) not enough information given

97. Under certain conditions, bacteria reproduce at a rapid rate. (1) true (2) false (3) not enough information given

98. Continued use of insulin from other animals may cause unpleasant reactions in some people. (1) true (2) false (3) not enough information given

99. The bacteria used in these experiments are normally found only in the nerve tissue of humans. (1) true (2) false (3) not enough information given

100. Bacteria other than *E. coli* are unable to produce insulin. (1) true (2) false (3) not enough information given

CHAPTER 7

Evolution

Evolution is the process of change over time. The theory of evolution suggests that existing forms of life on Earth have evolved from earlier forms over long periods of time. These earlier forms were usually very different from the related organisms living today. Evolution accounts for the differences in structure, function, and behavior among all life-forms, as well as for the changes that occur within populations over many generations.

EVIDENCE OF EVOLUTION

Observations that support the theory of evolution have been obtained from the study of the geologic record and from studies of comparative anatomy, embryology, cytology, and biochemistry.

Geologic Record

Geologists estimate the age of Earth to be between 4.5 and 5 billion years old. This estimate is based on *radioactive dating* of the oldest known rocks from Earth's crust. (It is assumed that Earth is at least as old as the oldest rocks and minerals in its crust.)

In studying the geology of the planet, scientists have found many **fossils**, the remains or traces of organisms that no longer exist. From their studies of rocks and fossils, scientists have developed a picture of the changes that have occurred both in Earth itself and in living things on the planet.

Fossils

The earliest known fossils are traces of bacteria-like organisms that are about 3.5 billion years old. (The age of these fossils was determined by radioactive dating of the rocks in which they were found.)

Fossils of relatively intact organisms have been found preserved in ice, tar, and amber (a sticky plant resin that hardens). Mineralized bones, shells, teeth, and other hard parts of an-cient organisms are sometimes found intact. (The soft parts generally decay within a short time.)

Other fossils have been formed by *petrifaction*, a process in which the tissues are gradually replaced by dissolved minerals that produce a stone replica of the original material. Imprints, casts, and molds of organisms or parts of organisms are frequently found in *sedimentary* rock. This type of rock is formed from the deposition of thick layers of soft sediments that eventually harden and turn to rock from the weight of overlying sediments and water. The fossils form when the remains of dead organisms settle to the bottom of a body of water and are quickly covered by sediment. The overlying sediment slows or halts decay. When the layers of sediment harden, traces of the buried organisms are preserved in the rock.

In studying undisturbed sedimentary rock, scientists assume that each layer is older than all the layers, or *strata*, above it. Thus, fossils in the lower strata are older than fossils in the overlying strata. Fossils in the upper strata of a sedimentary rock sample are generally more complex than fossils in the lower strata, but there is often a resemblance between them. This suggests a link between recent forms and older forms. The fossil record may also provide evidence of divergent evolutionary pathways of some organisms from a common ancestor (Figure 7-1a).

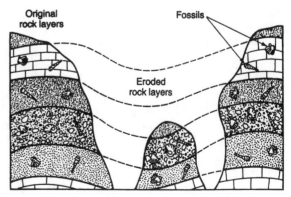

Figure 7-1a. A resemblance between fossils in the upper and lower rock strata often indicates an evolutionary link between recent and older forms.

Some fossils in older strata are unlike any organisms living today. This suggests that many previous species have died out, or undergone **extinction**. Other fossils have structures that show ancestral connections to present-day life-forms. On the other hand, there are fossils that are quite similar to modern organisms, suggesting that some species have existed for a long time without much evolutionary change.

Comparative Anatomy

Another line of evidence for evolution comes from observations of basic structural, or anatomical, similarities between various organisms. *Homologous structures* are anatomical parts found in different organisms that are similar in origin and structure, although they may differ in function. For example, the flippers of whales, the wings of bats, the forelimbs of cats, and the arms of humans are homologous structures; they serve different functions, but their basic bone structures are similar (Figure 7-1*b*). The presence of such homologous structures suggests that these mammals all evolved from a common ancestor.

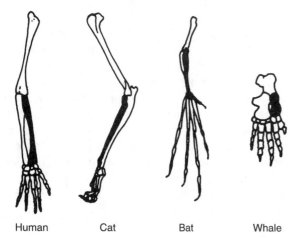

Human   Cat   Bat   Whale

Figure 7-1*b*. The presence of homologous structures in their limb bones suggests that these mammals all evolved from a common ancestor.

Comparative Embryology

Although adult organisms of different species may look very different from one another, a comparison of the early stages of their embryonic development may show similarities that suggest a common ancestry. For example, the very early embryos of such vertebrates as fish, reptiles, birds, and mammals show some similarities in structure, such as having a tail (Figure 7-2). As

embryonic development continues, the characteristic traits of each species become more apparent.

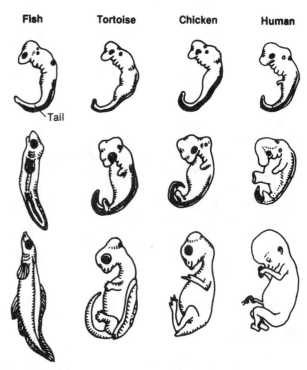

Figure 7-2. Similar features, such as a tail, in the early stages of embryonic development point to a common ancestry for these different vertebrates.

Comparative Cytology

As stated in the cell theory, all living things are made up of cells. Cell organelles, including the cell membrane, ribosomes, and mitochondria, are structurally and functionally similar in most living organisms.

Comparative Biochemistry

All living things contain similar biochemical compounds. For example, the structure and function of DNA, RNA, and proteins (including enzymes) are similar in all organisms. The closer the relationship between the organisms, the greater their biochemical and genetic similarities.

QUESTIONS

Multiple Choice

1. The forelegs of a frog and the front legs of a horse are examples of structures that are   (1) heterotrophic   (2) homozygous   (3) hermaphroditic   (4) homologous

2. Which conclusion may be made when comparing fossils in undisturbed strata of sedimentary rock? (1) The fossils in the upper strata are younger than those in the lower strata. (2) The fossils in the upper strata are older than those in the lower strata. (3) The fossils in the upper strata are generally less complex than those in the lower strata. (4) There are no fossils in the upper strata that resemble those in the lower strata.

3. The similarity among the blood proteins of all mammals may be taken as evidence of evolutionary relationships based on (1) comparative anatomy (2) geographic distribution (3) comparative embryology (4) comparative biochemistry

4. The diagram below represents a section of undisturbed rock and the general location of fossils of several closely related species. According to current theory, which assumption is probably the most correct concerning species *A*, *B*, *C*, and *D*? (1) *A* is most likely the ancestor of *B*, *C*, and *D*. (2) *B* was extinct when *C* evolved. (3) *C* evolved more recently than *A*, *B*, and *D*. (4) *D* was probably the ancestor of *A*, *B*, and *C*.

Species C & D
Species C
Species A & B & C
Species A & B
Species A

5. Which assumption is a basis for the use of fossils as evidence for evolution? (1) Fossils show a complete record of the evolution of all animals. (2) In undisturbed layers of Earth's surface, the oldest fossils are found in the lowest layers. (3) Fossils are always found deep in volcanic rocks. (4) All fossils were formed at the same time.

6. Many related organisms are found to have the same kinds of enzymes. This suggests that (1) enzymes work only on specific substrates (2) enzymes act as catalysts in biochemical reactions (3) organisms living in the same environment require identical enzymes (4) these organisms probably share a common ancestry

7. Which is an example of evidence of evolution based on comparative biochemistry? (1) Sheep insulin can be substituted for human insulin. (2) The structure of a whale's flipper is similar to that of a human hand. (3) Human embryos have

a tail during an early stage of their development. (4) Both birds and bats have wings.

8. The presence of gill pouches in early-stage human embryos is considered to be evidence of the (1) likelihood that all vertebrates share a common ancestry (2) theory that the first organisms on Earth were heterotrophs (3) close relationship between fish and human reproductive patterns (4) close relationship between humans and amphibians

9. If a rabbit is sensitized to human blood, the rabbit's blood will react to chimpanzee blood in much the same way it reacts to human blood. This is an example of which type of evidence supporting the theory of evolution? (1) comparative habitat (2) comparative anatomy (3) comparative embryology (4) comparative biochemistry

Short Answer
(Constructed Response)

10. Using a complete sentence for each item, list and describe the five main types of evidence used to support the theory of evolution.

11. The diagram below represents a cross section of undisturbed rock layers. A scientist discovers bones of a complex vertebrate species in layers *B* and *C*. In which layer would an earlier, less complex form of this vertebrate most likely first appear? In a complete sentence, explain the reasons for your answer.

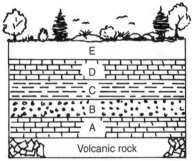

THEORIES OF EVOLUTION

Any theory of evolution must attempt to explain the origin and **diversity** of life on Earth. Such a theory must also account for the wide variety of *adaptations* found among both living and extinct species. Different theories may account for different aspects of the evolutionary process. However, taken together, they explain how life on Earth came to be and how it has progressed from the relatively simple and few to the complex and diverse.

THE HETEROTROPH HYPOTHESIS

The *heterotroph hypothesis* is one proposed explanation of how life arose and evolved on the primitive Earth. According to this hypothesis, the first life-forms were heterotrophic and therefore had to obtain organic nutrients from their environment.

The Primitive Earth

It is assumed that during the period preceding the development of the first life-forms, the primitive Earth was an exceptionally hot body consisting of inorganic substances in solid, liquid, and gaseous states.

The **atmosphere** of the primitive Earth had no free oxygen; instead, it is thought to have consisted of hydrogen (H_2), ammonia (NH_3), methane (CH_4), and water vapor. As Earth cooled, much of the water vapor condensed and fell as rain, which carried dissolved atmospheric gases (ammonia, methane, and hydrogen) and some minerals into the seas that formed. The seas became rich in these dissolved substances and minerals and are often described by biologists as having been a "hot, thin soup."

The primitive Earth provided an energy-rich environment. In addition to the heat, there was electrical energy in the form of lightning, **radiation** (X rays and ultraviolet rays) from the sun, and radioactivity from rocks.

Synthesis of Organic Compounds

The large amount of available energy was the driving force for synthesis reactions on the primitive Earth. In these reactions, the inorganic raw materials in the seas became chemically bonded to form organic molecules, including simple sugars and amino acids. These organic molecules were the building blocks for the first life-forms.

The scientist Stanley Miller devised an apparatus in which he simulated the conditions thought to exist in the primitive environment. His experiments showed that in the presence of heat and electrical energy, dissolved gases could combine to form simple organic compounds.

Formation of Aggregates

In time, the simple organic molecules accumulated in the seas. Eventually, they combined chemically in synthesis reactions to form more complex organic molecules. (Such interactions between organic molecules have been demonstrated in laboratories.) Some of the large, complex molecules formed groupings or clusters called *aggregates*. The aggregates developed a surrounding "membrane," which made it possible for the internal composition of the aggregate to differ from that of the surrounding water. It is thought that aggregates absorbed simple organic molecules from the environment for "food." Thus, they carried on a form of heterotrophic nutrition.

Reproduction of Aggregates

Over time, the aggregates became more complex and highly organized. Eventually, they developed the ability to reproduce. At that point in time, when their ability to reproduce had evolved, the aggregates are considered to have been living cells.

Heterotrophs to Autotrophs

It is thought that these early heterotrophic life-forms carried on a form of anaerobic respiration, or *fermentation* (in which glucose is converted to energy and CO_2 without O_2 being present). As a result of very long periods of fermentation, carbon dioxide was added to the atmosphere. Eventually, as a result of evolution, some heterotrophic forms developed the capacity to use carbon dioxide from the atmosphere in the synthesis of organic compounds. These organisms became the first autotrophs (self-feeders). Some bacteria are autotrophs, but most of the autotrophs alive today are green plants and algae.

Anaerobes to Aerobes

Autotrophic activity (photosynthesis) added oxygen molecules to the atmosphere. Over time, the capacity to use free oxygen in respiration (aerobic respiration) evolved in both autotrophs and heterotrophs.

There are both autotrophs and heterotrophs on Earth today. Some life-forms still carry on anaerobic respiration; but in most life-forms, respiration is aerobic. This is because aerobic respiration releases much more energy from food than does anaerobic respiration.

QUESTIONS

Multiple Choice

12. According to the heterotroph hypothesis, the first living things probably were anaerobic because their environment had no available (1) food   (2) energy   (3) water   (4) oxygen

13. Which is one basic assumption of the heterotroph hypothesis? (1) More complex organisms appeared before less complex organisms. (2) Living organisms did not appear until there was oxygen in the atmosphere. (3) Large autotrophic organisms appeared before small photosynthesizing organisms. (4) Autotrophic activity added oxygen molecules to the environment.

14. The heterotroph hypothesis is an attempt to explain (1) how Earth was originally formed (2) why simple organisms usually evolve into complex organisms (3) why evolution occurs very slowly (4) how life originated on Earth

15. The heterotroph hypothesis states that heterotrophic life-forms appeared before autotrophic forms as the first living things. A major assumption for this hypothesis is that (1) sufficient heat was not available in the beginning for the food-making process (2) the heterotrophic organisms were able to use molecules from the sea as "food" (3) lightning and radiation energy were limited to terrestrial areas (4) moisture in liquid form was limited to aquatic areas

Short Answer
(Constructed Response)

16. In two or more full sentences, explain how autotrophs evolved from heterotrophs.

17. In two complete sentences, identify the source of oxygen in Earth's early atmosphere and tell how this was important to the subsequent evolution of life.

EVOLUTION BY NATURAL SELECTION

Darwin's Theory of Natural Selection

Darwin's theory was based on the presence of variations among members of a species and their interaction with the process he called "natural selection." Darwin's theory includes the following main ideas:

Overpopulation: Within a population, there are more offspring produced in each generation than can possibly survive.

Competition: The natural resources, such as food, water, and space, available to a population are limited. Because there are more organisms produced in each generation than can survive, there must be *competition* among them for the resources needed for survival.

Survival of the fittest: Variations among members of a population make some of them better adapted to the environment than others. Such **variability** within populations means that, due to competition, the best-adapted individuals are most likely to survive.

Natural selection: The environment is the agent of **natural selection**, determining which adaptations or variations are helpful and which are harmful. For example, in an environment that is undergoing a particularly cold period, animals that have thicker fur than most other members of their population are more likely to survive. In this case, the variation—thicker fur—is helpful in terms of the environmental pressure.

Reproduction: Individuals with helpful variations tend to survive and reproduce at a higher rate than other members of their population, thus transmitting these variations to their offspring.

Speciation: The development of new species, a process called *speciation*, occurs as certain variations or adaptations accumulate in a population over many generations.

According to Darwin's theory, environmental pressures act as a force for the natural selection of the best-adapted individuals—those with helpful adaptations that enable them to survive and reproduce successfully. However, Darwin's theory did not explain *how* variations arise in members of a species. (The scientific study of heredity, genes, and mutations had not yet begun.)

QUESTIONS

Multiple Choice

18. Darwin's theory of evolution did *not* contain the concept that (1) genetic variations are produced by mutations and sexual recombination (2) organisms that are best adapted to their environment survive (3) population sizes are limited due to the struggle for survival (4) favorable traits are passed from one generation to the next

19. Natural selection is best defined as (1) survival of the strongest organisms only (2) elimination of the smallest organisms by the largest organisms (3) survival of those organisms best adapted to their environment (4) reproduction of those organisms that occupy the largest area in an environment

20. Although similar in many respects, two species of organisms exhibit differences that make each one well adapted to the environment in which it lives. The process of change that helps account for these differences is (1) evolution by natural selection (2) parthenogenesis (3) comparative embryology (4) inheritance of acquired traits

21. A key idea in Darwin's theory of evolution is that members of a population (1) are always identical (2) compete for limited resources in the environment (3) all get to reproduce and pass on their traits (4) are all equally well adapted to the environment

22. The development of new species, as variations accumulate in a population over time, is called (1) competition (2) reproduction (3) speciation (4) selection

Short Answer
(Constructed Response)

23. In two or more complete sentences, describe four main ideas that make up Darwin's theory of evolution.

24. Explain what is meant by "the environment is the agent of natural selection." Give one example to illustrate your answer (real or hypothetical).

MODERN EVOLUTIONARY THEORY

The modern theory of evolution includes both Darwin's ideas of variation and natural selection and the genetic basis of variations within populations.

Sources of Genetic Variations
Variations within a population result from two kinds of genetic events. First, recombination of alleles during sexual reproduction is a source of variations. Second, random and spontaneous gene and chromosome mutations produce genetic variations. Mutations may arise spontaneously in organisms, or they may be caused by exposure to *mutagenic* (mutation-causing) chemicals or radiation, such as ultraviolet rays and X rays. The accumulation of genetic recombination, variations, and mutations provides the raw material for evolution within a population.

Natural Selection and Genetic Variation
Natural selection involves the struggle of organisms to survive and reproduce in a given environment. Because of variability in traits, some individuals may have characteristics that help

them survive better than other members of their population. Natural selection favors those characteristics: individuals having favorable traits are more likely to survive, reproduce, and pass those traits on to future generations.

Favorable Variations. Favorable characteristics tend to increase in (genetic) frequency within a population. Favorable variations may include physical traits, such as larger muscles and increased speed, or behavioral traits, such as better food-finding or nest-building skills.

If environmental conditions change, traits that formerly had low survival value may come to have greater survival value. Likewise, traits that were favorable may no longer be so adaptive. The survival value of traits that had been neither helpful nor harmful may also change. In all of these cases, those traits that prove to be favorable under the new environmental conditions will increase in frequency within the population.

Unfavorable Variations. Unfavorable characteristics tend to decrease in frequency from generation to generation. Individuals with non-adaptive or unfavorable traits may be so severely selected against that, over time, populations that have unfavorable traits may become extinct. Indeed, the fossil record shows that extinction is a fairly common event, having been the fate of about 99 percent of all species that have ever existed on Earth.

Geographic Isolation
Changes in gene frequencies that lead to the development of a new species are more likely to occur in small populations than in large ones. Small groups may be segregated from the main population by a geographic barrier, such as a body of water or a mountain range. As a result of this *geographic isolation*, the small population cannot interbreed with the larger, main population. In time, the isolated population may evolve into a new species.

The following factors may be involved in the evolution of a new species: (a) the gene frequencies in the isolated population may already have been different from the gene frequencies in the main population, a difference known as the founder effect; (b) different mutations occur in the isolated population and the main population; and (c) different environmental factors exert different selection pressures on each population.

Darwin observed the effect of geographic isolation in his study of finches on the Galápagos Islands. Darwin hypothesized that the 14 different species he observed had evolved from a single species that had originally migrated to the islands from the mainland of South America. Over time, the different environment of each island had gradually resulted in the evolution of the separate species (Figure 7-3).

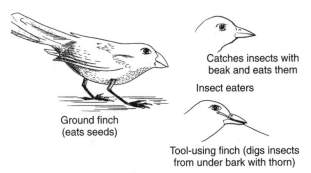

Figure 7-3. These Galápagos finches show a variety of adaptations for getting food.

Reproductive Isolation

Geographic isolation may eventually lead to *reproductive isolation*. The isolated population becomes so different from the main population that members of the two groups cannot interbreed, even if the geographic barriers were to be removed. When two populations can no longer interbreed and produce fertile offspring, they have become two distinct species.

Time Frame for Evolution

Although scientists generally agree on the basic factors involved in evolutionary change, there is some disagreement about the time frame in which such change occurs.

According to Darwin's original theory, evolutionary change occurs very gradually and continuously over the course of **geologic time** (millions of years). This theory, called *gradualism*, proposes that new species develop as a result of the gradual accumulation of small genetic variations that eventually, together, cause reproductive isolation and lead to speciation.

The more recent theory of *punctuated equilibrium* proposes that most species have long periods (several million years) of relative stability, or stasis, interrupted by geologically brief periods during which major changes occur, possibly leading to the evolution of new species. It is thought that drastic environmental changes, for example, a global cooling event, could cause species to evolve—or become extinct.

In the fossil records of some evolutionary lineages, there are transitional forms that support the theory of gradualism. However, in many evolutionary lineages, there is an apparent lack of transitional forms, which better supports the theory of punctuated equilibrium.

Impact of Humans on Natural Selection

It has been found that some insects have a genetic mutation that makes them resistant to the effects of insecticides, the group of **pesticides** developed to kill insect pests. Before the widespread use of insecticides, this trait was of no particular survival value. With the increased use of insecticides, however, this trait developed a very high survival value. Because the insects that are resistant to insecticides have survived and reproduced, the frequency of insecticide resistance has increased greatly in insect populations.

Resistance to **antibiotics** (drugs that fight bacterial infections) in populations of bacteria has followed the same pattern. The frequency of resistant individuals in bacterial populations has increased with the increasing use of certain antibiotics.

It is important to note that resistance to insecticides and antibiotics did not arise as a result of exposure to these substances. The traits were already present in some members of the organisms' populations, and the insecticides and antibiotics simply acted as the selecting agents.

Humans and Artificial Selection

In nature, evolution is not goal-oriented; that is, there is no particular preconceived idea of how each organism must evolve. Rather, during the course of evolution, many variations appear within the lineages of organisms, similar to the branching of twigs on a tree. Natural selection continuously "prunes" these lineages, eliminating branches with unfavorable adaptations while allowing those with favorable adaptations to continue growing and evolving.

In contrast, humans can and do have an effect on the inheritance of traits in some populations of organisms. The changes that occurred in the genetic makeup of resistant populations of insects and bacteria were unintentional consequences of human actions. However, modern humans have intentionally altered the traits of numerous plants and animals. In the process of domesticating organisms, people have selectively bred plants and animals for desired traits. In such cases, it is a person, not the environment, that is the selecting agent. (See Chapter 6.) Advances in

biotechnological procedures have also had an impact on the genetic composition of some plant and animal populations.

QUESTIONS

Multiple Choice

25. A population of mosquitoes is sprayed with a new insecticide. Most of the mosquitoes are killed, but a few survive. In the next generation, the spraying continues, but still more mosquitoes hatch that are immune to the insecticide. How could these results be explained according to the present concept of evolution?   (1) The insecticide caused a mutation in the mosquitoes.   (2) The mosquitoes learned how to fight the insecticide.   (3) A few mosquitoes in the first population were resistant and transmitted this resistance to their offspring.   (4) The insecticide caused the mosquitoes to develop an immune response, which was inherited.

26. What would be the most likely effect of geographic isolation on a population?   (1) It has no effect on variations in the species.   (2) It favors the production of new species.   (3) It prevents the occurrence of mutations.   (4) It encourages the mixing of gene pools.

27. Two organisms can be considered to be of different species if they   (1) cannot mate with each other and produce fertile offspring   (2) live in two different geographical areas   (3) mutate at different rates depending on their environment   (4) have genes drawn from the same gene pool

28. Certain strains of bacteria that were susceptible to penicillin have now become resistant. The probable explanation for this is that   (1) the gene mutation rate must have increased naturally   (2) the strains have become resistant because they needed to do so for survival   (3) a mutation that gave some of them resistance was passed on to succeeding generations because it had high survival value   (4) the penicillin influenced the bacterial pattern of mating

29. The continents of Africa and South America were once a single landmass but have drifted apart over millions of years. The monkeys of both continents, although similar, show several genetic differences from each other. Which factor is probably the most important for causing and maintaining these differences?   (1) fossil records   (2) comparative anatomy   (3) use and disuse   (4) geographic isolation

30. A change in the frequency of any mutant allele in a population most likely depends on the   (1) size of the organisms possessing the mutant allele   (2) adaptive value of the trait associated with the mutant allele   (3) degree of dominance of the mutant allele   (4) degree of recessiveness of the mutant allele

31. Modern evolutionary biologists have accepted the main ideas of Darwin's theory of evolution but have added genetic information that gives a scientific explanation for   (1) overproduction   (2) the struggle for existence   (3) the survival of the fittest   (4) variations

32. As a result of sexual reproduction, the potential for evolutionary change in plants and animals is greatly increased because   (1) the offspring show more variability than those from asexual reproduction   (2) characteristics change less frequently than in asexual reproduction   (3) environmental changes never affect organisms produced by asexual reproduction   (4) two parents have fewer offspring than one parent

33. Populations of a species may develop traits that are different from each other if they are geographically isolated for sufficient lengths of time. The most likely explanation for these differences is that   (1) acquired traits cannot be inherited by the offspring   (2) the environmental conditions in the two areas are identical   (3) mutations and selective forces will be different in the two populations   (4) mutations will be the same in both populations

Short Answer
(Constructed Response)

34. In two or more complete sentences, explain how genetic variations and natural selection drive the evolutionary process.

35. How did Darwin explain the evolution of 14 finch species from one ancestral finch species? Use the terms *geographic isolation* and *reproductive isolation* in your answer.

Base your answers to questions 36 through 39 on the following information and data table .

A population of snails was living on a sandy beach. The snails' shells appeared in two colors: either tan or black. The sand on the beach was a tan color. One day, a volcano in a nearby mountain range erupted, spewing out tons of ash and debris. The ash and debris coated the sand on the beach, blackening it. Biologists had kept careful records of the snail population before and after the volcanic eruption. The data are presented in the table on page 97.

Time	Number of Tan Snails	Number of Black Snails
Before volcano erupted	6000	50
After volcano erupted (one year later)	400	3000

36. Using the data in the table, prepare a bar graph that shows the information on snail populations before and after the volcanic eruption.

37. Explain why the numbers of tan snails and black snails changed.

38. How does this event support the idea of evolution by natural selection?

39. Why might the tan snails in this population disappear within a few years?

Essay
(Extended Constructed Response)

40. A species of wildflower grows in a meadow. The flowers are of two color varieties: yellow and purple. There are about the same number of yellow flowers and purple flowers. A biologist observes that bees frequently visit the yellow flowers but seldom go to the purple ones.

Use the above data and your knowledge of biology to write a brief essay that includes the following:
   a) A testable question prompted by the information given
   b) A reasonable hypothesis that addresses your question
   c) A brief experimental procedure that could be used to test your hypothesis
   d) A description of the main selecting force on the flowers in this meadow
   e) A prediction of what may happen to this population of plants in 50 years

41. Describe how the continued widespread use of antibiotics (in people and livestock) may result in the evolution of more resistant strains of bacteria. How does the antibiotic act as a selecting agent? How does this illustrate the concept of natural selection?

42. Attempts to develop a vaccine to combat HIV infection have been unsuccessful so far. Discuss why it is very difficult to produce an effective vaccine against this virus. (Base your answer on scientific knowledge about the reproductive strategy of HIV.)

Reading Comprehension

Base your answers to questions 43 through 46 on the information below and on your knowledge of biology.

The Process of Plant Cloning

Today some plants are cloned to produce millions of offspring from a small piece of the original plant. Plant cloning is possible because the plant's diploid cells have the same genetic potential as the zygote that originally produced the plant and because of the action of the plant hormones auxin and cytokinin. These hormones are combined with other organic and inorganic substances in a growth medium that stimulates the production of new plants. The cloning process occurs in a sterile environment. The new plants produced are genetically identical to the original plant and to each other.

The process and equipment used for cloning are more expensive than for other forms of vegetative propagation. The advantage of cloning is that large numbers of desirable plants can be produced in a short period of time. For example, a million plants of a new variety can be cloned in about six months.

43. For which reason is cloning used to reproduce plants?   (1) Plants with a large degree of genetic variation are produced.   (2) Plants are produced more cheaply than by other vegetative methods.   (3) Plants are produced by pollination, resulting in seeds.   (4) A large number of plants are produced in a short period of time.

44. If the diploid chromosome number of a cloned plant is 12, the chromosome number of the plant cell used to produce the cloned plant would be   (1) 3   (2) 6   (3) 12   (4) 24

45. Which statement describes the hormones auxin and cytokinin?   (1) They are new forms of vegetative propagation.   (2) They can develop into a zygote.   (3) They help stimulate the growth of new plants.   (4) They inhibit the production of new plants.

46. Cloning is defined as   (1) a form of sexual reproduction   (2) a form of vegetative propagation   (3) an inorganic plant hormone   (4) an inorganic component of the growing medium

8 Ecology

Ecology is the study of the relationships between organisms and between organisms and their physical environment. No organism exists in nature as an entity apart from its environment.

ECOLOGICAL ORGANIZATION

In ecology, the relationships between organisms and the environment may be considered at various levels. The smallest, least inclusive level in terms of ecological organization is the population; the largest and most inclusive level is the biosphere.

Levels of Organization

All members of a species living in a given location make up a **population**. For example, all the water lilies in a pond make up a population, and all the goldfish in a pond make up a population. Together, all the interacting populations in a given area make up a **community**. For example, all the plants, animals, and microorganisms in a pond make up the pond community.

An **ecosystem** includes all the members of a community along with the physical environment in which they live. The living and nonliving parts of an ecosystem function together as an interdependent and relatively stable **system**. The *biosphere* is the portion of Earth in which all living things exist. The biosphere, which is composed of numerous, complex ecosystems, includes the water, soil, and air.

QUESTIONS

Multiple Choice

1. All the different species within an ecosystem are collectively referred to as the (1) niche (2) community (3) consumers (4) population

2. Which term includes the three terms that follow it? (1) population: community, ecosystem, organism (2) community: ecosystem, organism, population (3) ecosystem: organism, population, community (4) organism: ecosystem, community, population

3. Which sequence shows increasing complexity of levels of ecological organization? (1) biosphere, ecosystem, community (2) biosphere, community, ecosystem (3) community, ecosystem, biosphere (4) ecosystem, biosphere, community

4. The members of the mouse species *Microtus pennsylvanicus* living in a certain location make up a (1) community (2) succession (3) population (4) phylum

5. Which term includes all of the terrestrial and aquatic regions in which life exists? (1) marine biome (2) climax community (3) biosphere (4) tundra

Short Answer (Constructed Response)

6. In a complete sentence, list the four levels of ecological organization in order of increasing complexity.

7. Define, and give an example of, each of the four ecological levels: *ecosystem, population, community, biosphere.*

CHARACTERISTICS OF ECOSYSTEMS

Ecosystems are the structural and functional units studied in ecology.

Requirements of Ecosystems

An ecosystem, which involves interactions between living and nonliving factors, is a self-sustaining unit when the following two conditions are met.

First, there must be a constant flow of energy into the ecosystem, and there must be organisms within the ecosystem that can use this energy for the synthesis of organic compounds. The primary source of energy for most ecosystems on Earth is sunlight; the organisms that can use this energy for the synthesis of organic compounds are green plants, algae, and other photosynthetic autotrophs. Second, there must be a cycling of materials between the living organisms and the physical, nonliving parts of an ecosystem.

Abiotic Factors of Ecosystems

The components of an ecosystem include nonliving, or **abiotic**, factors, and living, or **biotic**, factors. The abiotic factors of the environment are physical factors that sustain the lives and reproductive cycles of organisms. These factors are: intensity of light; temperature range; amount of water; type of soil; availability of minerals and other inorganic substances; supply of gases, including oxygen, carbon dioxide, and nitrogen; and the pH (acidity or alkalinity) of the soil or water.

Abiotic factors vary from one environmental area to another. The abiotic conditions in any particular environment determine the types of plants and animals that can exist there. Thus, abiotic factors are *limiting factors*. For example, the small amount of available water in a desert limits the kinds of plants and animals that can live in that environment.

Biotic Factors of Ecosystems

The biotic factors of an ecosystem are all the living things that directly or indirectly affect the environment. The organisms of an ecosystem interact in many ways. These interactions include nutritional and symbiotic relationships.

Nutritional Relationships. Nutritional relationships involve the transfer of nutrients from one organism to another within the ecosystem.

Autotrophs are organisms that can use energy from the environment to synthesize their own food from inorganic compounds. Most autotrophs are photosynthetic, using energy from sunlight and carbon dioxide and water from the environment to synthesize organic compounds.

Heterotrophs cannot synthesize their own food and must obtain nutrients from other organisms. Depending on their source of food, heterotrophs are classified as saprophytes, herbivores, carnivores, or omnivores.

Saprophytes are organisms that obtain nutrients from the remains of other organisms. Types of saprophytes include bacteria, fungi, and heterotrophic plants. Animals that feed exclusively on plants are called **herbivores**. Animals that consume other animals are called **carnivores**. The carnivores include **predators**, which kill and eat their **prey**, and **scavengers**, which feed on the remains of animals that they have not killed. **Omnivores** are animals that consume both plant and animal matter.

Symbiotic Relationships. Different kinds of organisms sometimes live together in a close association. Such a close relationship, or **symbiosis**, may or may not be beneficial to the organisms involved.

A type of symbiotic relationship in which one organism benefits while the other is neither helped nor harmed is called *commensalism*. Barnacles living on whales, remora living on sharks, and orchids living on large, tropical trees all obtain favorable places to live without doing any noticeable harm to the other organism (Figure 8-1).

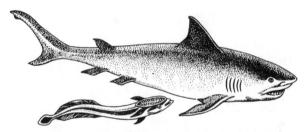

Figure 8-1. The shark and remora have a type of symbiosis known as commensalism.

A symbiotic relationship in which both organisms benefit is called *mutualism*. For example, certain protozoans live in the digestive tracts of termites. Wood eaten by the termite is digested by the protozoans. The nutrients released supply both organisms. Another example of mutualism is found in lichens, which are made up of both algal and fungal cells. The algal cells carry on photosynthesis, which provides food for the lichen, while the fungal cells provide moisture and minerals, and anchor the lichen to a surface.

Nitrogen-fixing bacteria live in the roots of legumes. The relationship between these organisms is mutualistic because the bacteria provide nitrogen compounds for the plant, while the plant provides the bacteria with nutrients and a good place to live (Figure 8-2, page 100).

A symbiotic relationship in which one organism, the **parasite**, benefits while the other, the **host**, is harmed is called *parasitism*. Examples include the athlete's foot fungus that can live on

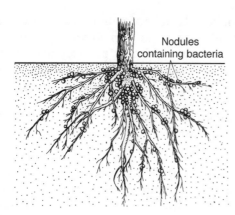

Figure 8-2. Nitrogen-fixing bacteria live in the roots of legumes in a type of symbiosis known as mutualism.

humans, and tapeworms and heartworms that can live in dogs.

QUESTIONS

Multiple Choice

8. Different species of animals in a community would most likely be similar in their (1) physical structure (2) size (3) abiotic requirements (4) number of offspring produced

9. Interactions between organisms, which influence their survival, are considered to be types of (1) biotic factors (2) inorganic substances (3) physical conditions (4) chemical factors

10. A study made over a period of years in a certain part of the country showed that there was a low amount of rainfall, a wide seasonal variation in temperature, and short periods of daylight. These environmental factors are (1) abiotic factors of little importance to living things (2) abiotic factors that limit the type of organisms that live in the area (3) biotic factors important to saprophytes in the area (4) biotic factors that are affected by the abiotic factors

11. The presence of nitrogen-fixing bacteria in nodules on the roots of legumes such as the peanut plant illustrates an association known as (1) commensalism (2) mutualism (3) parasitism (4) saprophytism

12. At times, hyenas will feed on the remains of animals that they have not killed themselves. At other times, they will kill other animals for food. Based on their feeding habits, hyenas are best described as both (1) herbivores and parasites (2) herbivores and predators (3) scavengers and parasites (4) scavengers and predators

13. Which is an abiotic factor in the environment? (1) water (2) earthworm (3) fungus (4) human

14. The organisms that prevent Earth from becoming littered with the remains of dead organisms are known as (1) herbivores (2) parasites (3) autotrophs (4) saprophytes

15. A particular species of fish has a very narrow range of tolerance for changes in water temperature and dissolved oxygen content. For this fish, the temperature and oxygen content represent (1) autotrophic conditions (2) a community (3) limiting factors (4) symbiosis

16. Which of the following is an example of parasitism? (1) tapeworms living in the digestive tract of a dog (2) algal and fungal cells living together in the form of a lichen (3) barnacles living on whales (4) wood-digesting protozoa living in the gut of termites

17. Parasitism is a type of nutritional relationship in which (1) both organisms benefit (2) both organisms are harmed (3) neither organism benefits (4) one organism benefits and the other is harmed

18. For an ecosystem to be self-sustaining, it must (1) contain more animals than plants (2) receive a constant flow of energy (3) have a daily supply of rainwater (4) contain only heterotrophs

19. Heterotrophs include (1) autotrophs, saprophytes, and herbivores (2) omnivores, carnivores, and autotrophs (3) saprophytes, herbivores, and carnivores (4) herbivores, autotrophs, and omnivores

20. The primary source of energy for most ecosystems is (1) radioactivity (2) sunlight (3) animal proteins (4) carbon dioxide

Short Answer
(Constructed Response)

21. In two complete sentences, describe the two main conditions that must exist for an ecosystem to be self-sustaining.

22. Explain why abiotic factors are considered to be limiting factors. Give an example.

Energy Flow Relationships

For an ecosystem to be self-sustaining, there must be a flow of energy between organisms. The pathways of chemical energy from food through the organisms of an ecosystem are represented by food chains and food webs.

Food Chains

The transfer of energy from green plants through a series of organisms with repeated stages of eating and being eaten is described as a **food chain** (Figure 8-3). Green plants obtain energy for their life processes from the radiant energy of sunlight (that is, **solar energy**), which they convert to usable chemical energy by photosynthesis. For all other organisms in the food chain, energy is obtained from the breakdown of food. The organisms in a food chain are described in terms of the following categories.

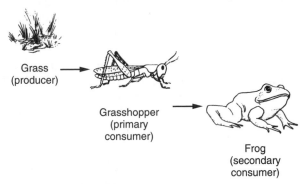

Figure 8-3. A food chain.

Green plants and other autotrophs are the **producers** in the food chain. All the energy for a community is derived from the organic compounds synthesized by the producers (for example, grass in a savannah and algae in the sea).

All the heterotrophic organisms in a community are **consumers**. They must obtain energy from the food that they eat. Animals that feed on green plants and algae are called *primary consumers*, or herbivores. Animals that feed on primary consumers are called *secondary consumers*, or carnivores. Omnivores may be either primary or secondary consumers.

Saprophytes are **decomposers**, the organisms that break down the **residue**, or remains, of dead organisms and organic wastes. Decomposers return substances in the remains and wastes of plants and animals to the environment, where they can be used again by other living organisms. Most decomposers are either bacteria or fungi.

Food Webs. In a natural community, most organisms eat more than one species and may be eaten, in turn, by more than one species. Thus, the various food chains in a community are interconnected, forming a **food web** (Figure 8-4). Food webs have the same levels of organisms (producers, consumers, and decomposers) as food chains, but the flow of energy and materials is much more complex.

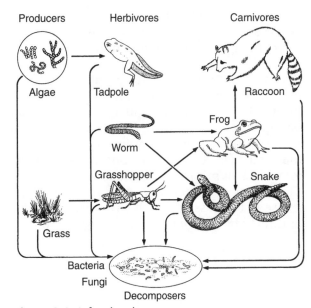

Figure 8-4. A food web.

Pyramid of Energy. The greatest amount of energy in a community is present in the organisms that make up the producer level. Only a small portion of this energy is passed on to primary consumers, and only a small portion of that energy in the primary consumers is passed on to secondary consumers. An **energy pyramid** can be used to illustrate the loss of usable energy at each feeding, or *trophic*, level (Figure 8-5).

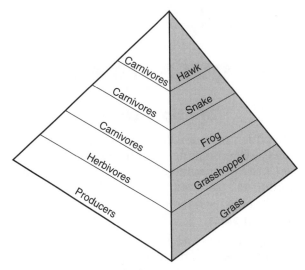

Figure 8-5. A pyramid of energy.

At each consumer level in an energy pyramid, only about 10 percent of the ingested nutrients are used to synthesize new tissues, which represent the food available for the next feeding level. The remaining energy is used by the consumers for their life functions and is eventually converted to heat, which is lost from the ecosystem. Thus, an ecosystem cannot sustain itself without the constant input of energy from the sun.

Pyramid of Biomass. In general, the decrease in available energy at each higher feeding level means that less organic matter, or *biomass*, can be supported at each higher level. Thus, the total mass of producers in an ecosystem is greater than the total mass of primary consumers, and the total mass of primary consumers is greater than the total mass of secondary consumers. This decrease in biomass at each higher feeding level is illustrated by a *biomass pyramid* (Figure 8-6).

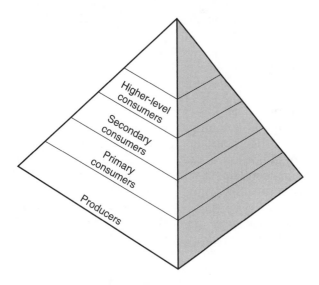

Figure 8-6. A pyramid of biomass.

QUESTIONS

Multiple Choice

23. Which occurs within self-sustaining ecosystems? (1) Consumers produce most of the oxygen. (2) Consumers eventually outnumber producers. (3) Energy is created and destroyed. (4) Organisms interact with their environment and each other.

24. Which food chain relationship illustrates the nutritional pattern of a primary consumer? (1) seeds eaten by a mouse (2) an earthworm eaten by a mole (3) a mosquito eaten by a bat (4) a fungus growing on a dead tree

25. Which term describes both the bird and the cat in the following food chain?

sun → grass → grasshopper → bird → cat

(1) herbivores (2) saprophytes (3) predators (4) omnivores

26. The elements stored in living cells of organisms in a community will eventually be returned to the soil for use by other living organisms. The organisms that carry out this process are the (1) producers (2) herbivores (3) carnivores (4) decomposers

27. In the food chain below, what is the nutritional role of the rabbit?

lettuce plant → rabbit → coyote

(1) parasite (2) saprophyte (3) primary consumer (4) primary producer

28. Fly larvae consume the body of a dead rabbit. In this process, they function as (1) producers (2) scavengers (3) herbivores (4) parasites

Base your answers to questions 29 through 32 on the diagram below and on your knowledge of biology. The diagram represents different species of organisms interacting with each other in and around a pond environment.

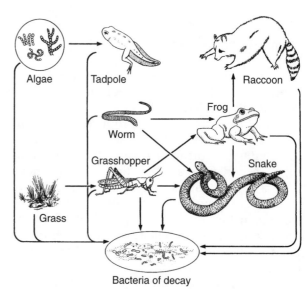

Bacteria of decay

29. The adult frog represents a type of consumer known as a (1) producer (2) carnivore (3) saprophyte (4) parasite

30. Which organisms are classified as herbivores? (1) algae, tadpole, raccoon (2) worm, snake, bacteria (3) tadpole, worm, grasshopper (4) grasshopper, bacteria, frog

31. Which statement about the algae and grass is true? (1) They are classified as omnivores. (2) They are parasites in the animals that eat them. (3) They contain the greatest amount of stored energy. (4) They decompose nutrients from dead organisms.

32. The interactions among organisms shown in this diagram illustrate (1) a food web (2) geographic isolation   (3) abiotic factors   (4) organic evolution

33. Which level of the food pyramid shown below represents the largest biomass? (1) bass (2) minnows   (3) copepods   (4) algae

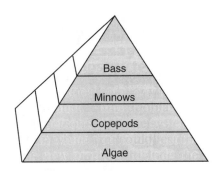

34. Which diagram best represents the usual relationships of biomass in a stable community? (1) 1   (2) 2   (3) 3   (4) 4

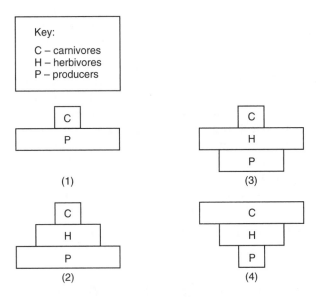

Base your answers to questions 35 through 37 on the food chain represented below and on your knowledge of biology.

rosebush → aphid → ladybird beetle
→ spider → toad → snake

35. Which organism in the food chain can transform light energy into chemical energy?   (1) spider   (2) ladybird beetle   (3) rosebush   (4) snake

36. At which stage in the food chain will the population with the smallest number of animals probably be found? (1) spider   (2) aphid   (3) ladybird beetle   (4) snake

37. Which organism in this food chain is a primary consumer? (1) rosebush   (2) aphid   (3) ladybird beetle   (4) toad

38. Which level in an energy pyramid has the highest amount of available energy?   (1) highest

level consumers   (2) secondary consumers   (3) primary consumers   (4) producers

Base your answers to questions 39 through 42 on the diagram below, which represents four possible pathways for the transfer of energy stored by green plants.

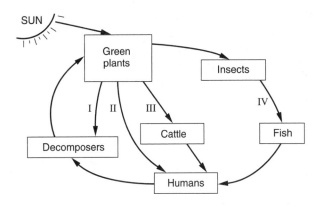

39. The pathway labeled IV represents   (1) a food chain   (2) a population   (3) an ecosystem (4) an abiotic factor

40. Through which pathway would the sun's energy be most directly available to humans?   (1) I (2) II   (3) III   (4) IV

41. In this diagram, humans are shown to be (1) herbivores only   (2) carnivores only   (3) omnivores   (4) parasites

42. The cattle in the diagram represent   (1) primary consumers   (2) secondary consumers (3) producers   (4) autotrophs

Short Answer
(Constructed Response)

43. Draw, using specific organisms as examples, a pyramid of energy.

44. Distinguish between a pyramid of energy and a pyramid of biomass. Explain the relationship between them. Be sure to write your answer in complete sentences.

Essay
(Extended Constructed Response)

45. Explain why an ecosystem could not sustain itself without the constant input of energy from the sun.

Carrying Capacity

In every ecosystem on Earth, there are limited amounts of available resources. These resources include food, water, energy, minerals, and space (territory). Even though some of these resources may be recycled through the actions of bacteria and fungi, the pace of recycling may not keep up with the demand for these materials. The amount of resources available limits the number of organisms that an ecosystem can support. The maximum number of organisms of a particular type that can be supported in an area is known as the **carrying capacity**. In a stable ecosystem, a population of organisms will fluctuate slightly, as shown in Figure 8-7. If the population increases significantly above its carrying capacity, many individuals will die off because there are insufficient resources available to support them.

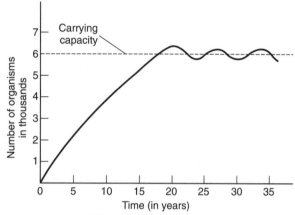

Figure 8-7. The carrying capacity for a population of organisms will fluctuate slightly in a stable ecosystem.

Competition

Different species living in the same environment, or **habitat**, may require some of the same resources for their survival. Since resources (such as food, water, space, light, and minerals) are usually limited, **competition** occurs among the various species. Competition is the struggle between different organisms for the same limited resources.

The more similar the needs of the species, the more intense the competition. For example, lions, leopards, and hyenas may compete to consume the same type of antelope. In addition, because their requirements are most similar, the strongest competition for resources often occurs among members of the same species. For example, competition for antelope prey (or water, mates, territory, and so on) may be more intense between neighboring prides of lions than between lions and other nearby large predators.

Each species occupies a particular ecological niche in a community. A **niche** is the role that the species fills in its habitat. A species' niche includes the type of food, or nutrients, it requires; where and how it lives; where and how it reproduces; and its relationships with other species in

the area. When two species compete for the same niche, the one that is more successful at utilizing the available resources will outcompete the other, thereby maintaining just one species per niche in the community.

QUESTIONS

Multiple Choice

46. Carrying capacity is best thought of as the amount of (1) abiotic factors present in an ecosystem (2) light available for photosynthesis (3) organisms the ecosystem can support (4) producers compared to consumers in the ecosystem

47. A stable ecosystem is characterized by (1) a greater number of consumers than producers (2) population sizes at or near the carrying capacity (3) a greater need for energy than is available (4) a lack of decomposers to recycle materials

48. In a freshwater pond community, a carp eats decaying matter from around the bases of underwater plants, while a snail scrapes algae from the leaves and stems of the same plant. They can survive at the same time in the same pond because they occupy (1) the same niche but different habitats (2) the same habitat but different niches (3) the same habitat and the same niche (4) different habitats and different niches

49. The role a species plays in a community is called its (1) habitat (2) biotic factor (3) territory (4) niche

50. When two different species live in the same environment and use the same limited resources, which interaction will usually occur? (1) competition (2) cooperation (3) commensalism (4) mutualism

Short Answer
(Constructed Response)

51. Some bacteria can reproduce once every 20 minutes. As a result, their populations can double several times an hour. Even at this phenomenal rate of reproduction, bacteria do not overrun the planet. Give a brief, scientifically valid explanation for this.

52. In a complete sentence, explain why competition between individuals of the same species is often more intense than competition between members of different species.

Cycles of Materials

In a self-sustaining ecosystem, various materials are recycled between the organisms and the abiotic environment. The recycling process allows materials to be used over and over again by living things.

Carbon-Hydrogen-Oxygen Cycle. The elements carbon, hydrogen, and oxygen are recycled through the environment by the processes of respiration and photosynthesis (Figure 8-8). During aerobic cellular respiration, plants and animals use oxygen (O_2) from the air and release carbon dioxide (CO_2) and water (H_2O) via the breakdown of glucose. During photosynthesis, plants use carbon dioxide (CO_2) from the air and water (H_2O) from the environment in the synthesis of glucose ($C_6H_{12}O_6$), and oxygen (O_2) is given off as a by-product.

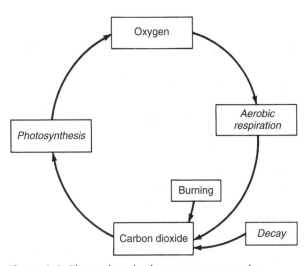

Figure 8-8. The carbon-hydrogen-oxygen cycle.

Water Cycle. In the water cycle, water moves between Earth's surface and the atmosphere (Figure 8-9). The main processes involved in this cycle are *evaporation* and *condensation*. Liquid water on Earth's surface changes to a gas by the process of evaporation and enters the atmosphere in the form of water vapor. As a result of condensation, water vapor is returned to the liquid state (precipitation) and falls to Earth. Some water vapor is added to the atmosphere by aerobic respiration in plants and animals and by transpiration in plants. Water is also an essential nutrient for all living things, allowing them to carry out essential life processes and chemical reactions.

Nitrogen Cycle. The element nitrogen is needed by all living things because it is part of the structure of amino acids and proteins. Plants ab-

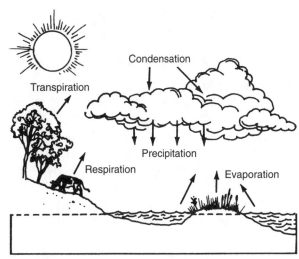

Figure 8-9. The water cycle.

sorb nitrogen-containing compounds from the soil; animals obtain nitrogen in the form of proteins in the foods they eat. These proteins are broken down by digestion to amino acids, which are then used in the synthesis of animal proteins.

The nitrogen cycle involves decomposers and other soil bacteria. Figure 8-10 shows the various components of the nitrogen cycle, which are described below.

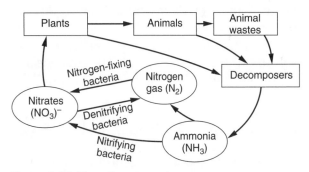

Figure 8-10. The nitrogen cycle.

Nitrogen-fixing bacteria, which live in nodules inside the roots of some plants (refer to Figure 8-2), convert free nitrogen (N_2) from the air into nitrogen-containing compounds called nitrates (NO_3). *Nitrates* are absorbed from the soil by plants and used in protein synthesis. Animals that eat plants convert the nitrogen-containing plant proteins into animal proteins. The nitrogenous wastes of living animals, and the nitrogen compounds in the remains of dead plants and animals, are broken down by decomposers and converted to ammonia (NH_3). *Nitrifying bacteria* in the soil convert ammonia into nitrates, which can be used again by plants. *Denitrifying bacteria* break down some nitrates into free nitrogen (N_2), which is released into the atmosphere as a gas.

QUESTIONS

Multiple Choice

53. In which form is nitrogen normally absorbed from the soil by grasses?   (1) nitrates   (2) amino acids   (3) ammonia   (4) free nitrogen

54. The processes involved in the recycling of carbon, hydrogen, and oxygen are   (1) evaporation and condensation   (2) photosynthesis and respiration   (3) nitrification and denitrification   (4) respiration and transpiration

55. Nitrogen is both removed from the atmosphere and returned to the atmosphere by the activities of   (1) plants only   (2) animals only   (3) plants and animals   (4) bacteria

56. Animals obtain their nitrogen from   (1) proteins in their food   (2) nitrates in the soil   (3) gas in the atmosphere   (4) bacteria in their intestines

57. Carbon dioxide is added to the atmosphere by   (1) photosynthesis in plants   (2) evaporation of water   (3) respiration in animals only   (4) respiration in plants and animals

58. Oxygen (O_2) is added to the atmosphere by   (1) evaporation and photosynthesis   (2) respiration in plants   (3) photosynthesis only   (4) denitrifying bacteria

59. Which of the following processes is *not* involved in the water cycle?   (1) condensation   (2) nitrification   (3) evaporation   (4) transpiration

60. Nitrogen compounds in animal wastes and in the remains of dead organisms are broken down and converted into other compounds that can be used by living organisms by   (1) bacteria   (2) photosynthesis   (3) aerobic respiration   (4) absorption

Base your answers to questions 61 through 63 on the diagram below, which represents a cycle in nature, and on your knowledge of biology.

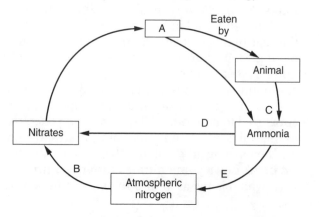

61. The cycle represented by the diagram is the   (1) nitrogen cycle   (2) carbon cycle   (3) water cycle   (4) oxygen cycle

62. Nitrifying bacteria in the soil are represented by the letter   (1) *A*   (2) *E*   (3) *C*   (4) *D*

63. The letter *B* most likely represents   (1) bacteria of decay   (2) denitrifying bacteria   (3) a leguminous plant   (4) nitrogen-fixing bacteria

Short Answer
(Constructed Response)

64. In two complete sentences, describe how carbon dioxide and oxygen are recycled via the processes of respiration and photosynthesis.

65. In two or more complete sentences, explain why both nitrogen-fixing bacteria and nitrifying bacteria are particularly important for the survival of plants.

ECOSYSTEM FORMATION

Ecosystems tend to change over a long period of time until a stable ecosystem is formed. Both the communities (living things) and the nonliving part of the ecosystem change.

Succession

The replacement of one kind of community by another in an ecosystem is called ecological, or biological, **succession**. Ecological succession is usually a long-term process, happening over the course of many years (and many generations of different plants and animals). The kind of stable ecosystem that eventually develops in a particular geographical area depends on the region's climate.

Pioneer Organisms.   Depending on climate and other abiotic environmental factors, succession on land can begin in an area that has no living things and end with a forest. Succession begins with *pioneer organisms*, which are the first plants, or plantlike organisms, to populate an area. Lichens and algae are typical pioneer organisms on bare rock, such as that found on a newly emerged volcanic island (Figure 8-11).

Starting with pioneer plants, each community modifies the environment, often making it less favorable for itself and more favorable for other kinds of communities. One sequence of plant succession in New York State might be lichens → grasses → shrubs → conifers (pine trees) → deciduous (beech and maple) woodlands.

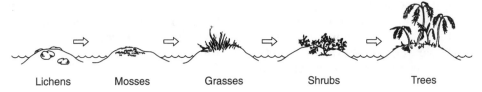

Lichens   Mosses   Grasses   Shrubs   Trees

Figure 8-11. Ecological succession on a new island.

Since plants are the basic source of food for a community, the types of plants present in a community determine the types of animals that can live in the community. As the plant populations change, the animal populations also change.

Climax Communities. Succession ends with the development of a *climax community* in which populations of plants and animals exist in balance with each other and with the environment. In New York State, for example, the oak-hickory and hemlock-beech-maple associations represent two climax communities. In the Midwest, where there is less rain, grasslands are the typical climax community.

The climax community remains stable until a catastrophic change, such as a volcanic eruption or forest fire, alters or destroys it. Thereafter, succession begins again, leading to the development of a new climax community. This new community may be of the same type as the previous one or, if the catastrophe has changed the environment in some important way, it may be of another kind.

Biodiversity

In addition to the factors mentioned above, a stable community or stable ecosystem requires **biodiversity**. This term refers to the presence of a wide range of different species of organisms living and interacting with each other and with their nonliving environment. These organisms play a variety of roles that contribute to the overall stability of an ecosystem. For example, green plants and algae act as producers; fungi and bacteria act as decomposers, recycling vital materials; and animals act as consumers. Some roles are readily apparent while others may not be so obvious. Nevertheless, the removal of any one species from its natural environment may have profound negative effects on the overall health of the ecosystem.

Biodiversity also increases the probability that at least some organisms would be able to survive a catastrophic environmental event, such as climate change or a volcanic eruption. In time, the surviving organisms could reestablish a healthy community.

In addition, stable ecosystems that are rich in species, such as tropical rain forests, contain a wealth of genetic material that may have beneficial uses in medicine, agriculture, or other areas. It is critical to preserve the biodiversity of Earth, not only for the needs of humans or individual ecosystems but also for the health and stability of the entire planet.

QUESTIONS

Multiple Choice

66. The natural replacement of one community by another until a climax stage is reached is known as (1) ecological balance (2) organic evolution (3) dynamic equilibrium (4) ecological succession

67. In an ecological succession in New York State, lichens growing on bare rock are considered to be (1) climax species (2) pioneer organisms (3) primary consumers (4) decomposers

68. In an ecological succession leading to the establishment of a pond community, which of the following organisms would be among the first to establish themselves? (1) grasses (2) algae (3) minnows (4) deciduous trees

69. Ecological succession ends with the development of a (1) climax community (2) pioneer community (3) ecological niche (4) abiotic community

70. Which two groups of organisms are most likely to be pioneer organisms? (1) songbirds and squirrels (2) lichens and algae (3) deer and black bears (4) oak and hickory trees

71. Following a major forest fire, an area that was once wooded is converted to barren soil. Which of the following sequences describes the most likely series of changes in vegetation after the fire?
(1) shrubs → maples → pines → grasses
(2) maples → pines → grasses → shrubs
(3) pines → shrubs → maples → grasses
(4) grasses → shrubs → pines → maples

72. Biodiversity in an ecosystem is important because it   (1) allows one species to dominate the others in its habitat   (2) slows down the pace at which species evolve   (3) provides stability to the ecosystem   (4) limits the amount of variation among organisms

73. Stable ecosystems are characterized by (1) only two major species interacting with each other   (2) an infinite amount of available resources   (3) a variety of different species interacting with one another   (4) very little recycling of materials between the biotic and abiotic components

Short Answer
(Constructed Response)

74. In a complete sentence, list the stages that precede a beech-maple forest in New York State. Identify the pioneer organism and the climax community in this succession.

Base your answers to questions 75 through 77 on the following information and on your knowledge of biology:

A group of western ranchers was very concerned about a local wolf population that they thought was preying on their livestock. After several attempts, they persuaded a court to authorize a hunt in order to eliminate the wolf population in their area. The court set a quota of 200 wolves, to be eliminated over the course of six months.

75. State a negative impact that the removal of these wolves might have on the habitat.

76. How would this hunt affect the biodiversity of the area's natural ecosystem?

77. Suppose that you are a local environmental official in the area. Propose a plan that would preserve the wolves yet keep them away from the ranchers' livestock.

BIOMES

Earth can be divided into broad geographic regions by climate. The kind of climax ecosystem that develops in these large climatic areas is called a **biome**. Biomes may be terrestrial (land biomes) or aquatic (water biomes). The stretch of tropical rain forests around the equator is a land biome. The ocean is an aquatic biome.

Terrestrial Biomes

The major plant and animal associations (biomes) on land are determined by the large climate zones of Earth. These climate zones are, in turn, determined by geographic factors, including *latitude* (distance north or south of the equator) and *altitude* (distance above or below sea level). Other major geographic features, including large bodies of water, mountains, and deserts, modify the climate of nearby regions.

Climate includes the temperature range and the amounts of precipitation and solar radiation received by a region. The presence or absence of water is a major limiting factor for terrestrial biomes and determines the kinds of plant and animal communities that can be established.

Kinds of Terrestrial Biomes.   Land biomes are described in terms of, and sometimes named for, the dominant kind of climax vegetation found there. Table 8-1 lists the major land biomes, their

Table 8-1. The Major Terrestrial Biomes on Earth

Biome	Characteristics	Plants	Animals
Tundra	Permanently frozen subsoil	Lichens, mosses, grasses	Snowy owl, caribou
Taiga	Long, severe winters; summers with thawing subsoil	Conifers	Moose, black bear
Temperate forest	Moderate precipitation; cold winters; warm summers	Deciduous trees (maple, oak, beech)	Fox, deer, gray squirrel
Tropical forest	Heavy rainfall; constant warmth	Many broad-leaved plant species	Snake, monkey, leopard
Grassland	Variability in rainfall and temperature; strong winds	Grasses	Antelope, bison, prairie dog
Desert	Sparse rainfall; extreme daily temperature fluctuations	Drought-resistant plants and succulents	Lizard, tortoise, kangaroo rat

characteristics, dominant plant life, and some representative animals.

Effects of Latitude and Altitude.
At the equator, the temperature and amount of rainfall remain relatively constant throughout the year. With increasing distance from the equator, temperature and rainfall show more variation during the year.

Increasing altitude may have the same effect on climate as increasing latitude. Thus, the temperature and kind of climax vegetation found at the top of a high mountain near the equator may be very much like that of a sea-level region far north of the equator. This relationship is shown in Figure 8-12.

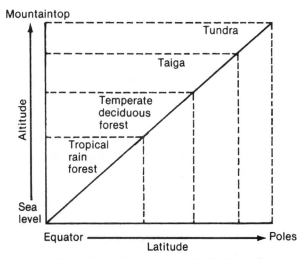

Figure 8-12. Relationship between latitude and altitude and terrestrial biomes.

Aquatic Biomes
Aquatic biomes make up the largest ecosystem on Earth. More than 70 percent of Earth's surface is covered by water; the majority of living things on Earth are water-dwellers.

Aquatic biomes are more stable than terrestrial biomes; they show less variation in temperature because water has a greater capacity to absorb and hold heat. The kinds and numbers of organisms present in an aquatic biome are affected by various factors, such as the amounts of dissolved oxygen and carbon dioxide, water temperature, intensity of light, and the kinds and amounts of dissolved minerals and suspended particles in the water.

Aquatic organisms are well adapted for the removal of dissolved oxygen from water. They also have adaptations for maintaining a proper water balance in their cells. (Water balance is affected by the concentration of salts in the water.)

In aquatic biomes, most photosynthesis takes place near the surface of the water, since the light intensity is strongest there. At greater depths, where sunlight does not penetrate, there is no photosynthesis.

Marine Biome.
The marine, or saltwater, biome includes all the oceans of Earth, which actually make up one continuous body of water. The most important characteristics of the marine biome are that it: (a) is the most stable environment on Earth; (b) absorbs and holds large quantities of solar heat, thereby stabilizing Earth's temperature; (c) contains a relatively constant supply of nutrients and dissolved salts; (d) serves as a habitat for a large number and wide variety of organisms; and (e) includes the area in which most of the photosynthesis on Earth occurs (in coastal waters, along the edges of landmasses).

Freshwater Biomes.
The freshwater biome includes ponds, lakes, and rivers. Because these are separate bodies of water, they vary widely in size, temperature, oxygen and carbon dioxide concentrations, amounts of suspended particles, current velocity, and rate of succession.

Ponds and lakes tend to fill in over time. Dead plant material accumulates on the bottom and around the banks, gradually making the body of water shallower and smaller. Thus, in all but the largest lakes, there is a gradual succession from a freshwater to a terrestrial climax community.

QUESTIONS

Multiple Choice

78. In which of the following biomes does most of the photosynthesis on Earth occur? (1) forests (2) oceans (3) deserts (4) grasslands

79. Drastic changes in air temperature would be *least* likely to affect which biome? (1) tundra (2) temperate forest (3) marine (4) tropical forest

80. Land biomes are characterized and named according to the (1) secondary consumers in the food webs (2) primary consumers in the food webs (3) climax vegetation in the region (4) pioneer vegetation in the region

81. The largest and most stable ecosystems are the (1) aquatic biomes (2) terrestrial biomes (3) high-altitude biomes (4) high-latitude biomes

82. Which is the most common sequence of major land biomes encountered from the equator to the polar region? (1) tundra, taiga, temperate forest, tropical forest (2) tropical forest, temperate forest, taiga, tundra (3) temperate forest, tropical forest, taiga, tundra (4) tropical forest, temperate forest, tundra, taiga

For each description given in questions 83 through 87, select the biome, from the list below, that is most closely associated with that description.

(A) Desert (D) Temperate deciduous forest

(B) Grassland (E) Tundra

(C) Taiga

83. This area has a short growing season and low precipitation, mostly in the form of snow. The soil is permanently frozen and the vegetation includes lichens and mosses. (1) A (2) B (3) C (4) D (5) E

84. This area has 25 to 50 centimeters of rainfall annually. The growing season does not produce trees, but the soil is rich and well suited for growing domesticated plants such as wheat and corn. Grazing animals are found here. (1) A (2) B (3) C (4) D (5) E

85. There are many lakes in this area and the vegetation is coniferous forest composed mainly of spruce and fir. There are many large animals, such as bear and deer. (1) A (2) B (3) C (4) D (5) E

86. This area has broad-leaved trees, which shed their leaves in the fall. Winters are fairly cold, and the summers are warm with well-distributed rainfall. (1) A (2) B (3) C (4) D (5) E

87. This area has a low annual rainfall and a rapid rate of evaporation. In order for plants to survive, they must be adapted to conserve moisture. Animals here are active mainly at night. (1) A (2) B (3) C (4) D (5) E

88. Which biome is characterized by its ability to absorb and hold large quantities of solar heat, which helps to regulate Earth's temperature? (1) desert (2) marine (3) grassland (4) taiga

89. Generally, an increase in altitude has the same effect on the habitat of organisms as an increase in (1) latitude (2) moisture (3) available light (4) longitude

Short Answer
(Constructed Response)

90. In two or more complete sentences, explain the relationship between latitude and altitude in terms of how these factors similarly affect the types of organisms in a biome.

91. Use complete sentences to describe the two main types of aquatic biomes and list at least five

important abiotic factors that affect the kinds of organisms that live in them.

HUMANS AND THE BIOSPHERE

Humans, more than any other organisms, have the capacity to change the environment. Some human activities have negative effects on the environment, while others have positive effects.

Negative Aspects

Some human activities have upset the natural balance of ecosystems. These activities have brought about undesirable and lasting changes in one or more of the biotic or abiotic factors in some ecosystems, harming humans and other living things.

Human Population Growth. The human population of Earth is increasing at a rapid rate (Figure 8-13). A major factor in this increase involves medical advances that have increased human survival rates and the average life span. In most parts of the world, population growth is no longer limited by disease to the extent that it was in the past. However, in many places, the population has grown faster than the food-producing capacity, resulting in hunger and starvation. In addition, as the human population grows, there is a greater encroachment on, and loss of, natural habitat for wildlife.

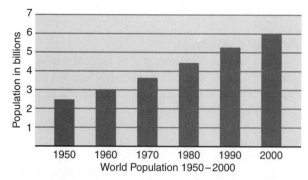

Figure 8-13. Human population growth over the past 50 years.

Human Activities. Some human activities have led to the endangerment or extinction of numerous species of plants and animals, and also have produced less favorable living conditions for many species. Such activities include overhunting, importation of organisms, exploitation of wild organisms, poor land-use practices, and technological oversights.

Uncontrolled hunting, fishing, and trapping, which still occur in many parts of the world, have resulted in the extinction of some species and the endangerment of others. Several vertebrate species, such as the passenger pigeon and Steller's sea cow, have been hunted to extinction already; hundreds of other animals are currently listed as threatened or endangered as a result of such human activities.

Humans have both accidentally and intentionally imported species into areas where they have no natural enemies. These imported organisms have increased in numbers, leading to the disruption of existing ecosystems. Imported organisms that have caused serious damage include the European starling, Japanese beetle, gypsy moth, zebra mussel, and various plant species.

People have exploited plants and animals for their own use for centuries, often with negative impacts on wild populations. For example, the extensive cutting down, or **deforestation**, of tropical rain forests has led to habitat loss for wildlife and erosion of topsoil; elephants and walrus have been overhunted for their ivory tusks; tropical parrots and monkeys have been captured and sold as pets.

The increased building of cities and suburbs has reduced the amount of farmland and disrupted natural habitats, threatening the existence of various native plant and animal species. Overgrazing and poor agricultural practices have caused valuable soil nutrients and topsoil to be lost, or **depleted**.

Some technological developments have contributed to the pollution of air, land, and water. In many areas, the water has been polluted by chemical wastes from homes, factories, and farmlands. Major chemical wastes include phosphates, heavy metals, and PCBs (an industrial by-product). Radioactive materials have been dumped or have leaked into the water supply from factories and waste-storage areas. Such chemical and radioactive wastes are *toxins* that can cause harm to people and wildlife alike.

The increased temperature, or *thermal pollution*, of river water occurs when water is taken from a river and used for cooling in factories and then returned to the waterway. Untreated sewage, which contains harmful bacteria, has been dumped into rivers and oceans. Water pollutants have killed fish and other animals, as well as plant life.

Exhaust gases from the burning of fossil fuels in factories, automobiles, and other places have polluted the air. The major air pollutants include carbon dioxide, carbon monoxide, hydrocarbons, and particulate matter. The increasing levels of carbon dioxide and other greenhouse gases in the atmosphere have been linked to **global warming** trends. (The destruction of rain forests also adds to an increase in atmospheric carbon dioxide.) Compounds used in aerosol sprays have weakened Earth's **ozone shield**, allowing more ultraviolet radiation to penetrate the atmosphere, causing harm to both plants and animals. Nitrogen oxides and sulfur dioxides are gaseous pollutants that combine with water vapor in the atmosphere, forming acids. Precipitation of these acids, called *acid rain*, kills plants and lowers the pH of lakes and ponds, thereby harming and killing aquatic wildlife.

Several biocides (pesticides and herbicides) that are used to kill insects and to prevent the growth of weeds have had negative effects on the environment. Biocides have contaminated the soil, air, and water supplies. The *residue*, or chemical remains, of their use has also entered food chains and caused harm to some organisms, thereby disrupting whole food webs. For example, the pesticide DDT was linked to reproductive failure and population decrease among bald eagles and peregrine falcons. Its use has been banned in the United States, and eagle and falcon populations are now on the increase.

Technological developments have resulted in the increased production of solid, chemical, and nuclear wastes. Disposal of these wastes, many of them highly toxic, is a major problem. In addition, disposal of household garbage is becoming a problem, as more landfills are filled to capacity and shut down.

Positive Aspects

People are becoming increasingly aware of the negative effects of some of their activities on the environment. As a result, they are making many efforts to correct past damage and avoid future harmful effects.

Population Control.   Methods for limiting the high rate of human population growth have been, and continue to be, developed.

Conservation of Resources.   Measures have been taken to conserve water, fossil fuels (oil, coal, and natural gas), and other natural resources (such as trees and wildlife). Reforestation projects help prevent further loss of trees, and planting of cover crops helps conserve topsoil. People are now realizing the economic and environmental benefits of recycling various materials, such as newspapers, aluminum cans, and glass bottles.

Pollution Control. Laws have been enacted to control the pollution of air and water. New techniques for limiting pollution from cars and factories, and for better sanitation and disposal of hazardous wastes, have been developed.

Species Preservation. Endangered species are being protected, and efforts are being undertaken to increase their populations in the wild and in captivity. This is accomplished through captive breeding programs, protection of wild habitats, and the establishment of wildlife refuges and national parks. Management of various forms of wildlife also includes laws that regulate hunting and fishing.

Examples of animals that are, or were, endangered but are now increasing in numbers include the American bison, alligator, whooping crane, fur seal, and bald eagle (Figure 8-14). However, the future of many species is still very much in doubt.

Figure 8-14. Bald eagle populations are now on the increase due to protective measures.

Biological Control. Biological control of insect pests reduces the use of chemical pesticides. One method of biological control involves the use of sex hormones to attract and trap insect pests. Another method of biological control involves the use of natural parasites that kill harmful insects. Biological control methods are less likely than chemical methods to affect species that are beneficial to humans, disrupt food webs, or contaminate the land.

The Future
A greater awareness of ecological principles and careful use of energy and other natural resources will help to ensure a suitable environment for future generations.

QUESTIONS

Multiple Choice

92. Which accomplishment by people has had the most positive ecological impact on the environment? (1) the importation of organisms such as the starling and Japanese beetle into the United States (2) reforestation efforts and planting of cover crops to prevent soil erosion (3) the extinction or near extinction of many predators to protect prey animals (4) the use of pesticides and other chemical compounds to reduce the insect population

93. When a garden became infested with a large population of aphids, some ladybird beetles were introduced into the community as predators on the aphids. The resultant decrease in the aphid population was due to (1) biological control (2) parthenogenesis (3) vegetative propagation (4) chemical control

94. An increased burning of coal would cause additional tons of sulfur dioxide to be released into the atmosphere, which could increase environmental problems associated with (1) acid rain (2) PCBs (3) DDT (4) dioxin

95. The number of African elephants has been greatly reduced by poachers who kill the animals for their ivory tusks. This negative aspect of human involvement in the ecosystem could best be described as (1) poor land-use management (2) importation of organisms (3) poor agricultural practices (4) exploitation of wildlife

96. Gypsy moth infestations in rural areas of New York State may pose a potentially serious threat to many forested areas. Which would probably be the most ecologically sound method of gypsy moth control? (1) widespread application of DDT (2) introduction of a biological control (3) removal of its forest habitat (4) contamination of its food sources

97. Recent evidence indicates that lakes in large areas of upstate New York are being affected by acid rain. The major effect of acid rain in these lakes is the (1) increase in game fish population levels (2) stimulation of a rapid rate of evolution (3) elimination of various species of aquatic wildlife   (4) increase in local agricultural productivity

98. Compared to other organisms, humans have had the greatest ecological impact on the biosphere due to their   (1) internal bony skeleton   (2) homeostatic regulation of metabolism   (3) adaptations for respiration   (4) ability to modify the environment

99. The rapid increase in the human population over the past few hundred years has been due mainly to   (1) increasing levels of air and water pollution   (2) depletion of topsoil from farmable lands   (3) medical advances that increase survival rates   (4) increasing resistance levels of insect species

100. Which illustrates the human population's increased understanding of, and concern for, ecological interrelationships?   (1) importing organisms in order to disrupt existing ecosystems   (2) allowing the air to be polluted only by those industries that promote technology   (3) removing natural resources from Earth at a rate equal to or greater than the needs of an increasing population   (4) developing wildlife game laws that limit the number of organisms that may be hunted each year

101. When plant and animal species are introduced into a new area, they often become pests in the new habitat, even though they were not pests in their native habitats. The most probable reason for this is that, in their new habitat, they   (1) have fewer natural enemies   (2) have a much lower mutation rate   (3) develop better resistance to the new climate   (4) learn to use different foods

102. Recent studies have found traces of the insecticide DDT accumulated in the fat tissue of many wild animals. A correct explanation for this accumulation is that   (1) fat tissue absorbs DDT directly from the air   (2) fat tissue cells secrete DDT   (3) DDT is needed for proper metabolic functioning   (4) DDT is passed along in many food chains

Short Answer
(Constructed Response)

103. In two complete sentences, state three positive and three negative impacts that humans have on the natural environment.

104. In your opinion, what are some of the most important precautions we must take to protect our environment for future generations?

Essay
(Extended Constructed Response)

105. Tropical rain forests around the world are being cleared at an alarming rate to make room for the increasing human population and its needs. Describe two reasons why the remaining tropical forests must be preserved. Suggest a plan by which people might be able both to protect and utilize tropical rain forests in a way that is sustainable.

Reading Comprehension

Base your answers to questions 106 through 109 on the passage below and on your knowledge of biology.

PCBs in the Water

Polychlorinated biphenyls (PCBs) are microcontaminants that are found in some water. Microcontaminants do not change the appearance, smell, or taste of the water, yet they affect the health of the ecosystem. After PCBs get into water, they are absorbed by some algae, which concentrate them. Then fish, which feed on the algae, concentrate the PCBs many more times. PCBs are usually thousands of times more concentrated in the fish than they are in the water in which the fish live. At this level of contamination, the survival of some species in the food web is endangered. The health of other species, including humans who consume some predator fish such as salmon, is also endangered.

Identifying microcontaminants in huge bodies of water is a painstaking and time-consuming procedure. The procedure involves a long chain of activities; it includes filtering, extracting with solvents, and analyzing by chromatographic techniques. Although detecting microcontaminants is a difficult process, it is essential that humans continuously monitor the environment for their presence to help preserve our food webs.

106. In which of the following are PCBs usually the most concentrated?   (1) dissolved oxygen   (2) water molecules   (3) algae   (4) fish

107. Which is a harmful effect of microcontaminants on an aquatic ecosystem?   (1) They decrease the density of the water.   (2) They cause water used for human consumption to taste bad.   (3) They accumulate in certain organisms, making them toxic to other organisms.   (4) They cause water to appear cloudy.

108. The producer organisms in the aquatic food web described in the passage are the (1) bacteria (2) fish (3) humans (4) algae

109. The presence of microcontaminants such as PCBs in the water supply is an example of a negative way that humans have modified their environment due to (1) technological oversight (2) pollution controls (3) importation of species (4) deforestation

Base your answers to questions 110 through 113 on the passage below and on your knowledge of biology.

Acid Rain in the Air

Acid rain is a serious environmental problem in large areas of Canada and the northeastern United States, including New York State. It forms, partly, as rain "washes out" sulfur and nitrogen pollutants from the air. Acid rain alters the fundamental chemistry of sensitive freshwater environments and results in the death of many freshwater species. The principal sources of this pollution have been identified as smokestack gases released by coal-burning facilities located mainly in the midwestern region of the United States.

Unpolluted rain normally has a pH of 5.6. Acid rain, however, has been measured at pH values as low as 1.5, which is more than 10,000 times more acidic than normal. Commonly, acid rain has a pH range of 3 to 5, which changes the acidity level of the freshwater environment into which it falls. The effect of the acid rain depends on the environment's ability to neutralize it. Evidence is accumulating, however, that many environments are adversely affected by the acid rain. As a result, the living things within lakes and streams that cannot tolerate the increasing acidity gradually die off.

Many environmental problems result from acid rain. Most of these problems center around the food web on which all living things, including humans, depend. If freshwater plants, animals, and protists are destroyed by the acidic conditions, then terrestrial predators and scavengers dependent on these organisms for food are forced to migrate or starve. These changes in a food web can eventually affect food consumption by people, too.

110. The following scale shows the pH of four common household substances. Acid rain has a pH closest to that of which of these substances? (1) ammonia (2) tap water (3) baking soda (4) vinegar

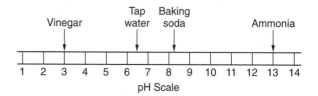

pH Scale

111. What is the most likely source of acid rain in New York State? (1) far western United States (2) midwestern United States (3) far eastern Canada (4) far western Europe

112. Which food chain includes organisms that would most immediately be affected by acid rain?
(1) grass → rabbit → fox → decay bacteria
(2) algae → aquatic insect → trout → otter
(3) shrub → mouse → snake → hawk
(4) tree → caterpillar → bird → lynx

113. Acid rain is generally considered a negative effect of human interaction with the environment. As such, it would most correctly be classified as an example of (1) biological control (2) conservation of resources (3) technological oversight (4) a land-use practice

Laboratory Skills

As part of the Regents Living Environment course, students are expected to master a number of specific science-related skills. Some of these skills involve application of the scientific method, while others are actual laboratory techniques and procedures.

Skills using the scientific method:

- Formulate a question or define a problem for investigation and develop a hypothesis to be tested in an investigation.
- Distinguish between controls and variables in an experiment.
- Collect, organize, and graph data.
- Make predictions based on experimental data.
- Formulate generalizations or conclusions based on the investigation.
- Apply the conclusion to other experimental situations.

Skills involving laboratory procedures:

- Given a laboratory problem, select suitable lab materials, safety equipment, and appropriate observation methods.
- Demonstrate safety skills in heating materials in test tubes or beakers, use of chemicals, and handling dissection equipment.
- Identify the parts of a compound light microscope and their functions. Use the microscope correctly under low power and high power.
- Determine the size of microscopic specimens in micrometers.
- Prepare wet mounts of plant and animal cells and apply stains, including iodine and methylene blue.
- With the use of a compound light microscope, identify cell parts, including the nucleus, cytoplasm, chloroplasts, and cell walls.
- Use indicators, such as pH paper, Benedict solution (or Fehling solution), iodine solution (or Lugol solution), and bromthymol blue. Interpret changes shown by the indicators.
- Use measurement instruments, such as metric rulers, Celsius thermometers, and graduated cylinders.

- Dissect plant or animal specimens, exposing major structures for examination.

The Scientific Method

Defining a problem and developing a hypothesis. Scientists do research to answer a question or solve a problem. Thus, the first step in planning a research project is to define specifically the problem to be solved.

After the research problem has been defined, the next step is to develop an idea of the possible solution to the problem. This educated guess, or *hypothesis*, is a statement that provides the researcher with the factor (or factors) to be tested in the experiment.

For example, a scientist interested in studying the enzyme amylase might want to measure the rate of enzyme action at various temperatures. The basic hypothesis for such an experiment would be that the rate at which amylase hydrolyzes, or breaks down, starch is affected by temperature. The scientist might also hypothesize that the maximum rate of enzyme action would occur at normal body temperature (37°C).

Designing and conducting an experiment. Biologists often use controlled experiments when doing research. In one kind of controlled experiment, there are actually two setups: an experimental setup and a control setup. The experimental and control setups are identical except for the single factor, or *variable*, that is being tested.

In another type of controlled experiment, all conditions are kept constant except for one, which is varied. Any changes observed during the experiment can then be explained in terms of the variable factor.

In an experiment to determine the effect of temperature on the rate of action of the enzyme amylase, temperature is the variable.

The scientist could set up two types of controls in this experiment. A basic controlled experiment would use two setups—one containing a starch solution only, the second containing exactly the same amount of the same starch solution plus the enzyme amylase. Both setups would then be tested at various temperatures to determine how much starch had undergone hydrolysis. The setup with no enzyme is the control; the setup with the enzyme is the experimental one. The control can show that no hydrolysis occurs without the enzyme.

In the experimental setup, all conditions are kept constant except temperature. Thus, the scientist knows that changes in the rate of hydrolysis are caused by the effects of temperature on the enzyme amylase.

Collecting, organizing, and graphing data.
During an experiment, the scientist collects data. These data are the results of the experiment. The data may be recorded in a log in the form of a chart or data table. Sometimes the results are plotted on a graph. Scientists also use computers to record and organize experimental results.

In an experiment to determine the rate of action of amylase at various temperatures, the data collected might be written in a table, as shown in Figure 1.

Temperature (°C)	Grams of starch hydrolyzed per minute
0	0.0
10	0.2
20	0.4
30	0.8
40	1.0
50	0.3
60	0.2

Figure 1.

The relationship between two varying factors can also be shown clearly on a line graph. The graph in Figure 2 shows the same information as the data table above.

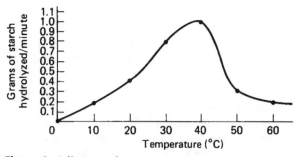

Figure 2. A line graph.

Making predictions based on experimental data.
Scientists may make predictions based on experimental data. The validity of these predictions can then be tested by further experimentation.

For example, on the basis of the data shown in Figure 1, a scientist might predict that the number of grams of starch hydrolyzed at normal body temperature (37°C) would be between 0.8 and 1.0 gram/minute. Further measurements might show that the prediction was correct, or they might show that at 37°C the rate was higher than 1.0 gram/minute. Scientists must be extremely careful not to make any assumptions that are not supported by the data.

Making generalizations and drawing conclusions.
The results of an experiment are collected and analyzed. For a conclusion to be meaningful, the experiment must be repeated many times, and all the results obtained must be included in the analysis. The scope of the conclusion must be limited by the experimental data.

In the experiment on the effect of temperature on the rate of action of amylase, the data in the table show that the enzyme functions most efficiently at 40°C. However, if measurements were made only at 10° intervals, you could not say definitely that 40°C is the optimum temperature for amylase without making measurements at other, intermediate, temperatures. Still, it is probably safe to conclude that the optimum temperature is close to 40°C.

QUESTIONS

Multiple Choice

1. The diagram below represents a setup at the beginning of a laboratory investigation.

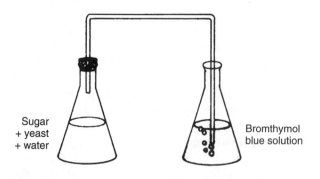

Which hypothesis would most likely be supported by observing and collecting data from this investigation? (1) The fermentation of a yeast-sugar solution results in the production of carbon dioxide. (2) Yeast cells contain simple sugars. (3) Oxygen is released when a yeast-sugar solution is illuminated with green light. (4) Yeast cells contain starches.

Base your answers to questions 2 and 3 on the information and data table below.

A green plant was placed in a test tube, and a light was placed at varying distances from the plant. The bubbles of O_2 given off by the plant were counted. The table below shows the data collected during this experiment.

Distance of light from plant (cm)	Number of bubbles per minute
10	60
20	25
30	10
40	5

2. A variable in this investigation is the (1) color of the light used (2) distance between the light and the plant (3) size of the test tube (4) type of plant used

3. Which conclusion can be drawn from this investigation? (1) As the distance from the light increases, the number of bubbles produced decreases. (2) As the distance from the light increases, the number of bubbles produced increases. (3) As the distance from the light decreases, the number of bubbles produced decreases. (4) There is no relationship between the number of bubbles produced and the distance of the plant from the light.

Base your answers to questions 4 through 6 on the following information, diagram, and data table, and on your knowledge of biology.

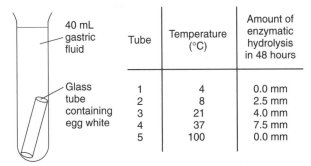

Tube	Temperature (°C)	Amount of enzymatic hydrolysis in 48 hours
1	4	0.0 mm
2	8	2.5 mm
3	21	4.0 mm
4	37	7.5 mm
5	100	0.0 mm

A student is studying the effect of temperature on the hydrolytic action of the enzyme gastric protease, which is contained in gastric fluid. An investigation is set up using five identical test tubes, each containing 40 milliliters of gastric fluid and 20 millimeters of glass tubing filled with cooked egg white, as shown in the diagram below. After 48 hours, the amount of egg white hydrolyzed in each tube was measured. The data collected are shown in the data table below.

4. Which is the variable in this investigation? (1) gastric fluid (2) length of glass tubing (3) temperature (4) time

5. If an additional test tube were set up identical to the other test tubes and placed at a temperature of 15°C for 48 hours, what amount of hydrolysis might be expected? (1) less than 2.5 mm (2) between 2.5 mm and 4.0 mm (3) between 4.0 mm and 7.5 mm (4) more than 7.5 mm

6. Which set of axes would produce the best graph for plotting the data from the results of this investigation? (1) 1 (2) 2 (3) 3 (4) 4

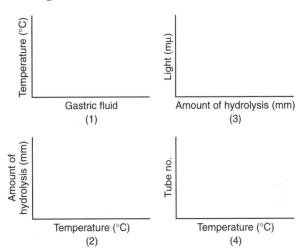

Base your answers to questions 7 through 11 on the two charts below and on your knowledge of biology.

Chart I

Substance	% of blood	% of urine
Protein	7.0	7.0
Water	91.5	96.0
Glucose	0.1	0.0
Sodium	0.33	0.29
Potassium	0.02	0.24
Urea	0.03	2.7

Chart II

Substance	Number of Molecules		
	In blood entering glomerulus	Beginning of tubule	End of tubule
Protein	100	0	0
Water	100	30	1
Glucose	100	20	0
Sodium	100	30	1
Potassium	100	23	12
Urea	100	50	90

Chart I shows the percentages of certain materials in the blood entering the kidney and the percentages of the same materials in the urine leaving the body. Chart II shows the number of molecules in the beginning and end of the kidney tubule for every 100 molecules of each substance entering the glomerulus.

7. According to Chart I, which substance is more highly concentrated in the urine than in the blood? (1) water (2) sodium (3) protein (4) glucose

8. According to Charts I and II, which substance enters the tubules but does *not* appear in the urine leaving the body? (1) protein (2) water (3) glucose (4) potassium

9. According to the data, which substance did *not* pass out of the blood into the tubule? (1) water (2) urea (3) glucose (4) protein

10. The data in the two charts would best aid a biologist in understanding the function of the (1) heart of a frog (2) nephron of a human (3) nerve cell of a fish (4) contractile vacuole of a paramecium

11. Which substances enter the tubule and then are reabsorbed back into the blood as they pass through the tubule? (1) urea and potassium (2) water and sodium (3) urea and protein (4) protein and glucose

Base your answers to questions 12 through 14 on the information provided by the graph below. The graph shows the average growth rate for 38 pairs of newborn rats. One member of each pair was injected with anterior pituitary extract. The other member of each pair served as a control.

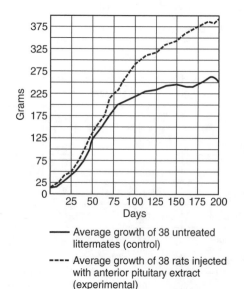

Grams / Days

— Average growth of 38 untreated littermates (control)

---- Average growth of 38 rats injected with anterior pituitary extract (experimental)

12. At 75 days, what was the average weight of the rats injected with pituitary extract? (1) 65 grams (2) 125 grams (3) 200 grams (4) 225 grams

13. Based on the graph, it can be correctly concluded that the pituitary extract (1) is essential for life (2) determines when a rat will be born (3) affects the growth of rats (4) affects the growth of all animals

14. The graph shows the relationship between the weight of treated and untreated rats and the (1) age of the rats (2) sex of the rats (3) size of the rats' pituitary glands (4) type of food fed to the rats

Base your answers to questions 15 and 16 on the following information, diagrams, and data table, and on your knowledge of laboratory procedures used in biology.

Fruits (not drawn to scale)

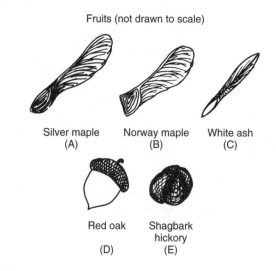

| Silver maple (A) | Norway maple (B) | White ash (C) |

Red oak (D)   Shagbark hickory (E)

Tree type	Average fall time of 100 fruits
Silver maple	3.2 sec
Norway maple	4.9 sec
White ash	1.5 sec
Red oak	0.8 sec
Shagbark hickory	0.8 sec

Diagrams *A* through *E* show the general appearance of five tree fruits that were used by a science class in an experiment to determine the length of time necessary for each type of fruit to fall from a second-floor balcony to the lobby floor of their school. One hundred fruits of each type were selected by the students, and the average time of fall for each type of fruit is shown in the table below.

15. Based on this experimental evidence, what inference seems most likely to be true concerning the distribution of these fruits during windstorms in nature? (1) Silver maple fruits would land closer to the base of their parent tree than would shagbark hickory fruits. (2) White ash fruits would land farther from the base of their parent tree than would silver maple fruits. (3) White ash fruits would land closer to the base of their parent tree than would shagbark hickory fruits. (4) Norway maple fruits would land farther from the base of their parent tree than would silver maple fruits.

16. Which graph best shows the average fall time for each fruit type tested during this experiment?

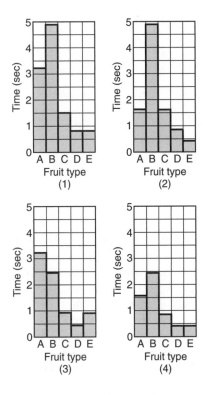

17. The graph below was developed as a result of an investigation of bacterial counts of three identical cultures grown at different temperatures. Which conclusion might be correctly drawn from this graph?

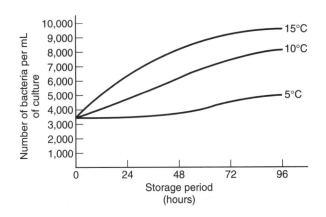

(1) The culture contains no bacteria. (2) Refrigeration retards bacterial reproduction. (3) Temperature is unrelated to the bacteria reproduction rate. (4) Bacteria cannot grow at a temperature of 5°C.

Base your answers to questions 18 through 20 on the graphs below, which show data on some environmental factors affecting a large New York lake.

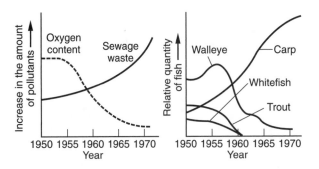

18. Which relationship can be correctly inferred from the data presented? (1) As sewage waste increases, oxygen content decreases. (2) As sewage increases, oxygen content increases. (3) As oxygen content decreases, carp population decreases. (4) As oxygen content decreases, trout population increases.

19. The greatest change in the lake's whitefish population occurred between which years? (1) 1950 and 1955 (2) 1955 and 1960 (3) 1960 and 1965 (4) 1965 and 1970

20. Which of the fish species appears able to withstand the greatest degree of oxygen depletion? (1) trout (2) carp (3) walleye (4) whitefish

Laboratory Procedures

Selecting suitable lab equipment. In planning and carrying out an experiment, knowledge of the correct lab equipment is essential. Figure 3 on page 120 shows the basic lab equipment that you should know.

Safety in the laboratory. Following are some safety precautions that you should practice in the laboratory.
- Do not handle chemicals or equipment unless you are told by your teacher to do so.
- If any of your lab equipment appears to be broken or unusual, do not use it. Report it to your teacher.
- Report any personal injury or damage to clothing to your teacher immediately.
- Never directly taste or inhale unknown chemicals. Never eat or drink in the lab.

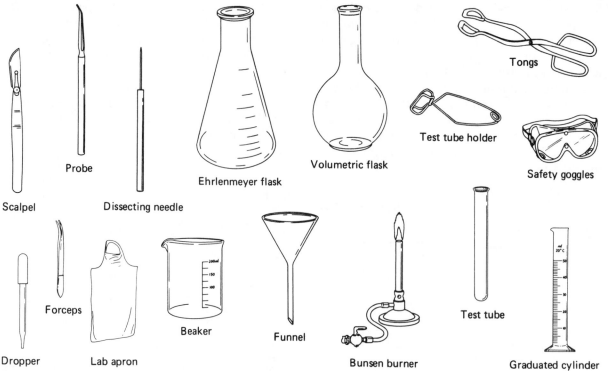

Figure 3. Laboratory equipment.

- Never pour chemicals back into stock bottles or exchange stoppers.
- When heating a liquid in a test tube, always wear safety goggles and point the opening away from yourself and all others.
- Handle all sharp instruments with care.

Using a compound light microscope. Review the parts of the compound light microscope and their functions by studying Figure 1-2 and Table 1-1 (in Chapter 1).

In using the compound microscope, the observer should begin by viewing the specimen with the low-power objective, focusing first with the coarse adjustment, then with the fine adjustment. The objectives can then be switched from low power to high power. All focusing under high power should be done with the fine adjustment. The field appears dimmer under high power than under low power. Opening the diaphragm allows more light to reach the specimen.

The image of an object seen under the microscope is enlarged, reversed (backward), and inverted (upside down). When viewed through the microscope, an organism that appears to be moving to the right is actually moving to the left. An organism that appears to be moving toward the observer, or up, is actually moving away from the observer, or down.

Determining the size of microscopic specimens. To determine the size of a specimen being examined under a microscope, you must know the diameter of the microscope field. You can actually measure the field diameter with a clear plastic centimeter ruler. Place the ruler over the opening in the stage of the microscope, as shown in Figure 4. Focus on the ruler markings and adjust the position of the ruler so that a millimeter marking is at the left.

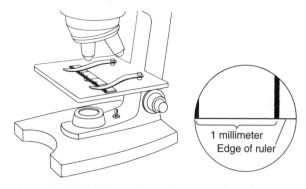

Figure 4. Measuring with a microscope.

Once you have estimated the field diameter under low power, you can estimate the size of specimens observed under low power by how much of the field they cover. For example, if the diameter of the field is 1.5 mm and a specimen is about one-third the diameter of the field, the specimen is about 0.5 mm in length.

The unit most commonly used in measuring microscopic specimens is the *micrometer*, symbol μm, which is one-thousandth of a millimeter.

$$1 \text{ mm} = 1000 \text{ μm} \qquad 1 \text{ μm} = 0.001 \text{ mm}$$

In the example above, the field diameter is 1.5 mm, which is equal to 1500 μm. The specimen is 0.5 mm long, which equals 500 μm.

When you switch from low power to high power, the field diameter decreases. For example, if the magnification under low power is 100× and under high power it is 400×, then the field diameter under high power will be one-fourth that under low power. If the low-power magnification is 100× and the high-power magnification is 500×, then the diameter of the high-power field will be one-fifth that of the low-power field.

Preparing a wet mount and applying stains. A wet mount is a temporary slide preparation used for viewing specimens with a compound light microscope. Any specimen to be examined must be thin enough for light to pass through it.

The preparation of a wet mount involves the following steps:
1. Use a medicine dropper to put a drop of water in the center of the slide.
2. Place the tissue or organism to be examined in the drop of water on the slide.
3. Cover the specimen with a coverslip, as shown in Figure 5.
4. To stain the section, add a drop of iodine solution or methylene blue at one edge of the coverslip. Touch a small piece of paper towel to the opposite side of the coverslip to draw the stain across the slide and through the specimen.

Identifying cell parts with a compound light microscope. Review the structure of plant cells and animal cells (Figure 1-1) and the functions of cell organelles (Chapter 1).

Unstained cells viewed with a compound light microscope show relatively little detail. The use of stains, such as iodine or methylene blue, enhances contrast. With such stains, the nucleus becomes clearly visible, and in plant and algal cells the cell wall becomes visible, too. Chloroplasts are visible as small oval green structures. Most other cell organelles, including mitochondria and the endoplasmic reticulum, are not visible with the compound light microscope.

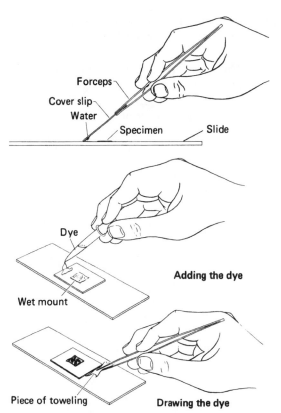

Figure 5. Making a wet mount (above) and staining a specimen.

Using indicators and interpreting changes. Indicators are used to test for the presence of specific substances or chemical characteristics.

Litmus paper is an indicator used to determine whether a solution is an acid or a base. An acid turns blue litmus paper red. A base turns red litmus paper blue.

pH paper is an indicator that is used to determine the actual pH of a solution. When a piece of pH paper is dipped into a test solution, it changes color. The color of the pH paper is then matched against a color chart, which shows the pH.

Bromthymol blue is an indicator used to detect carbon dioxide. In the presence of carbon dioxide, bromthymol blue turns to bromthymol yellow. If the carbon dioxide is removed, the indicator changes back to bromthymol blue.

Benedict solution is an indicator used to test for simple sugars. When heated in the presence of simple sugars, Benedict solution turns from blue to yellow, green, or brick red, depending on the sugar concentration.

Lugol, or *iodine, solution* is an indicator used to test for starch. In the presence of starch, Lugol solution turns from red to blue-black.

Biuret solution is an indicator used to test for protein. In the presence of protein, Biuret solution turns from light blue to purple.

Using measurement instruments. The following tools are used for making scientific measurements.

- *Metric rulers.* The basic unit of length in the metric system is the meter, abbreviated *m*. One meter contains 100 centimeters. As shown in Figure 6, metric rulers are generally calibrated in centimeters and millimeters (mm). Each centimeter contains 10 millimeters, thus each meter is equal to 1000 mm.

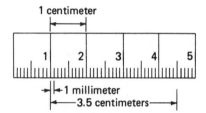

Figure 6. A centimeter ruler.

- *Celsius thermometers.* In the metric system, temperature is commonly measured in degrees Celsius. On the Celsius scale, 0°C is the freezing point of water and 100°C is the boiling point of water. Figure 7 shows a thermometer calibrated in degrees Celsius. Note that each degree is marked by a short line (such as 37°C), and every tenth degree is labeled with the number (such as 30°C and 40°C).

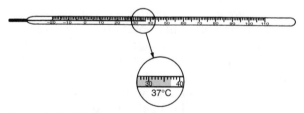

Figure 7. A Celsius thermometer.

- *Graduated cylinders.* The basic unit used for measuring the volume of a liquid in the metric system is the liter, symbol *L*. A liter contains 1000 milliliters (mL). Most laboratory measurements involve milliliters rather than liters.

The volume of a liquid is frequently measured in graduated cylinders, which come in many sizes. When you need an accurately measured amount of liquid, use a graduated cylinder of appropriate size—that is, to measure 5 mL of liquid, use a 10-mL graduated cylinder, not a 1000-mL graduated cylinder.

The surface of water and similar liquids curves upward along the sides of the cylinder (Figure 8). This curved surface, or *meniscus*, is caused by the strong attraction of liquid molecules to the glass surface. For an accurate measurement, the reading should be done at eye level, and the measurement should be taken from the bottom of the meniscus, as shown. With other types of liquids, the meniscus curves the other way. A meniscus of this type should be read across the top.

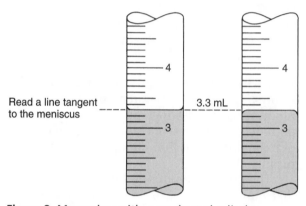

Figure 8. Measuring with a graduated cylinder.

Dissecting plant and animal specimens. Dissections are done to expose major structures for examination. The specimen is generally placed in a dissection pan and fastened down with pins. While doing a dissection, you should be very careful with the dissection instruments, which are sharp. Scalpels, forceps, scissors, and stereomicroscopes are used. You should also be careful in cutting into and handling the specimen so that you do not damage important structures. Follow all instructions and record your observations by making labeled diagrams as you proceed with the dissection.

QUESTIONS

Multiple Choice

Base your answers to questions 21 through 23 on the four sets of laboratory materials listed on page 123 and on your knowledge of biology.

Set A	Set B	Set C	Set D
Light source	Droppers	Scalpel	Compound microscope
Colored filters	Benedict solution	Forceps	Glass slides
Test tubes	Iodine	Scissors	Water
Test-tube stand	Test tubes	Pan with wax bottom	Forceps
	Test-tube rack	Stereo-microscope	
	Heat source	Pins	
	Goggles	Goggles	

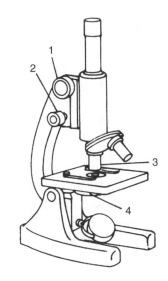

21. Which set should a student select to test for the presence of a carbohydrate in food? (1) Set *A* (2) Set *B* (3) Set *C* (4) Set *D*

22. Which set should a student select to determine the location of the ovules in the ovary of a flower? (1) Set *A* (2) Set *B* (3) Set *C* (4) Set *D*

23. Which set should a student use to observe chloroplasts in elodea (a water plant)? (1) Set *A* (2) Set *B* (3) Set *C* (4) Set *D*

24. To view cells under the high power of a compound light microscope, a student places a slide of the cells on the stage and moves the stage clips over to secure the slide. She then moves the high-power objective into place and focuses on the slide with the coarse adjustment. Two steps in this procedure are incorrect. For this procedure to be correct, she should have focused under (1) low power using coarse and fine adjustments and then under high power using only the fine adjustment (2) high power first, then low power using only the fine adjustment (3) low power using the coarse and fine adjustments and then under high power using coarse and fine adjustments (4) low power using the fine adjustment and then under high power using only the fine adjustment

Base your answers to questions 25 and 26 on the following diagram of a compound light microscope.

25. The part labeled 1 is used to (1) increase the amount of light reaching the specimen (2) focus with the high-power objective (3) hold the lenses in place (4) focus with the low-power objective

26. To adjust the amount of light reaching the specimen, you would use the part labeled (1) 1 (2) 2 (3) 3 (4) 4

Base your answers to questions 27 through 29 on the information below and on your knowledge of biology.

A student prepares a wet mount of onion epidermis and observes it under three powers of magnification with a compound light microscope (40×, 100×, and 400×).

27. An adjustment should be made to allow more light to pass through the specimen when the student changes the magnification from (1) 100× to 400× (2) 400× to 100× (3) 400× to 40× (4) 100× to 40×

28. Iodine stain is added to the slide. Under 400× magnification, the student should be able to observe a (1) mitochondrion (2) nucleus (3) ribosome (4) centriole

29. A specimen that is suitable for observation under this microscope should be (1) stained with Benedict solution (2) moving and respiring (3) alive and reproducing (4) thin and transparent

30. A microscope is supplied with 10× and 15× eyepieces, and with 10× and 44× objectives. What is the maximum magnification that can be obtained from this microscope? (1) 59× (2) 150× (3) 440× (4) 660×

31. Under low power (100×), a row of eight cells can fit across the field of a certain microscope. How many of these cells could be viewed in the high power (400×) visual field of this microscope? (1) 1 (2) 2 (3) 8 (4) 32

32. A compound light microscope has a 10× ocular, a 10× low-power objective, and a 40× high-power objective. A student noted that under high power, four cells end to end extended across the diameter of the field. If the microscope were switched to low power, approximately how many cells would fit across the field? (1) 1 (2) 8 (3) 16 (4) 4

33. The diagram below shows a section of a metric ruler scale as seen through a compound light microscope. If each division represents 1 millimeter, what is the approximate width of the microscope's field of view in micrometers? (1) 3700 μm (2) 4200 μm (3) 4500 μm (4) 5000 μm

Base your answers to questions 34 through 37 on your knowledge of biology and on the diagrams below, which represent fields of vision under the low power of the same compound microscope (100×). Diagram A shows the millimeter divisions of a plastic ruler, and diagram B shows a sample of stained onion epidermal cells.

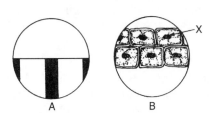

34. Structure X in diagram B was most likely stained by adding (1) water (2) iodine solution (3) Benedict solution (4) bromthymol blue

35. Structure X in diagram B indicates (1) a nucleus (2) a mitochondrion (3) the cell wall (4) the cytoplasm

36. The diameter of the field of vision in diagram A is approximately (1) 500 μm (2) 1000 μm (3) 1500 μm (4) 2000 μm

37. What is the approximate length of each onion epidermal cell in field B? (1) 200 μm (2) 660 μm (3) 1000 μm (4) 2500 μm

38. Iodine solution is used to test for the presence of (1) proteins (2) simple sugars (3) oxygen (4) starch

39. In the presence of carbon dioxide, bromthymol blue (1) shows no color change (2) turns yellow (3) turns blue-black (4) turns red-orange

40. Benedict solution is used to test for (1) disaccharides (2) oxygen (3) starch (4) simple sugars

41. Which piece of equipment should be used to transfer a protist onto a microscope slide? (1) scissors (2) dissecting needles (3) medicine dropper (4) forceps

42. While a student is heating a liquid in a test tube, the mouth of the tube should always be (1) corked with a rubber stopper (2) pointed toward the student (3) allowed to cool off (4) aimed away from everybody

Science, Technology, and Society

Enzymes in the Body

The human body performs an unimaginable number of chemical reactions each day. These reactions carry out such important tasks as digesting food, utilizing energy, processing oxygen and carbon dioxide, and releasing cellular wastes. Under ordinary circumstances, many of these reactions would occur too slowly for the body to survive. In the body, however, substances called catalysts speed up certain chemical reactions.

The molecules that serve as catalysts in the human body are enzymes. Almost all enzymes are proteins. Enzymes speed up chemical reactions by reducing the amount of energy required for the reaction to occur. The operation of an enzyme is somewhat like that of a lock and key. Molecules called substrates bind to the enzyme at a region called the active site. Only substrates that fit into the enzyme, like a key fits into a lock, can bind there. Once the reaction is complete, the products are released and the enzyme is free to bind to new substrates.

Because of the important roles that enzymes play in the body, any changes to enzyme production or use will cause health problems in the body. With this information, doctors have another tool for diagnosing and treating disease. The reason is that enzymes are normally concentrated in the cells and tissues where they perform their catalytic function. When a disease occurs, however, certain enzymes tend to leak into the blood from the injured cells and tissues. As a result, the activity of specific enzymes in a sample of blood serum can be measured and a disease detected.

Over 50 enzymes have been found in human blood serum. Blood serum can be studied with enzyme assays that have been automated with devices called autoanalyzers. This makes it possible to obtain data from one sample of serum about the activity of up to 20 or more enzymes.

One enzyme that is studied in blood serum is called amylase. This enzyme is formed in the pancreas and salivary glands, and it is involved in the digestion of starch. When the pancreas becomes inflamed, the amount of amylase in the blood is usually elevated. An enzyme called acid phosphatase, found in most body tissues, is found in particularly high concentration in the adult prostate gland. This enzyme is released into the blood when the prostate suffers from metastatic cancer. Another enzyme, called alkaline phosphatase, also is found in most body tissues, notably in bone marrow and liver. This enzyme usually shows elevated values in the blood in such conditions as Paget's disease, which is inflammation of the bone, and osteomalacia, which is softening of the bone, as well as in hepatitis and some forms of jaundice.

As researchers study the role that enzymes play in disease, they can begin to learn how the disease develops and how it might be treated. Recent efforts have been making headway for several major diseases. One such disease is Fabry's disease. Fabry's disease is caused by a deficiency of an enzyme involved in the breakdown of lipids in the body. This allows a fatty substance to build up in the tissues. The disease is characterized by a burning sensation in the hands and feet along with raised blemishes on the skin. Over time, people with Fabry's disease may develop heart and kidney problems. The enzyme involved in Fabry's disease is known as ceramidetrihexosidase, or alpha-galactosidase A. In experiments, researchers have been able to successfully treat Fabry's disease by injecting patients with the missing enzyme.

Another enzyme-related disease is Gaucher's disease. A chemical called glucocerebroside accumulates in the body as it replaces worn tissues. In most people, an enzyme known as glucocerebrosidase breaks down the accumulated chemical. People with Gaucher's disease do not produce enough glucocerebrosidase, so glucocerebroside builds up in certain cells. The disorder affects the spleen, liver, and bones, and has been successfully treated by injecting the missing enzyme into the patient's blood.

The key to treating diseases with enzymes is through research. Successful research is used to identify the specific enzyme responsible for a disease and then to deliver it to the patient. As a result, scientists continue to search for the enzymes involved in other disorders. For example, scientists are investigating an enzyme suspected of playing a major role in causing Alzheimer's disease. Similarly, researchers are investigating a family of enzymes that appear to play a role in both cancer and cardiovascular disease. Through research, doctors may some day be able to treat a variety of enzyme-related diseases.

Questions

1. What role do enzymes play in the human body?
2. How can enzymes be used to diagnose disease?
3. How can enzymes be used to treat certain diseases?
4. How might scientific research be involved in identifying and treating enzyme-related diseases?

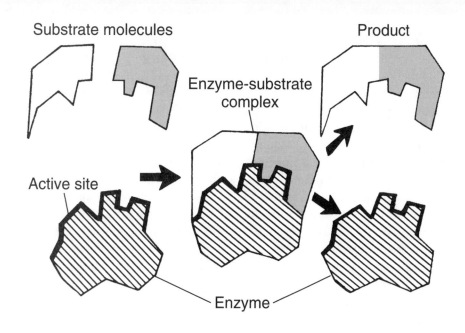

The Lungs of the Planet

Earth's organisms inhabit a variety of ecosystems throughout the world. These ecosystems are grouped into biomes according to the plants and animals that are relatively stable and abundant within them. One of the most important biomes on Earth is the tropical rain forest.

Tropical rain forests are found primarily in South and Central America, West and Central Africa, Indonesia, parts of Southeast Asia, and tropical Australia. As the name suggests, rainfall is plentiful in the tropical rain forest biome and the dry season is limited to a few months. Temperatures remain high, usually about 30°C during the day and 20°C at night. These warm, moist conditions allow for abundant vegetation and wildlife.

Rain forests may be best known for the great diversity of organisms that live within them. Aside from the rare beauty of many of these plants and animals, it is thought that some rainforest organisms hold the secrets to cures for many human diseases and ailments. Maybe less well known is that rain forests are the planet's biggest producers of biomass, they intercept solar radiation, they change the flow of winds, and they influence the exchange of energy between the atmosphere and the ground. In addition, rain forests influence global rainfall patterns and give rise to some of the world's greatest rivers.

One of the most important roles of the rain forest, however, is to convert carbon dioxide (CO_2) in the atmosphere into oxygen (O_2) through the process of photosynthesis. Animals continuously release CO_2 into the atmosphere through the process of respiration. In addition, industrial processes and combustion release CO_2 into the atmosphere. We depend on trees and other plants to remove CO_2 from the atmosphere and return the O_2 that we and other aerobic organisms need to survive. Tropical rain forests are responsible for much of this gas exchange because of the tremendous amount of vegetation within them. It is estimated that over 20 percent of Earth's O_2 is produced in the Amazon rain forest alone! Because of its role of continuously recycling CO_2 into O_2 the Amazon rain forest has been described as the "lungs of our planet."

This delicate natural balance of gas exchange is being threatened. For one thing, emissions of CO_2 continue to increase as a result of industrialization and human population growth. In addition, rain forests are being destroyed at an alarming rate. Over 500 million acres of tropical forests have been lost worldwide since 1980. That is an area larger than Mexico and Indonesia combined. If deforestation continues at current rates, scientists estimate that nearly 80 to 90 percent of tropical rainforest ecosystems will be destroyed by the year 2020.

Why are the tropical forests being destroyed? There are several factors involved. Although widespread fires have consumed some forest regions, the most devastating cause of deforestation has been the practices of struggling human populations. Most of the world's important tropical forests are located in developing countries. These nations are under financial pressure to use their rain forests to raise funds to meet their immediate domestic needs and to pay off debts owed to industrial nations. Rain forests are converted into money by clearing the land and selling the trees through logging operations and other resources through mining operations.

Another driving force in the loss of rain forests is subsistence farming. By tradition, lands in the rain forest are free to those who clear the forest and farm the soil. Poor farmers clear rainforest lands to raise cattle or grow crops. Unfortunately, rainforest soils are not suitable for sustained agriculture. Rain forests are deceptive, because their lush vegetation is able to flourish on soils that are low in nutrients. Rainforest soil is comparable to wet desert soil. Therefore, the soil is difficult to cultivate for agriculture. The soil is generally depleted in three or four crop cycles and can no longer sustain farming. When this happens, farmers must move on and clear additional rainforest land.

Whatever the cause, deforestation has many dangerous consequences, including erosion of the soil, extinction of the plants and animals that lose their habitats, air and water pollution, and an increase in the amount of CO_2 in the atmosphere. In other words, as rainforest land diminishes, less CO_2 is removed from the atmosphere and less O_2 is returned for respiration.

Aside from the air quality, an increase in CO_2 in the atmosphere increases the natural greenhouse effect on Earth. In this process, CO_2 in the atmosphere acts like a blanket around the planet by keeping incoming solar heat near Earth's surface. As the amount of CO_2 increases, the atmospheric heat also increases, leading to a condition known as global warming.

The solution to the problem might seem obvious at first glance—tell the people to stop destroying the rain forests and find other sources of income. After all, these countries are sacrificing long-term, global resources for short-term, financial needs. The answer, however, isn't quite so simple. Industrialized nations, such as the United States, cleared vast areas of forest during their early development. So, is it fair, or even possible, to deny currently developing nations that same opportunity? Furthermore, is it fair to tell hungry people to change their way of life and sacrifice their means of survival for the sake of the rain forests?

The solution lies in international cooperation. Efforts are being made to create a new source of income related to rain forests that doesn't involve destroying them. If, for example, the medicinal plants, fruits, nuts, oil, and other sustainable resources found in the rain forest are harvested, such forests will become more valuable alive and intact than destroyed. Recent statistics show that rainforest land converted to cattle operations yields the landowner $60 per acre. If timber is harvested, the land is worth $400 per acre. However, if renewable and sustainable rainforest resources—i.e., the medicinal and edible plants—are harvested instead, the land will yield the landowner $2,400 per acre. The key to the success of this conversion is to create markets for these resources by educating people about them and educating landowners about the potential.

Another solution being explored involves having industrialized nations reduce debts owed to them in return for rainforest protection. In 1998, for example, the United States passed the Tropical Forest Conservation Act. Under this law, sometimes called the debt-for-nature swap, developing countries around the world would be permitted to reduce their debt to the United States in return for setting up trust funds to pay for the protection of their remaining tropical rain forests. Proponents say that this is a win-win situation, in which developing nations are released from debt, thereby supporting their economic development. And at the same time, tropical rain forests are being preserved. Opponents argue that industrialized nations are being forced to support the developing nations.

Both the problem and the solution of the destruction of tropical rain forests are economic. Governments need money to pay their debts, farmers need money to feed their families, and companies need to make profits. The simple fact is that tropical rain forests are being destroyed for the income and profits they yield. Yet, no matter where you live, you depend on the rain forests for the air you breathe and, therefore, you need to be concerned about their future.

Questions

1. What are the general characteristics of the tropical rain forest biome?
2. How is photosynthesis related to the importance of tropical rain forests?
3. What are three economic incentives currently causing inhabitants of developing nations to destroy tropical rain forests?
4. Why is it important for people of all nations to preserve tropical rain forests?
5. What are some possible approaches to helping developing nations protect the vast resources of tropical rain forests?

A Hard Time to Breathe

Imagine suddenly not being able to breathe. You start coughing and wheezing. Your chest feels tight. This frightening scenario is reality each day for millions of Americans who suffer from asthma. Asthma is a chronic disorder involving periodic attacks that occur when the muscles of the air passageways that branch through the lungs constrict. Sadly, asthma cases are reaching epidemic proportions in the United States. The number of asthma cases has more than doubled since 1980. Experts predict that the number of asthma cases will nearly double again, to 29 million, by the year 2020.

What is of particular concern is that, of the almost 18 million cases reported at the end of the last century, about 5 million of those were in children. At the present time, asthma is the most common chronic disease among children. The problem is not limited to the United States. Asthma rates in some countries, including Australia, New Zealand, Ireland, and the United Kingdom, surpass those in the United States.

Researchers are not absolutely sure why there has been such an increase in the number of asthma cases, but they have found several clues. There seems to be a hereditary predisposition present in asthma cases. In other words, the genetic makeup of some people makes them more likely to develop asthma. However, the actual attacks themselves seem to be triggered by a person's exposure to allergens, the substances that provoke an allergic reaction.

Since asthma involves breathing problems, the most obvious culprit for carrying allergens is the air. Until recently, most people looked only to outside air to find a connection between air pollution and asthma. The real connection, however, has been found inside. Today, people tend to spend more time indoors than ever before. In fact, on average, people spend about eighty percent of their lives indoors. As a result, the characteristics of indoor air have a more direct and sustained impact on people's health than outdoor air.

Common indoor allergens found to affect school-age children who suffer from asthma include dander, hair, and saliva from house pets, along with dust mites and mold spores. One of the most significant allergens turned out to be cockroaches. Other substances that showed some relationship to asthma included viruses and bacteria, pesticides, cleaning supplies, and building materials. In the case of preschool-aged children, secondhand smoke was also found to make asthma symptoms worse.

Many of these substances are common in homes because, without realizing it, most homeowners create environments in which these substances thrive. Dust mites and mold, for example, thrive in a warm, moist environment. Due to the availability and ease of home heating, people now tend to keep their homes warmer than they used to. In addition, cooking, bathing, hanging up wet clothes, and using humidifiers all increase the humidity in a home. Also, as people add carpeting, mattresses, curtains, and stuffed animals to their homes to make their lives more comfortable, they are unknowingly creating perfect breeding grounds for dust mites.

To make matters worse, most homes lack proper ventilation. This means that the air inside the home is not renewed. Consider the style of home heating. When homes were heated by fireplaces and by wood-burning stoves, air from the home was released through the chimney. Central heating, however, has no outlet for releasing either the air or the allergens it may carry. Instead, these substances stay within the home and are continuously recirculated. In addition, people who live in urban areas or along busy roadways generally keep their windows shut to avoid traffic exhaust and noise. Others add thick storm windows to increase insulation. These factors further serve to trap allergens within the home.

These relationships explain another trend in the asthma epidemic. The incidence of asthma among African-American children has increased faster than in other portions of the population. At first, some researchers thought that the disease was becoming more common only in African Americans. However, when they considered variables such as race, poverty, and urban residence, they found that all urban children, regardless of race, had a higher risk of asthma. This means that the high rate of asthma is most likely a result of increased urban living.

With knowledge of the relationship between allergens and asthma, there is the hope of curbing this epidemic. Most people are unaware of both the dangers of indoor pollution and the appropriate measures to protect themselves and their children from its effects. Once they are educated about the factors that may lead to the expression of asthma symptoms, people can begin to eliminate the allergens. A variety of strategies, such as removing a pet, cleaning intensively, prohibiting smoking, and controlling indoor humidity, may help alleviate asthma symptoms. In addition, people can try to increase the ventilation in their homes to create healthier home environments.

Unfortunately, in many cases these solutions are easier said than done. Many people in urban homes cannot control certain allergens, such as the presence of cockroaches. The workplace is another place where people do not have complete control over their environment. Additional allergens may be present in the workplace, including toxic chemicals, airborne mineral dusts, fumes from welding, as well as various gases, smokes, mists, and vapors. Curbing the asthma epidemic will prove to be a serious challenge for years to come.

Questions

1. What is asthma? Is the number of asthma cases increasing or decreasing? Explain.
2. What types of allergens have been linked to asthma?
3. Suggest five ways to cut down on asthma-inducing allergens.
4. Why might urban living result in a high rate of asthma cases?

Healthy Habits for Life

Unlike the bodies of some other animals, the human body has the ability to maintain its normal functions under a wide variety of conditions. The body system that helps maintain this internal stability is the endocrine system. It ensures that the composition of the body fluids surrounding the cells remains constant.

One role of the endocrine system is to regulate blood glucose levels. Glucose is a sugar found in foods. It acts as the energy source for most body cells and as the only energy source for cells of the central nervous system under normal conditions. When blood glucose levels rise, beta cells in the pancreas produce a hormone called insulin. Insulin triggers cells to take up the carbohydrate glucose so that the cells can use this energy-yielding sugar. When blood glucose levels fall, an opposite process occurs. Chemicals produced by the pancreas cause energy reserves to be used and proteins to be broken down into amino acids. The liver then converts the amino acids and lipids into glucose that is released into circulation. In this way, the body maintains homeostasis whether or not food is being ingested.

When the endocrine system operates improperly, the body is unable to maintain homeostasis. The most common disorder of the endocrine system is *diabetes mellitus*, a disease in which the body does not produce or properly use insulin. Since the glucose in the blood is not being processed, the blood glucose levels rise. This condition is known as hyperglycemia, or high blood sugar. As glucose accumulates in the blood, excess levels of this sugar are excreted in the urine. The high levels of glucose cause more water to be excreted with it. The result is frequent urination and thirst, along with other symptoms that include itching, hunger, weight loss, and weakness.

There are two types of diabetes: Type I and Type II. In Type I diabetes, the body does not produce any insulin. This form of diabetes is an autoimmune disease in which the body mistakes some of its own cells for foreign invaders. The insulin-producing beta cells of the pancreas are destroyed and the pancreas can no longer produce insulin. Type I diabetes, which occurs most often in children and young adults, was once known as juvenile-onset diabetes. People with Type I diabetes must take daily insulin injections several times each day to lower their high blood sugar. This treatment controls, but does not cure, the disease.

In Type II diabetes, the body is unable to make enough, or properly use, insulin. This form of the disease develops either when the pancreas slows in its production of insulin or when the cells of the body become less responsive to insulin. Type II diabetes, once known as adult-onset diabetes, usually occurs after 40 years of age and becomes more common with increasing age. People with Type II diabetes can control blood glucose levels through diet and exercise and, if necessary, by taking insulin injections. Despite once being called juvenile or adult, either type of diabetes can occur at any age.

Diabetes is a serious condition because it upsets the body's homeostasis. As a result, diabetes is a major factor in the cause of many other health problems, including heart disease, stroke, high blood pressure, and kidney disease. One recent study estimates that one of every seven health care dollars is spent on complications related to diabetes. According to the Centers for Disease Control, diabetes is the seventh leading cause of death in the United States.

Unfortunately, the number of people with diabetes continues to rise in the United States. Approximately 800,000 new cases are diagnosed every year. One portion of the population that is experiencing a rapid increase in diabetes cases is children. According to the Juvenile Diabetes Foundation, 35 more American children are found to have Type I diabetes every day. What is particularly alarming is that more and more children are being diagnosed with Type II diabetes. A panel of the American Diabetes Association

(ADA) reports that up to 45 percent of newly diagnosed cases of childhood diabetes are Type II. This is particularly troubling because pediatric endocrinologists, doctors who treat children for diabetes, report that children with Type II diabetes may be at even higher risk for heart disease, stroke, blindness, kidney failure, poor circulation, and infections of the feet and legs that can result in amputation than children with Type I.

Recent statistics indicate that Type II diabetes is nearing epidemic proportions. Some doctors argue that the growing number of Type II cases in children is simply because cases were misdiagnosed in past years. However, most others argue that the change is due to trends in unhealthy habits among America's youth. Although the exact cause of diabetes is unknown, both genetics and environmental factors appear to play a role in its expression. The first factor, genetics, is unchangeable. Yet, it has long been known that less than five percent of people with the diabetes gene develop the disease. What then sets the disease in motion in susceptible children? The answer appears to involve diet and exercise. Almost four out of five people who are newly diagnosed with diabetes are obese.

Why are more children overweight? One reason is that the eating habits among young people in the United States have declined in recent years. Children are eating more processed foods, fast foods, and refined sugars than ever before. Perhaps even more dramatic, though, is that young people today are considerably less active than their parents were at the same age. Due to the preponderance of electronic gadgets and the busy lifestyles of working parents, children watch too much television. Almost two-thirds of children watch at least two hours of television each day, and more than one quarter of children watch four or more hours of television each day. When television viewing and body fatness were compared, children who watched four or more hours of television per day had a higher body fat and greater body mass index than those who watched less than two hours per day.

The general conclusion is that children who overeat, are inactive, and have a family history of diabetes are most at risk of contracting Type II diabetes. Most children are currently diagnosed with Type II diabetes during middle-to-late puberty. Physicians fear that as the childhood population becomes more overweight and less active, Type II diabetes may begin occurring in younger children. While all cases of diabetes cannot be prevented by diet alone, some cases may be prevented if children (and adults) make an effort to adopt a more active lifestyle. A healthy diet and regular exercise can help in the fight against obesity, diabetes, and heart disease, too.

Questions

1. What is insulin and how is it used in the body?
2. Compare Type I diabetes and Type II diabetes.
3. How has the frequency of Type II diabetes changed in recent years?
4. How does the modern American lifestyle contribute to an increase in diabetes? What changes should be made?

Making Extinction Extinct

Some of the most beautiful and interesting organisms that have ever lived on Earth no longer exist. In other words, they are extinct. Most species became extinct because conditions on Earth changed over time. Other species disappeared because their habitats were destroyed by the expansion of the human population. Whatever the cause, additional species are lost to extinction every year. At present, a large number of species are listed as endangered, because their numbers are so small that they are in danger of becoming extinct in the near future.

One controversial approach being explored to prevent endangered species from becoming extinct is cloning. The term *clone* comes from the Greek word *klon*, meaning a twig, as in a cutting used to grow plants. Cloning has also come to mean the production of genetically identical animals. A clone is generally defined as an individual organism (or group of identical organisms) that was produced from a single cell of a parent organism; as such, a clone is genetically identical to its parent.

The science of cloning is not new. Scientists were able to clone frogs in the 1950s and mice in the 1980s. In the 1990s, scientists were able to clone their first large mammal—a sheep. The basic technique used in each cloning experiment is straightforward. Scientists remove the nucleus, and therefore the genetic material, from an egg cell of one animal. They then insert the nucleus of a cell from the donor animal to be cloned into the empty egg cell. Using an electrical impulse to simulate the burst of energy that occurs during fertilization, scientists fuse the material from the two cells together. The egg then begins dividing normally and becomes an embryo, which eventually forms a cloned offspring.

Until 1997, the donor cell used for cloning was, in most cases, either from an embryo or an adult cell from plants and small animals such as frogs. All attempts to use an adult cell, rather than an embryonic cell, to clone a mammal had failed. It was thought that the reason for the failure was that, as mammalian cells develop and differenti-ate, the DNA changes, which makes it impossible to use adult cells for cloning. Almost all of an animal's cells contain the complete genetic information needed to reproduce a copy of the organism. However, as cells differentiate into tissues and organs, they express only that genetic information needed to reproduce their own cell type. Researchers concluded that donor cells for cloning were therefore limited to embryonic cells, which have not yet differentiated into blood, skin, bone, or other specialized cells.

In 1997, a team of British researchers led by Ian Wilmut at the Roslin Institute in Edinburgh, Scotland, made history when they successfully cloned a sheep from the cell of an adult. They took the nucleus of a cell from the mammary gland of an adult sheep and implanted it into another sheep's unfertilized egg whose nucleus had been removed. The key to their success was getting the two cells to the same point in the cell cycle at which they prepare for cell division. To achieve this, they deprived the mammary cell of nutrients before implanting it. Removing the nutrients stopped its cell cycle, preventing it from dividing. Once it was fused to the egg cell, normal division began. The lamb that was born, Dolly, is a clone of the sheep that donated the mammary cell nucleus.

Researchers around the world immediately saw a multitude of possibilities for the new technology. One such application is to use cloning to preserve endangered species. By using cells from adults of the species, scientists would be able to add to the remaining population at a faster rate than would otherwise be possible.

One obstacle first identified in cloning endangered species is that researchers would have to remove endangered females from the wild or from a zoo in order to form and implant the engineered egg cell. Any such medical procedure would expose the animal to stresses that might endanger its health. Because success rates are still quite low, the risk of harming a healthy female is higher than the possibility of producing offspring.

The proposed solution is to create the clone embryo and implant it into a similar, related species that is not endangered. The animal of the related species would serve as a surrogate mother for the embryo, thereby decreasing researcher interactions with females of the endangered species.

Whether cloning that uses more than one species could actually work on a large scale is the subject of considerable debate. If it does, giant pandas of China would be one of the first animals to benefit. Researchers are considering black bears as surrogate mothers for the cloned pandas. Plans are also underway to clone the rare African bongo antelope and the Sumatran tiger, among others.

Although most everyone agrees that every effort should be made to preserve the diversity of life by protecting species from extinction, there are many issues to consider. Perhaps the most important concerns are ethical. Is it ethical to create identical copies of living organisms? The public response to cloning suggests that countries differ widely in their perceptions of this new technology. Immediately after the announcement of Dolly's birth, for example, Italy banned the cloning of any mammal, whereas a number of groups in the United States welcomed the technique.

Another question that must be answered is, "Will cloning do more harm than good in the attempt to protect endangered species?" Opponents argue that this plan will restrict an already dwindling amount of genetic diversity in remaining populations of endangered species. Supporters disagree. They explain that researchers can collect tissues from as many individuals of an endangered species as possible. This will create a diverse genetic bank to draw on for donor cells.

In addition, cloning enables researchers to introduce new genes back into the gene pool of a species that has few remaining animals. By cloning animals whose body cells have been preserved, scientists can keep the genes of that individual alive. In this way, they can maintain or increase the overall genetic diversity of endangered populations of that species.

Yet there is the concern that cloning might have unforeseen consequences. Recent studies have found that mice cloned from embryonic stem cells had unique genetic abnormalities even though they looked identical. There is a possibility that negative characteristics might unknowingly be added to the gene pool during the cloning process.

Another danger is that cloning could overshadow efforts to preserve habitats. Saving the habitats of species is the best long-term method of protecting endangered species. If attention and funds are funneled toward cloning, habitats will continue to diminish, thereby making the plight of endangered species hopeless. Supporters argue that while conservation of habitats is urgent, some countries are too poor or unstable to support conservation. Cloning offers the opportunity to maintain the species despite the loss of habitats.

There is also a concern that the technology will be abused. Overzealous researchers might attempt to clone extinct animals that no longer have natural habitats and natural predators. Supporters argue that the chances of successfully cloning such organisms are low because it is nearly impossible to obtain a complete set of preserved DNA. A similar abuse might come from owners of prized animals, such as racehorses, who might clone identical copies of the animals in order to make money. Since the technology is relatively simple, tight constraints would have to be developed to prevent such abuse.

It is clear that there is no easy answer. While the goal of protecting biodiversity is noble, the issues are complex and the risks are real.

Questions

1. What is a clone?
2. How was Dolly different from previous mammal clones?
3. How might cloning be used to protect endangered species from extinction?
4. What are some of the issues surrounding the use of cloning in endangered species?

Healing Through Gene Therapy

Scientific knowledge about diseases and their cures has progressed gradually over the years. As a result, researchers have developed a wide range of techniques to use in diagnosing, treating, and researching diseases. A major breakthrough occurred in the 1970s when restriction enzymes were first discovered. Restriction enzymes cut DNA at specific sequences. Researchers were then able to cut, remove, and join genes together. In this way, they were able to start exploring the roles that genes play in disease.

Recall that a gene is a linear sequence of DNA that codes for a particular protein. On rare occasions, usually during cell division, the order of the DNA base pairs of a gene can be mixed or mutated so that the resulting protein is faulty. Such an event will cause a genetic disease such as cystic fibrosis, adenosine deaminase (ADA) deficiency, or sickle-cell anemia. By studying how genes are related to disease, and how such genes can be manipulated, researchers are attempting to treat diseases by making changes to a person's genes. This form of treatment is known as *gene therapy*.

There are essentially two types of gene therapy. One type, called somatic gene therapy, involves gene expression in cells that will affect the patient but that will not be passed on to the next generation. The other type, called germline gene therapy, involves modifying genes in germ cells that will pass the change on to the next generation.

Germline gene therapy is the more controversial of the two forms. The possible benefits of germline gene therapy in humans could be significant. However, the long-term effects of each transferred gene will have to be carefully monitored and analyzed. Because of the potential for abuse, germline gene therapy in humans needs to be widely discussed and the associated safety issues evaluated before this approach can be used for the treatment of diseases.

Aside from ethical issues, gene therapy faces other challenges. For one thing, researchers must find ways to get the new genes into the billions of target cells where they are needed in the body. To do so, researchers must first isolate the disease-related gene. Then they must package the repair gene in something that can deliver it to the target cells. The delivery vehicle is usually a disabled virus that cannot reproduce and cause disease, but that can transport the gene inside the patient's cells.

Creating an effective delivery vehicle has proven to be difficult. Scientists first tried using a type of mouse virus that can easily infect human cells and integrate the new genes into the cell's chromosomes. The mouse virus, however, infects only dividing cells. So, researchers switched to adenovirus, a type of human virus that causes the common cold. Because its own genes needed to reproduce are removed from the adenovirus, the remaining viral container is unable to cause illness.

Once inserted, the new genes need to function properly. Frequently, the body suppresses gene expression, essentially turning the new genes off, or destroys the transplanted genes. Then, once all of this is accomplished, researchers must show that the procedure is safe. In other words, they must confirm that the expression of the transferred gene will be controlled, that it will occur only in those cells that are targeted, and that the transferred gene will not cause any disease.

The first human trials of gene therapy began in 1990 by using a strategy called *ex vivo* gene therapy. *Ex vivo* gene therapy is the transfer of genes into cells that have been temporarily removed from the patient. The first trials that were done using this approach attempted to treat two genetic disorders—one in children who have an inherited form of immune deficiency and another in both children and adults who have extremely high levels of serum cholesterol.

The research quickly moved into more practical approaches for delivering genes by using *in vivo* gene therapy. *In vivo* gene therapy transfers genes directly into the target cells where they are found in the body. The first attempt at *in vivo* gene therapy involved using a weakened version of the adenovirus to treat people who have cystic fibrosis.

Since the first trials in 1990, researchers around the world have launched more than 400 clinical trials to test gene therapy on a wide array of illnesses. Unfortunately, high hopes have gone unfulfilled because there have been no true cures through gene therapy. Even more devastating is the fact that one clinical trial not only failed to cure its volunteer, it led to his death. In September 1999, a patient died from a reaction to a gene therapy treatment at the University of Pennsylvania's Institute of Human Gene Therapy in Philadelphia. Eighteen-year-old Jesse Gelsinger had a rare genetic disease that was diagnosed sometime after his birth. Researchers are not completely sure why the gene therapy treatment caused his death, but it appears that his immune system attacked the adenovirus carrier.

In the investigation that followed, the FDA found a series of serious deficiencies in the way that the gene therapy trial had been conducted. Similar errors were found in other gene therapy trials. Gene therapy researchers were not following all of the federal rules requiring them to report unexpected adverse events associated with the gene therapy trials. Even worse, some scientists were asking that such problems not be made public. As a result, many gene therapy programs were instantly suspended.

However, not all the news about gene therapy is bad. Although dramatic cures have not been seen yet, there are signs that such advances are not far off. For example, Ashanthi DeSilva, the first child to receive gene therapy for an immune disorder in 1990, continues to do well. Cynthia Cutshall, the second child to receive gene therapy for the same immune disorder, also continues to do well. Some scientists do not count them as true successes because both girls began receiving a drug treatment just before receiving the gene therapy. So, it is not clear which treatment can be credited for their health.

Nonetheless, there is little question that the technological advances in gene therapy research hold great promise. It is now possible to be optimistic about future developments, but it is also of the utmost importance that society becomes educated about the possible dangers of gene therapy along with the potential advantages.

Questions

1. What is the goal of gene therapy?
2. How is somatic gene therapy different from germline gene therapy?
3. How are researchers attempting to transfer genes into patients?
4. What failures have made gene therapy trials disappointing thus far? What successes have there been?

A Sea Change at the North Pole

When you look outside each morning, what do you observe? Perhaps you notice that the sun is shining, there are clouds in the sky, or that branches are swaying in the breeze. These observations all relate to the weather. Weather is the temporary condition of the atmosphere, and it includes such characteristics as temperature, precipitation, and wind. The general or long-term weather conditions in a region are known as the climate. Climates range from hot and wet, as in a tropical rain forest, to cold and dry, as in the tundra. Several different climate types can be found throughout the world.

The organisms that live within a region are adapted to the conditions of that area's climate. An organism that depends on the moisture of a rain forest, for example, would probably not survive in the dry climate of a desert. Yet there are organisms that do thrive in dry climates. As you might expect, then, a change in the climate of an area would have a serious impact on the organisms that live there.

What changes can a climate experience? For one thing, a climate might become warmer. Over the past century or so, temperatures on Earth have been slowly, but steadily, rising. In fact, the 1990s was the hottest decade on record in the past millennium. The major reason for this is modern society's dependence on fossil fuels. When fossil fuels are burned, they release gases into the atmosphere. These gases trap heat near Earth's surface in much the same way that the glass of a greenhouse traps heat inside. For this reason, these gases are called greenhouse gases, and their effect on the atmosphere is referred to as global warming.

You probably have not noticed the warming trend in your climate. After all, some days are warm and some are not. But there is evidence for such a warming, and it is found in perhaps in the last place you might expect—the Arctic. The arctic region is characterized by barren land and frigid temperatures, which give rise to thick layers of snow and ice. Yet the Arctic is warming faster than anywhere else on Earth. In fact, American scientists have reported that, for the first time in 50 million years, part of the North Pole has actually melted—a stretch of open water that spans over one mile wide has been discovered. In addition, a report in the Norwegian science journal *Cicerone* predicted that the Arctic was melting so quickly that the polar icecap could vanish completely during the summer within 50 years. Similarly, the British journal *Science Progress* reported that the Arctic was melting three times faster than theoretical models had predicted. Since the late 1970s, the Arctic's winter ice has receded by six percent. That means a loss of area roughly equal to the size of Texas.

Does it matter if the arctic ice melts a little? It matters a lot. Some of Earth's last great wilderness areas are located in this region. Many of the world's most distinctive mammals are found only in the Arctic, such as polar bears, walruses, arctic foxes, collared lemmings, arctic and tundra hares, musk oxen, bowhead whales, and several species of seals. In addition, the arctic region is perhaps most important to migratory birds. An estimated 15 percent of the world's bird species use the Arctic during the breeding season.

All of the organisms that live in the Arctic have developed unique characteristics that enable them to thrive in the area's extreme climate. If mainland areas of tundra largely disappear in the next 50 to 100 years, as some scientists predict, the uniquely adapted plants and animals will no longer be well suited to the climate. If the climate change were slower and more gradual, many of the arctic species would be able to adapt to the new conditions. But these changes are expected to occur at a rate that is too fast to allow arctic species the time to adapt. Also, climate changes that affect one species can have wide-reaching effects on the ecosystem as a whole.

Consider as an example the relationship between the polar bear and its principal prey, the ringed seal. Ringed seals give birth in caves, or dens, of snow. The seals' success in raising their young depends on the quality of the snow caves. Warming at the southern edge of the snow pack can cause snow caves to collapse. The young born in the spring have a protective coat of fur, but they do not yet have their protective layer of blubber. That means they are not ready to withstand the extreme conditions outside the snow caves. Scientists suspect that warming in the Arctic will lead to more collapsed caves, and ultimately to a reduction of areas suitable for seal denning.

Polar bears require deeper snow to make their dens. As snowdrifts become thinner, polar bears will be less successful at raising their young. In addition, the normal hunting routine of the polar bears is being disturbed by the warming trend. Because ringed seals are prey for polar bears, a decline in seal prey will result in an inevitable decline in polar bear populations. Also, as the length of time during which the ocean is covered by ice shortens, polar bears have less opportunity to hunt. Adult polar bears near Churchill, Manitoba, for example, fast during the summer and early fall because they are forced to stay on land due to the lack of sea ice. When the sea ice returns, the bears immediately move out onto Hudson Bay to begin hunting. If their hunting time is cut short or even eliminated, the polar bears' population will suffer.

Changes in the arctic climate have other implications as well. The Inuit people of northern Russia, Alaska, Canada, and Greenland are also being affected. As the sea ice becomes thinner and the climate becomes warmer, dangerous animals from the south, such as the grizzly bear and moose, are moving farther north than ever before. This change disrupts the delicate balance that exists in the region. Warmer weather also leads to more tourists, more sports hunters, and perhaps, most seriously, more ships. As a result, the melting Arctic threatens the Inuit lifestyle and culture.

In terms of ships, opening the Arctic to cargo shipping would cut about 7700 kilometers off existing ocean trade routes connecting Germany and Japan. Oil-burning cargo vessels, however, are among the most polluting vehicles on Earth. The gases they release contribute directly to global warming. And, once ships make their way into Arctic waters, it is only a matter of time before the Arctic's valuable oil resources are tapped. Not only does this remove limited resources and ultimately lead to the release of additional greenhouse gases, it poses a new threat of oil spills and other pollution that this fragile ecosystem cannot withstand.

The effects of global warming are being observed all over the world, in both the northern and southern hemispheres. Just as it did not start on its own, the warming trend will not go away on its own. Only when businesses create products with lower energy demands, and make better use of resources in the manufacturing process, can society hope to curb this damaging trend. Shareholders, customers, and the media must demand that companies act responsibly to reduce emissions of greenhouse gases. Governments must also demand the reduction of greenhouse gas emissions. Unless urgent actions are taken to control the burning of fossil fuels, we may well witness the end of an ecosystem within the next few generations.

Questions

1. How is climate different from weather? Give one example of each.
2. What is global warming? How is global warming related to fossil fuels?
3. How is global warming affecting the animals of the Arctic? How might global warming affect the arctic environment in other ways?
4. Suggest ways that people, located far from the Arctic, can help protect the Arctic from the effects of global warming?

Growing Out of Control

You have probably seen cities or towns described in terms of population. A population is the number of people living in an area. The world population is the number of people inhabiting Earth at any given time. In basic terms, the population grows when babies are born and shrinks when people die.

Throughout most of the time that people have existed on Earth, the world population has grown at a slow and steady rate. In the last half-century, however, the human population has exploded. Since 1950, the world population has more than doubled. Estimates placed the world population at 6 billion people in 2000. The United Nations predicts that by 2050, the human population will grow to between 7.7 and 11.2 billion people.

Why has the population grown so dramatically? For population size to remain stable, the rate at which babies are born (birth rate) must be roughly equal to the rate at which people die (death rate). If one of those rates changes relative to the other, the population will either grow or shrink. The growth of the world population can be attributed to a decrease in the death rate. Improvements in medical care and disease control along with increased availability of food have extended the life expectancy of people throughout the world. As a result, more babies are being born each year than people are dying. This causes the population to grow.

All populations, including humans, rely on the resources provided by the environment. Those resources include such things as food, water, air, and land. As the human population grows, the available resources are strained.

First, consider the strain on food resources. Up until the mid-1980s, the world harvest of grain increased at a greater rate than the rate at which the population grew. Since that time, however, the rate of population growth has exceeded the rate of grain harvest growth. As the population grows, the people not only eat more grain, but they move into regions that were once reserved for growing grain. Less land translates into less grain. In addition, the growing population uses more of the available fresh water. That leaves less water available for irrigating grain fields. Either way, at some point the world production of grain will not be able to keep up with the expanding human population.

Grain and related crops are not the only sources of food being strained. The once-vast supply of seafood in the oceans is also being depleted. Widespread overfishing is common as the industry attempts to supply the world demand for seafood. Experts predict that some species will soon be lost from seafood markets. The remaining supply will be subject to higher prices and lower quality. Eventually, the supply may need to come primarily from commercial fish farming. But these farms will then compete with land animals and humans for food resources, such as grain and soybean meal.

As the affluence of a society increases, the demand for meat also tends to increase. In the past, the meat demand was generally limited to western countries and Japan. However, meat consumption has increased in East Asia, the Middle East, and Latin America. As a result, world meat production has increased almost twice as fast as the human population has grown in recent years. Since livestock and poultry are fed mostly grain, increased meat production puts further demands on grain supplies, too.

Aside from the food supply, the population explosion strains the environment in other ways. For one thing, the expansion of the human population has resulted in a reduction in the size and quality of natural recreation areas. Consider, for example, the Florida Everglades. This unique combination of ecosystems is home to a tremendous number of species, some of which exist nowhere else on Earth. Population growth in that state has not only destroyed much of the Everglades, it has shifted the water patterns in such a way that many organisms have been forced to the brink of extinction. Natural habitats are being destroyed in similar ways on every continent.

Forests are one particular type of ecosystem that is being destroyed at an alarming rate. It is estimated that 75 percent of global forests were lost during the twentieth century. Much of the land was cleared to make room for people to live on or farm. This loss is significant because forests are responsible for recycling carbon dioxide in the atmosphere, controlling erosion, protecting water resources, and providing habitats for a tremendous number of organisms.

Marine ecosystems are also being destroyed as a result of the population explosion. Coastal regions are home to some of the most productive habitats on Earth. Coral reefs, for example, are possibly the most diverse ecosystem of all. As people expand to populate coastal regions, greater amounts of garbage, sewage, and industrial waste are added to landfills and waterways along the coasts. Runoff that contains pollution from these sources threatens aquatic habitats by damaging coral reefs, estuaries, marshes, and swamps.

In addition to directly damaging resources by changing Earth's landscape, population growth also depletes natural resources by using up those materials that exist in limited supplies. For example, more people on Earth leads to an increased demand for energy. This demand will continue to drain Earth of its supply of oil and other fossil fuels unless alternative energy sources are further developed.

Increased dependence on fossil fuels has another consequence. The burning of fossil fuels releases carbon dioxide into the atmosphere. Carbon dioxide is a greenhouse gas—a gas that traps heat near Earth's surface. In the last 50 years, carbon emissions have increased nearly twice as fast as the human population. About three-quarters of these emissions have come from the use of fossil fuels. This amount will increase as countries grow or industrialize. The question then arises, "How many people can Earth sustain?" In other words, is there a maximum number of people that can live on Earth? There is no clear answer to this question. Some suggest that limits must be placed on population growth by controlling the birth rate. Most of the world's population growth occurs in developing nations. These high rates are often deeply rooted in cultural, social, and economic traditions. Such longstanding traditions are difficult, perhaps impossible, to change. The future remains uncertain.

Questions

1. Describe a population in your own words. What factors increase the size of a population? What factors decrease the size of a population?
2. Make a list of factors that are affected by population growth. Briefly describe the relationship for each one.
3. How might the human population be different from other animal populations?
4. Some countries, such as China, already have limits on the number of children a married couple can have. Describe the pros and cons of this approach.
5. Your class will be debating the issue of proposed controls to limit population growth. Pose an argument for or against such controls.

Glossary

abiotic describes the nonliving parts of an organism's environment

acidity describes a low pH level due to dissolved acids, such as in acid rain

active transport movement of substances across a membrane from an area of lower concentration to an area of higher concentration; requires energy

adaptations special characteristics that make an organism well suited for a particular environment

AIDS (acquired immunodeficiency syndrome) an immunodeficiency disease, caused by HIV in humans

algae plantlike organisms, often single-celled, that carry out photosynthesis

alleles the two different versions of a gene for a particular trait

allergic reactions conditions caused by an overreaction of the immune system

amino acids organic compounds that are the building blocks of proteins

antibiotics chemicals that kill specific microorganisms; frequently used to combat infectious diseases

antibodies molecules that individuals produce as a defense against foreign objects in the body; antibodies bind to specific antigens

antigens proteins on a foreign object that stimulate the immune system to produce antibodies

asexually describes reproduction that requires only one parent to pass on genetic information; e.g., budding and fission

atmosphere the blanket of gases that covers Earth; commonly called "air"

atoms the smallest units of an element that can combine with other elements

ATP (adenosine triphosphate) the substance used by cells as an immediate source of chemical energy for the cell

autotrophic describes a self-feeding organism that obtains its energy from inorganic sources; e.g., plants and algae (producers)

bacteria single-celled organisms that have no nuclear membrane to surround and contain their DNA molecule

biodiversity the variety of different species in an ecosystem or in the world

biome a very large area characterized by a certain climate and types of plants and animals

biotechnological describes new procedures and devices that utilize discoveries in biology; usually refers to recombinant DNA technology

biotic describes the living parts of an organism's environment

cancer a disease that results from uncontrolled cell division, which damages normal tissues

carbon one of the six most important chemical elements for living things; carbon atoms form the backbone of nearly all organic compounds

carbon dioxide the inorganic molecule from which plants get carbon for photosynthesis; waste product of cellular respiration; a greenhouse gas

carnivores animals that obtain their energy by eating other animals; see also *consumers* and *heterotrophic*

carrying capacity the size of a particular population that an ecosystem can support

catalysts substances that increase the rate of a chemical reaction, but are not changed during the reaction

cell membrane a selectively permeable plasma membrane that separates and regulates substances that pass between the inside and the outside of a cell

cells the smallest functioning units of an organism; all living things are made up of at least one cell

cellular respiration the process that uses oxygen to create ATP for energy use

chloroplasts the organelles within plant cells that contain the pigment chlorophyll and carry out photosynthesis

chromosomes structures composed of DNA that contain the genetic material

circulation the movement of blood throughout the body of an animal

cloning the production of identical individuals (i.e., clones) from the cell of another individual

community populations of different species that interact within an area

competition the struggle between organisms for limited resources such as food and space

consumers organisms that obtain their energy by feeding on other organisms; heterotrophic life-forms

coordination the means by which body systems work together to maintain homeostasis; a property of living things

cytoplasm the watery fluid that fills a cell, surrounding its organelles

decomposers heterotrophic organisms that obtain their energy by feeding on decaying organisms

deforestation the cutting down and clearing away of forests; clear-cutting

deplete to use up natural resources that cannot be replaced within our lifetimes

development the changes in an organism that occur from fertilization until death

deviations changes in the body's normal functions that are detected by control mechanisms, which maintain a balanced internal environment

differentiation the creation of specialized cells from less specialized parent cells through controlled gene expression

diffusion the movement of molecules from an area of higher concentration to an area of lower concentration

digestion the process of breaking down food particles into molecules small enough to be absorbed by cells

diversity the variety of different traits in a species or different species in an ecosystem

DNA (deoxyribonucleic acid) the hereditary material of all organisms, which contains the instructions for all cellular activities

dynamic equilibrium in the body, a state of homeostasis in which conditions fluctuate yet always stay within certain limits

ecology the study of the interactions of living things with their environment

ecosystem an area that contains all living and nonliving parts that interact

egg the female gamete that supplies half the genetic information to the zygote

embryo an organism in an early stage of development before it is hatched, born, or germinated

energy pyramid describes the flow of energy through an ecosystem; most energy is at the base (producers) and decreases at each higher level (consumers)

enzymes protein compounds that act as catalysts for biological reactions

equilibrium in ecosystems, an overall stability in spite of cyclic changes

estrogen in females, along with progesterone, a major sex hormone that affects secondary sex characteristics and reproduction

evolution the change in organisms over time due to natural selection acting on genetic variations that enable them to adapt to changing environments

excretion the removal of metabolic wastes from the body

expression the use of genetic information in a gene to produce a particular characteristic, which can be modified by interactions with the environment

extinction the death of all living members of a species

feedback mechanisms systems that reverse an original response that was triggered by a stimulus; also, *negative feedback mechanisms* or *feedback loops*

fertilization in sexual reproduction, process by which an egg cell and a sperm cell unite to form a zygote

fetus a developing embryo after the first three months of development

food chain the direct transfer of energy from one organism to the next

food web the complex, interconnecting food chains in a community

fossils the traces or remains of dead organisms, preserved by natural processes

fungi (*singular,* **fungus**) heterotrophic organisms that obtain their energy by feeding on decaying organisms; e.g., yeast and mushrooms

gametes the male and female sex cells that combine to form a zygote during fertilization

gene expression see *expression*

genes the segments of DNA that contain the genetic information for a given trait or protein

genetic engineering recombinant DNA technology, i.e., the insertion of genes from one organism into the genetic material of another

genetic variation see *variability*

geologic time Earth's history divided into vast units of time by which scientists mark important changes in Earth's climate, surface, and life-forms

global warming an increase in the average global atmospheric temperature due to more heat-trapping CO_2 in the air, which causes the greenhouse effect

glucose a simple sugar that has six carbon atoms bonded together; a subunit of complex carbohydrates

habitat the place in which an organism lives; a specific environment that has an interacting community of organisms

herbivores animals that obtain their energy by eating plants; see also *consumers* and *heterotrophic*

hereditary describes the genetic information that is passed from parents to offspring

heterotrophic describes an organism that obtains its energy by feeding on other living things; e.g., animals (consumers)

homeostasis in the body, the maintenance of a constant internal environment

hormones chemical messengers that bind with receptor proteins to affect gene activity, resulting in long-lasting changes in the body

host the organism that a parasite uses for food and shelter by living in it or on it

hydrogen one of the six most important chemical elements for living things

immune system recognizes and attacks specific invaders, such as bacteria, to protect the body against infection and disease

immunity the ability to resist or prevent infection by a particular microbe

inheritance the process by which traits are passed from one generation to the next

inorganic in cells, substances that allow chemical reactions to take place; in ecosystems, substances that are cycled between living things and the environment

insulin substance secreted by the pancreas that maintains normal blood sugar levels

internal development describes an embryo's development within the female's body

internal fertilization describes the sperm fertilizing the egg cell within the female's body

kingdoms the major groupings into which scientists categorize all living things

lipids the group of organic compounds that includes fats, oils, and waxes

malfunction when an organ or body system stops functioning properly, which may lead to disease or death

meiosis the division of one parent cell into four daughter cells; reduces the number of chromosomes to one-half the normal number

membrane see *cell membrane*

metabolic describes the chemical reactions (building up and breaking down) that take place in an organism

microbes microscopic organisms that may cause disease when they invade another organism's body; e.g., microorganisms such as bacteria and viruses

mitochondria the organelles at which the cell's energy is released

mitosis the division of one cell's nucleus into two identical daughter cell nuclei

molecules the smallest unit of a compound, made up of atoms

movement the flow of materials between the cell and its environment; a property of living things, i.e., locomotion

multicellular describes organisms that are made up of more than one cell

mutations errors in the linear sequence (gene) of a DNA molecule that can affect gene expression

natural selection the process by which organisms having the most adaptive traits for an environment are more likely to survive and reproduce

nerve cells in animals, the cells that transmit nerve impulses to other nerve cells and to other types of cells

niche an organism's role in, or interaction with, its habitat and ecosystem

nitrogen one of the six most important chemical elements for living things

nucleotides the building blocks, or subunits, of DNA; they include four types of nitrogen bases, which occur in two pairs

nucleus the dense region of a (eukaryotic) cell that contains the genetic material

nutrients important molecules in food, such as lipids, proteins, and vitamins

nutrition the life process by which organisms take in and utilize nutrients

omnivores animals that eat both plants and animals; see also *consumers* and *heterotrophic*

organ describes a level of organization in living things, i.e., a structure made up of similar tissues that work together to perform the same task; e.g., the liver

organelles structures within a cell that perform a particular task; e.g., the vacuole

organic relating to compounds that contain carbon and hydrogen (in living things)

organisms   living things; life-forms

organ system   a group of organs that works together to perform a major task; e.g., the respiratory system

ovaries   the female reproductive organs that produce the mature egg cells

oxygen   one of the six most important chemical elements for living things; released as a result of photosynthesis; essential to cellular (aerobic) respiration

ozone shield   the layer of ozone gas that surrounds Earth high in the atmosphere and blocks out harmful ultraviolet (UV) radiation

pancreas   gland that secretes pancreatic juice (containing enzymes that aid digestion) and insulin (maintains normal blood sugar levels)

parasite   an organism that lives in or on another organism (the host), deriving nutrients from it and usually causing it harm

passive transport   movement of substances across a membrane; requires no use of energy

pathogens   microscopic organisms that cause diseases, such as certain bacteria and viruses; see also *microbes*

pesticides   chemicals used to kill agricultural pests, mainly insects, some of which have evolved resistance to the chemicals

pH   a measurement (on a scale of 0 to 14) of how acidic or basic a solution is

photosynthesis   the process that, in the presence of light energy, produces chemical energy (glucose) and water, and releases oxygen

placenta   the organ that forms in the uterus of mammals to nourish a developing embryo and remove its waste products

population   all the individuals of the same species that live in the same area

predators   organisms that feed on other living organisms (the prey); see also *carnivores, consumers,* and *heterotrophic*

pregnancy   in animals, the condition of having a developing embryo within the body

prey   an organism that is eaten by another organism (the predator)

producers   organisms on the first trophic level, which obtain their energy from inorganic sources (i.e., by photosynthesis); autotrophic life-forms such as plants and algae

progesterone   in females, along with estrogen, a major sex hormone; see *estrogen*

proteins   the group of organic compounds made up of chains of amino acids

radiation   a form of energy that can cause genetic mutations in sex cells and body cells

receptors   molecules that play an important role in the interactions between cells; e.g., molecules that bind with hormones

recombination   the formation of new combinations of genetic material due to crossing-over during meiosis or due to genetic engineering

recombining   during meiosis, the process that causes an increase in genetic variability due to the exchange of material between chromosomes

replicate   the process by which DNA makes a copy of itself during cell division and protein synthesis

reproduction   the production of offspring (i.e., the passing on of hereditary information), by either sexual or asexual means

residue   the remains of dead organisms, which are recycled in ecosystems by decomposers; also, the remains of chemicals in the soil, air, and water supplies

respiration   in the lungs, the process of exchanging gases; in cells, the process that releases the chemical energy stored in food; see also *cellular respiration*

response   an organism's reaction to an internal or external stimulus

ribosomes   the organelles at which protein synthesis occurs, and which contain RNA

scavengers   animals that eat the remains of a kill, rather than hunt the living animals

selective breeding   the process by which humans encourage the development of specific traits by breeding only the plants or animals that have those traits

sex cell   the male or female gamete; it has one-half the normal chromosome number as a result of meiosis

sexually   describes reproduction that requires two parents to pass on genetic information

simple sugars   single sugars that have six carbon atoms; e.g., glucose

solar energy   radiant energy from the sun that is a renewable resource

species   a group of related organisms that can breed and produce fertile offspring

sperm   the male gamete that supplies half the genetic information to the zygote

stability   the ability of an ecosystem to continue and to remain healthy; usually, the greater the species diversity, the more stable the ecosystem; see also, *homeostasis*

starch   a complex carbohydrate made up of many glucose molecules; used for energy storage in plants

stimulus (*plural,* **stimuli**)   any event, change, or condition in the environment that causes an organism to make a response

subunits   the four types of nucleotide bases that make up the DNA molecule; also, the components (i.e., amino acids) that make up a protein molecule

succession   the gradual replacement of one ecological community by another until it reaches a point of stability

symbiosis   a close relationship between two or more different organisms that live together, which is often but not always beneficial

synthesis   the building of compounds that are essential to life; e.g., protein synthesis

system   describes a level of organization in living things; e.g., in an ecosystem, the living and nonliving parts that function together, and, in a body, the groups of organs that work together to perform the same task; see also *organ system*

template   in DNA replication, the original molecule that is used to make copies

testes   the pair of male reproductive organs that produces the sperm cells

testosterone   in males, the main sex hormone that influences secondary sex characteristics and reproduction

tissues describes a level of organization in living things, i.e., groups of similar cells that work together to perform the same function; e.g., muscle tissue

toxins   chemicals that can harm a developing fetus if taken in by the mother during pregnancy; harmful chemicals that may get passed from one energy level to the next as they move up the food chain

uterus   in female mammals, the reproductive organ that holds the developing embryo

vaccination   a medical substance (usually an injection) that prepares the immune system to better fight a specific disease in the future

vacuoles   organelles that store materials, e.g., food or wastes, for plant and animal cells

variability   the differences that exist among offspring in their genetic makeup

virus   a particle of genetic material that can replicate only within a living host cell, where it usually causes harm

white blood cells   several types of cells that work to protect the body from disease-causing microbes and foreign substances

zygote   the fertilized egg cell that is formed when the nuclei of two gametes (a male and a female) fuse

Index

Sample Examinations

LIVING ENVIRONMENT
JUNE 1999

Part A

Answer all 35 questions in this part. [35]

Directions (1–35): For *each* statement or question, select the choice that best completes the statement or answers the question. Record your answer on the separate answer paper.

1 What occurs during the digestion of proteins?

1 Specific enzymes break down proteins into amino acids.
2 Specific hormones break down proteins into simple sugars.
3 Specific hormones break down proteins into complex starches.
4 Specific enzymes break down ·proteins into simple sugars.

2 Two organisms are shown in the diagrams below.

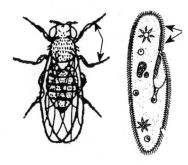

The arrows in the diagrams indicate structures that help these organisms to

1 carry out respiration
2 carry out photosynthesis
3 obtain food
4 excrete wastes

3 During a long-distance run on a hot day, an athlete produces large quantities of sweat. As a result, the kidneys change the rate of urine production. Why is this change important?

1 Decreased urine production increases the amino acids in the blood.
2 Increased urine production removes amino acids produced as a result of running.
3 Decreased urine production allows the body to conserve water.
4 Increased urine production allows more water to remain in the bloodstream.

4 An important method of communication between cells in an organism is shown in the diagram below.

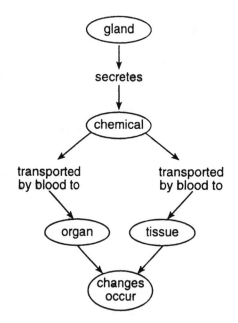

What is the chemical referred to in the diagram?

(1) a hormone important in maintaining homeostasis
(2) an enzyme detected by· a cell membrane receptor
(3) DNA necessary for regulating cell functions
(4) a food molecule taken in by an organism

5 All of the cell shapes shown in the diagrams below have the same volume. Which form could absorb nutrients most efficiently and quickly?

6 Molecules *A* and *B* come in contact with the cell membrane of the same cell. Molecule *A* passes through the membrane readily, but molecule *B* does not. Which statement could describe molecules *A* and *B*?

1 Molecule *A* is a protein, and molecule *B* is a fat.
2 Molecule *A* is a starch, and molecule *B* is a simple sugar.
3 Molecule *A* is an amino acid, and molecule *B* is a simple sugar.
4 Molecule *A* is a simple sugar, and molecule *B* is a starch.

7 When the bacterium *Serratia marcescens* is grown on a sterile culture medium in a petri dish at 30°C, the bacterial colonies are cream colored. When this same bacterium is cultured under identical conditions, except at a temperature of 25°C, the colonies are brick red. This difference in color is most likely due to the

1 type of nutrients in the culture medium
2 sterilization of the culture medium
3 effect of temperature on the expression of the gene for color
4 effect of colony size on the synthesis of color pigments

Note that question 8 has only three choices.

8 Which statement best describes the relationship between the number of genes and the number of chromosomes in human skin cells?

1 There are more genes than chromosomes in skin cells.
2 There are more chromosomes than genes in skin cells.
3 There are equal numbers of genes and chromosomes in skin cells.

9 A colony of red bacteria is allowed to reproduce for 16 generations. A scientist examines the colony at the end of this time and notes that all the individuals are almost identical in all characteristics. This evidence suggests that the bacteria

1 did not receive the proper nutrients
2 reproduced sexually
3 exchanged genetic material
4 reproduced asexually

10 A woman has a gene that causes a visual disorder. To prevent the disorder from appearing in future generations, the defective gene would have to be repaired in the mother's

1 nervous system   3 eye
2 reproductive cells   4 uterus

11 According to modern evolutionary theory, genes responsible for new traits that help a species survive in a particular environment will usually

1 not change in frequency
2 decrease gradually in frequency
3 decrease rapidly in frequency
4 increase in frequency

12 Thousands of years ago, a large flock of hawks was driven from its normal migratory route by a severe storm. The birds scattered and found shelter on two distant islands, as shown on the map below. The environment of island *A* is very similar to the hawk's original nesting region. The environment of island *B* is very different from that of island *A*. The hawks have survived on these islands to the present day with no migration between the populations.

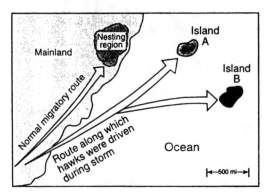

Which statement most accurately predicts the present-day condition of these island hawk populations?

1 The hawks that landed on island *B* have evolved more than those on island *A*.
2 The hawks that landed on island *A* have evolved more than those on island *B*.
3 The populations on islands *A* and *B* have undergone identical mutations.
4 The hawks on island *A* have given rise to many new species.

13 Exposure to cosmic rays, x rays, ultraviolet rays, and radiation from radioactive substances may promote

1 the production of similar organisms
2 diversity among organisms
3 an increase in population size
4 a change from sexual to asexual reproduction

14 Which statement best explains the significance of meiosis in the evolution of a species?

1 Meiosis produces eggs and sperm that are alike.
2 Meiosis provides for chromosomal variation in the gametes produced by an organism.
3 Equal numbers of eggs and sperm are produced by meiosis.
4 The gametes produced by meiosis ensure the continuation of any particular species by asexual reproduction.

15 The diagram below represents the male reproductive system in humans.

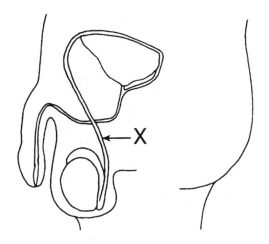

If structure *X* was cut and tied off at the arrow, which change would occur immediately?

1 Hormones would no longer be produced.
2 Sperm would no longer be produced.
3 Sperm would be produced but no longer released from the body.
4 Urine would be produced but no longer released from the bladder.

16 It was once thought that decaying meat turned into maggots (fly larvae). Careful experimentation by scientists demonstrated that maggots actually come from fly eggs and not meat. These experiments illustrate that new individuals result only from

1 genetic engineering
2 reproduction and development
3 nutrition and replication
4 metabolic homeostasis

17 Which event occurring in the life cycle of a bacterium most directly involves the replication of DNA?

1 The bacterium copies its single chromosome.
2 As the cell grows, the two copies of the chromosome separate.
3 The cell divides as a partition separates it into equal halves.
4 Each new cell receives one copy of the chromosome.

18 The graph below shows data on the average life expectancy of humans.

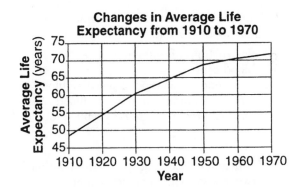

The change in life expectancy from 1910 to 1970 is most likely the result of

1 an increase in poor land-use management that affected the quality of topsoil
2 the introduction of technology that had a negative impact on air quality
3 a decrease in natural checks, such as disease, on the population
4 a widespread increase in the presence of lead and other heavy metals in water supplies

19 What will most likely result if a diabetic injects an overdose of insulin?

1 a serious infection in the pancreas
2 an increase in the production of pancreatic enzymes
3 an accumulation of wastes in the bloodstream
4 a dangerous drop in blood sugar levels

20 Cyanide is a poison that limits the ability of an animal cell to manufacture ATP. In a cell containing a small amount of cyanide, which process would be *least* affected?

1 movement   3 active transport
2 cell division   4 diffusion

21 One similarity between cell receptors and antibodies is that both

1 are produced by nerve cells
2 are highly specific in their actions
3 slow the rates of chemical reactions
4 are involved in digestion

22 Which phrase does *not* describe a way the human body responds to fight disease?

1 destruction of infectious agents by white blood cells
2 production of antibodies by white blood cells
3 increased production of white blood cells
4 production of pathogens by white blood cells

23 The diagram below illustrates the relationships between organisms in an ecosystem.

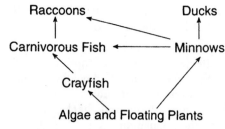

In addition to sunlight, which factor would need to be added to make this a stable ecosystem?

1 predators   3 decomposers
2 prey   4 herbivores

24 Which event does *not* occur between stages 2 and 11 in the process represented in the diagram below?

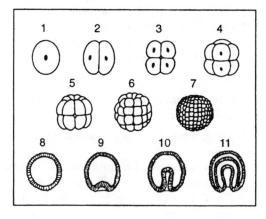

(1) a decrease in cell size
(2) DNA replication
(3) the development of embryonic layers
(4) fertilization

25 The table below shows the rate of water loss in three different plants.

Plant	Liters of Water Lost Per Day
Cactus	0.02
Potato plant	1.00
Apple tree	19.00

One reason each plant loses a different amount of water is that each has

1 different guard cells adapted to maintain homeostasis
2 different types of insulin-secreting cells that regulate water levels
3 the same number of chloroplasts but different rates of photosynthesis
4 the same rate of photosynthesis but different numbers of chloroplasts

26 A person with AIDS is likely to develop infectious diseases because the virus that causes AIDS

1 destroys cancerous cells
2 damages the immune system
3 increases the rate of antibody production
4 increases the rate of microbe destruction

27 Two test tubes were filled with a solution of bromthymol blue. A student exhaled through a straw into each tube, and the bromthymol blue turned yellow. An aquatic green plant was placed into each tube, and the tubes were corked. One tube was placed in the dark, and one was placed in direct sunlight. The yellow solution in the tube in sunlight turned blue, while the one in the dark remained yellow. Which statement best explains why the solution in the tube placed in sunlight returned to a blue color?

1 Oxygen was produced by photosynthesis.
2 Oxygen was removed by respiration.
3 Carbon dioxide was removed by photosynthesis.
4 Carbon dioxide was produced by respiration.

28 Organisms that eat cows obtain less energy from the cows than the cows obtain from the plants they eat because the cows

1 pass on most of the energy to their offspring
2 convert solar energy to food
3 store all their energy in milk
4 use energy for their own metabolism

29 Which human activity is most responsible for the other three human activities?

1 increasing demand for food
2 increasing loss of farmland
3 increasing human population
4 increasing air pollution

30 Endangered peregrine falcons have been bred in captivity and released in areas where they prey on pigeons and rodents. These activities are examples of

1 species preservation and biological control
2 overhunting and direct harvesting
3 recycling and technological development
4 conservation of resources and habitat destruction

31 Which change would usually increase competition among the squirrel population in a certain area?

1 an epidemic of rabies among squirrels
2 an increase in the number of squirrels killed on the highways
3 an increase in the number of hawks that prey on squirrels
4 a temporary increase in the squirrel reproduction rate

32 *Monocystis* is an organism that feeds on the sperm cells of earthworms. The activities of *Monocystis* eventually cause the infected earthworm to become sterile. The relationship between the earthworm and *Monocystis* is classified as

1 host — parasite
2 predator — prey
3 producer — consumer
4 scavenger — decomposer

Base your answer to question 33 on the graph below and on your knowledge of biology.

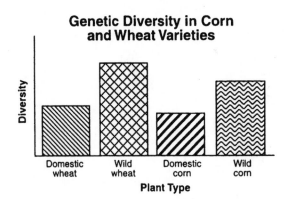

33 If the environment were to change dramatically or a new plant disease were to break out, which plant type would most likely survive?

1 wild wheat   3 wild corn
2 domestic wheat   4 domestic corn

Base your answers to questions 34 and 35 on the table below, which shows the type of food consumed by various animals in a community, and on your knowledge of biology.

Animals in the Community	Food Consumed in the Community				
	Shrews	Grasshoppers	Hawks	Snakes	Plants
Shrews		X			
Hawks	X			X	
Grasshoppers					X
Spiders		X			
Snakes	X				

34 Under normal conditions, which organisms in this community would have the greatest amount of stored energy?

1 grasshoppers   3 plants
2 snakes   4 hawks

35 Which animals in the community would be classified as herbivores?

1 snakes   3 spiders
2 hawks   4 grasshoppers

Part B

Answer all 30 questions in this part. [30]

For those questions that are followed by four choices, select the choice that best completes the statement or answers the question. For all other questions in this part, follow the directions given in the question. **Record your answers on the separate answer paper.**

Base your answers to questions 36 through 41 on the information below and on your knowledge of biology.

A student performed a laboratory investigation to determine the effect of temperature on the heart rate of Daphnia (water flea). The following temperatures and heart rates were recorded:

20°C — 260 beats/min; 10°C — 152 beats/min;
25°C — 300 beats/min; 5°C — 108 beats/min;
15°C — 200 beats/min

36 Organize the data by filling in the data table *provided on your answer paper.* Complete both columns in the data table so that the temperature either increases or decreases from the top to the bottom of the table. The data table below is provided for practice purposes only. Be sure your final answer appears *on your answer paper.*

Data Table

Temperature (°C)	Heart Rate (beats/min)

Directions (37–39): Using the information provided, construct a line graph on the grid *provided on your answer paper,* following the directions below. The grid on the next page is provided for practice purposes only. Be sure your final answer appears *on your answer paper.*

37 Mark an appropriate scale on the axis labeled "**Temperature** (°C)."

38 Mark an appropriate scale on the axis labeled "**Heart Rate** (beats/min)."

39 Plot the data from your data table. Surround each point with a small circle and connect the points.

Example:

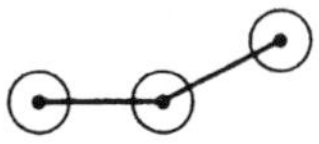

Heart Rate (beats/min)

Temperature (°C)

40 During which temperature interval did the greatest change in heart rate occur?

    (1) 5–10°C   (3) 15–20°C

    (2) 10–15°C   (4) 20–25°C

41 Using one or more complete sentences, state a valid conclusion that relates increasing temperature to heart rate in Daphnia.

_____

Base your answers to questions 42 through 45 on the passage below and on your knowledge of biology.

The Mystery of Deformed Frogs

Deformities, such as legs protruding from stomachs, no legs at all, eyes on backs, and suction cup fingers growing from sides, are turning up with alarming frequency in North American frogs. Clusters of deformed frogs have been found in California, Oregon, Colorado, Idaho, Mississippi, Montana, Ohio, Vermont, and Quebec.

Scientists in Montreal have been studying frogs in more than 100 ponds in the St. Lawrence River Valley for the past 4 years. Normally, less than 1% of frogs are deformed, but in ponds where pesticides are used on surrounding land, as many as 69% of the frogs were deformed. A molecular biologist from the University of California believes that the deformities may be linked to a new generation of chemicals that mimic growth hormones. The same kinds of deformities found in the ponds have been replicated in laboratory experiments.

Some scientists have associated the deformities with a by-product of retinoid, which is found in acne medication and skin rejuvenation creams. Retinoids inside a growing animal can cause deformities. For this reason, pregnant women are warned not to use skin medicines that contain retinoids. Recent laboratory experiments have determined that a pesticide can mimic a retinoid.

A developmental biologist from Hartwick College in Oneonta, New York, questioned whether a chemical could be the culprit because there were no deformed fish or other deformed animals found in the ponds where the deformed frogs were captured. He believes parasites are the cause. When examining a three-legged frog from Vermont, the biologist found tiny parasitic flatworms packed into the joint where a leg was missing. In a laboratory experiment, he demonstrated that the invasion of parasites in a tadpole caused the tadpole to sprout an extra leg as it developed. Scientists in Oregon have made similar observations.

42 Pregnant women are advised not to use skin medicines containing retinoids because retinoid by-products

1 may cause fetal deformities
2 may cause parasites to invade developing frogs
3 are the main ingredient in most pesticides
4 reduce abnormalities in maternal tissue

43 Which statement is most likely true, based on the information in the passage?

1 Only a few isolated incidents of frog deformities have been observed.
2 If frog parasites are controlled, all frog deformities will stop.
3 Deformities in frogs are of little significance.
4 Factors that affect frogs may also affect other organisms.

44 A possible reason for the absence of deformed fish in the ponds that contained deformed frogs is that

1 fish can swim away from chemicals introduced into the pond
2 fish cannot develop deformities
3 parasites that affect frogs usually do not affect fish
4 frogs and fish are not found in the same habitat

45 Using one or more complete sentences, describe how pesticides could cause deformities in frogs.

Base your answers to questions 46 through 48 on the diagram below, which represents the pathway of blood throughout the body, and on your knowledge of biology.

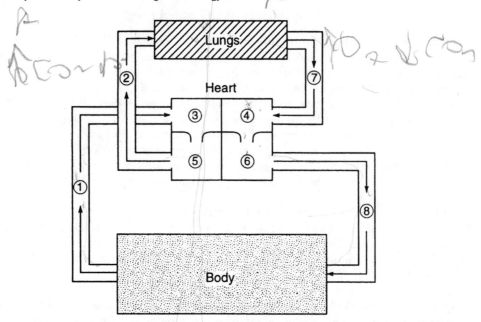

46 Which structure carries oxygenated blood to the body?

(1) 1   (3) 7

(2) 2   (4) 8

47 Which structure represents the chamber of the heart that receives oxygenated blood directly from the lungs?

(1) 5   (3) 3

(2) 6   (4) 4

48 Using one or more complete sentences, state one specific change that occurs in the gas composition of the blood as the blood moves from structure 6 to structure 3. Specify whether the change is an increase or a decrease in composition.

---

49 An aquatic food web is represented in the diagram below.

Using one or more complete sentences, predict how one of the populations in the food web will most likely change if the yellow perch population increases over a period of 3 years.

50 A process that occurs in the human body is shown in the diagram below.

Dipeptide (Substrate)   Active site   Enzyme   Enzyme-substrate complex   Amino acids   Enzyme

What would happen if a temperature change caused the shape of the active site to be altered?

1 The dipeptide would digest faster.
2 The dipeptide would digest slower or not at all.
3 The amino acids would combine faster.
4 The amino acids would combine slower or not at all.

---

51 A biologist in a laboratory reports a new discovery based on experimental results. If the experimental results are valid, biologists in other laboratories should be able to

1 repeat the same experiment with a different variable and obtain the same results
2 perform the same experiment and obtain different results
3 repeat the same experiment and obtain the same results
4 perform the same experiment under different experimental conditions and obtain the same results

52 A small piece of black paper was folded in half and used to cover part of the top and bottom portions of a leaf on a living geranium plant. After the plant was kept in sunlight for several days, the paper was removed. The leaf was then boiled in alcohol to remove the chlorophyll and placed in Lugol's iodine solution, which turns blue-black in the presence of starch. Only the part of the leaf that had *not* been covered turned blue-black. This investigation was most likely testing the hypothesis that

1 light is necessary for photosynthesis to occur
2 alcohol plus chlorophyll forms Lugol's iodine solution
3 green plants use carbon dioxide in photosynthesis
4 plants use alcohol in the production of chlorophyll

53 To locate a specimen on a prepared slide with a compound microscope, a student should begin with the low-power objective rather than the high-power objective because the

1 field of vision is smaller under low power than under high power
2 field of vision is larger under low power than under high power
3 specimen does not need to be stained for observation under low power but must be stained for observation under high power
4 portion of the specimen that can be observed under low power is less than the portion that can be observed under high power

54 Male reproductive cells from numerous lubber grasshoppers, lake trout, and field mice were examined and found to have flagella. A valid conclusion that can be made based on this observation is that

1 only lubber grasshoppers, lake trout, and field mice produce reproductive cells with flagella
2 all organisms produce male reproductive cells with flagella
3 only male organisms produce reproductive cells with flagella
4 all male lubber grasshoppers, lake trout, and field mice produce reproductive cells with flagella

55 Worker bees acting as scouts are able to communicate the distance of a food supply from the hive by performing a "waggle dance." The graph below shows the relationship between the distance of a food supply from the hive and the number of turns in the waggle dance every 15 seconds.

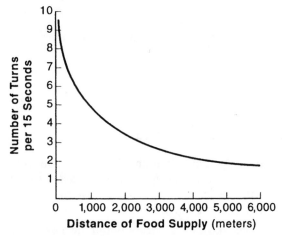

Distance of Food Supply (meters)

Using one or more complete sentences, state the relationship between the distance of the food supply from the hive and the number of turns the bee performs in the waggle dance every 15 seconds.

Base your answers to questions 56 and 57 on the investigation described below and on your knowledge of biology.

As part of an investigation, 10 bean seedlings in one setup were grown in the dark, while 10 seedlings in another setup were grown in sunlight. All other growth conditions were kept the same in both setups. The seedlings grown in the dark were white with long, slender stems. These seedlings soon died. The seedlings grown in the sunlight were green and healthy.

56 Which hypothesis was most likely being tested in this investigation?

1 Plants grown in the dark cannot perform the process of respiration.
2 Sunlight is necessary for the normal growth of bean plants.
3 Light is necessary for the germination of bean seeds.
4 Light is necessary for proper mineral absorption by plants.

57 Identify the independent variable in this investigation.

58 Substance X has a unique characteristic in that it fluoresces (glows) when exposed to ultraviolet light. An investigator added substance X to a dish containing a culture of cells. The investigator exposed the cells to ultraviolet light and found that substance X was highly concentrated only within mitochondria (cell organelles). Which assumption could the investigator make regarding the results of this experiment?

1 Substance X could be used to identify mitochondria in living cells.
2 Substance X could be used to stain nuclei of living cells.
3 All fluorescent substances will be absorbed by mitochondria.
4 All mitochondria synthesize fluorescent substances.

Base your answers to questions 59 through 61 on the graph below and on your knowledge of biology. The graph shows the relative rates of action of four enzymes, A, B, C, and D.

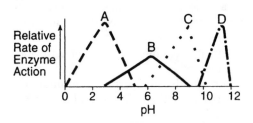

59 Which enzyme shows the greatest change in its rate of action with the *least* change in pH?

(1) A   (3) C
(2) B   (4) D

60 A solution with a pH of 6 contains enzyme C and its substrate. If a base is gradually added to this solution, the rate of action of enzyme C would most likely

1 remain constant
2 increase, then decrease
3 decrease, then increase
4 decrease constantly

61 Which two enzymes would function in a region of the human body having a neutral pH?

(1) A and B   (3) C and D
(2) B and C   (4) B and D

62 An investigation was designed to determine the effect of ultraviolet light on mold spore growth. Two groups of mold spores were grown under identical conditions, except one group was exposed only to ultraviolet light, while the other group was grown in total darkness. In this investigation, the group of mold spores grown without receiving any ultraviolet light is known as the

1 control
2 hypothesis
3 dependent variable
4 limiting factor

Base your answers to questions 63 and 64 on the diagram below of a **DNA** molecule and on your knowledge of biology.

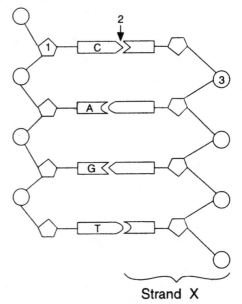

63 What is the base sequence of strand *X*?

(1) G–T–A–C (3) G–T–C–A
(2) T–G–C–A (4) A–T–C–G

64 What occurs in the process of replication?

1 Structure 1 is hydrolyzed.
2 Chemical bonds are broken in region 2.
3 Structure 3 is synthesized.
4 Proteins are formed in region 2.

Strand X

---

65 Which relationship can correctly be inferred from the data presented in the graphs below?

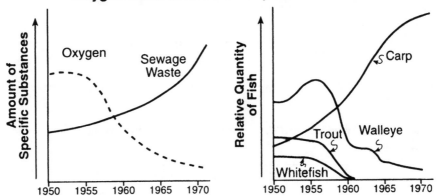

Oxygen Content and Fish Population in a Lake

1 As sewage waste increases, oxygen content decreases.
2 As sewage waste increases, oxygen content increases.
3 As oxygen content decreases, carp population decreases.
4 As oxygen content decreases, trout population increases.

Part C

Answer all 11 questions in this part. [20]

Answers to the following questions are to be written on paper provided by the school.

Base your answers to questions 66 and 67 on the information below and on your knowledge of biology. Use one or more complete sentences to answer each question.

In July 1997, about 25,000 *Galerucella pusilla* beetles were released at Montezuma Wildlife Refuge in western New York State. These beetles eat purple loosestrife, a beautiful but rapidly spreading weed that chokes wetlands. Purple loosestrife is native to Europe, but here it crowds out native wetland plants, such as cattails, and does not support wildlife the way the native plants do. Purple loosestrife grows too thick to allow birds to nest. Most native insects do not eat it, leaving little for insect-eating birds to eat. Bernd Blossey, a professor at Cornell University, spent 6 years in Europe trying to find out what limited the loosestrife population there.

66 Explain why the introduction of the beetle is an advantage over the use of herbicides to control the purple loosestrife population. [1]

67 Describe one possible environmental problem that may result from the introduction of this beetle. [1]

Base your answers to questions 68 through 70 on the information below and on your knowledge of biology. Use one or more complete sentences to answer each question.

When a drug manufacturer develops a new drug to treat some form of disease, the drug should be tested to ensure that it does what it is supposed to do. Usually, the drug is tested on animals and, if these tests are successful, it is then tested on humans.

A drug called Lowervil was developed by a drug company to lower blood pressure. Lowervil has been tested successfully on animals, and the drug company is now ready to test it on humans. The drug company claims that one dose of Lowervil per day will decrease blood pressure in individuals experiencing high blood pressure.

A researcher has been hired to determine whether or not Lowervil lowers blood pressure. Answer the following questions related to the experimental testing of the new drug Lowervil.

68 How should the experimental group and control group be treated differently? [1]

69 Why would it be important to use a large number of people in this experiment? [1]

70 How could the researcher determine if the drug is effective in reducing blood pressure? [1]

Base your answers to questions 71 through 73 on the information and data tables below and on your knowledge of biology. Use one or more complete sentences to answer each question.

Drinking alcohol during pregnancy can cause the class of birth defect known as fetal alcohol syndrome (FAS). Scientists do not yet understand the process by which alcohol causes damage to the fetus. There is evidence, however, that the more a pregnant woman drinks, the greater the chances that the child will be affected and the birth defects will be serious. Some evidence indicates that even low levels of alcohol consumption can cause intellectual and behavioral problems.

Infant Characteristics

Characteristics (Average)	Alcohol Use During Pregnancy	
	Drinker	Nondrinker
Weeks of development before birth	36.9	38.7
Birth weight (g)	2,555	3,094
Birth length (cm)	46.8	50.1
Head circumference (cm)	32.1	34.5

Physical Abnormalities Detected in Infants at Birth

Physical Abnormalities	Alcohol Use During Pregnancy	
	Drinker (Percentage of 40 Infants)	Nondrinker (Percentage of 80 Infants)
Low birth weight	73	12
Small brain	33	0
Flattened nasal bridge	8	0
Abnormal facial features	15	0
Spinal defects	8	0
Heart defects	8	0

71 Do the data in the tables justify scientists' conclusions that alcohol causes physical abnormalities at birth by interfering with the normal development of the fetus? Defend your position with supporting data. [1]

72 What additional data would be needed to better support the scientists' conclusions? [1]

73 Explain why alcohol consumption by the mother is especially harmful during the early stages of pregnancy. [1]

74 Using a specific example, illustrate how a feedback mechanism maintains homeostasis in a living organism. [2]

75 Give three examples of how the technology of genetic engineering allows humans to alter the genetic makeup of organisms. [3]

76 Habitat destruction is an environmental problem that affects our own generation and will affect future generations if it is not solved. Write an essay in which you identify a habitat that is being destroyed and explain how the destruction of this habitat relates to humans and the overall ecosystem. Your essay must include at least:

- *two* human activities that contribute to the destruction of this habitat [2]
- *three* ways the destruction of this habitat has affected plants, humans, and other animals [3]
- *two* ways to limit further destruction of this habitat [2]

LIVING ENVIRONMENT
JUNE 1999

_____

ANSWER PAPER

Student . . . .

Teacher . . . . School . . . .

Part A

Answer all questions in Part A.

1	13	25 . . . . . .
2	14	26 . . . . . .
3	15	27 . . . . . .
4	16	28 . . . . . .
5	17	29 . . . . . .
6	18	30 . . . . . .
7	19	31 . . . . . .
8	20	32 . . . . . .
9	21	33 . . . . . .
10	22	34 . . . . . .
11	23	35 . . . . . .
12	24	

36   **Data Table**

Temperature (°C)	Heart Rate (beats/min)

37–39

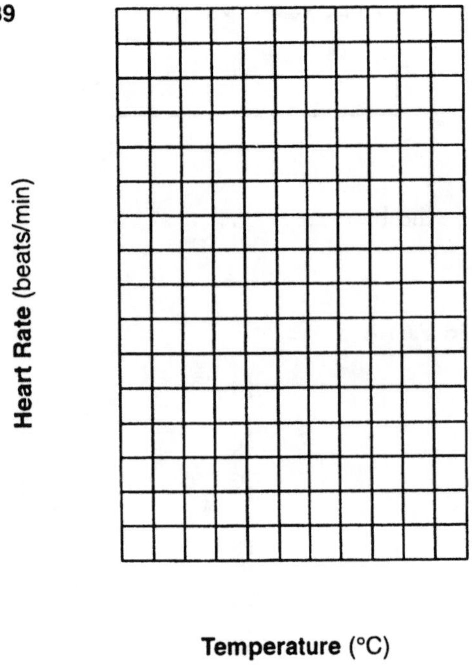

Heart Rate (beats/min)

Temperature (°C)

40 . . . .

41 _____

_____

_____

_____

_____

42 . . . .

43 . . . .

44 . . . .

45 _____

_____

_____

_____

_____

_____

_____

46 . . . .

47 . . . .

48 _____

_____

_____

_____

49 _____

_____

_____

_____

_____

50 . . . .

51 . . . .

52 . . . .

53 . . . .

54 . . . .

55 _____

_____

_____

_____

_____

56 . . . .

57 _____

_____

_____

_____

_____

58 . . . .

59 . . . .

60 . . . .

61 . . . .

62 . . . .

63 . . . .

64 . . . .

65 . . . .

Your answers for Part C should be placed on paper provided by the school.

LIVING ENVIRONMENT
JUNE 2000

Part A

Answer all 35 questions in this part.   [35]

Directions (1–35): For *each* statement or question, select the word or expression that, of those given, best completes the statement or answers the question. Record your answer on the separate answer paper in accordance with the directions on the front page of this booklet.

1 An experiment was performed to determine the effect of different mineral salts on plant growth. Forty pots containing genetically identical plants were divided into four equal groups and placed in a well-lighted greenhouse. Each pot contained an equal amount of nonmineral potting soil and one plant. Minerals were then added in equal amounts to each experimental group of pots as shown below.

Control Group	Experimental Groups		
	Water + Nitrogen salts	Water + Potassium salts	Water + Phosphorus salts

For the experiment to be valid, what should be added to the control group of pots?

1 water
2 nitrogen salts
3 potassium salts
4 potassium and phosphorus salts

---

2 A biologist observed a plant cell in a drop of water as shown in diagram *A*. The biologist added a 10% salt solution to the slide and observed the cell as shown in diagram *B*.

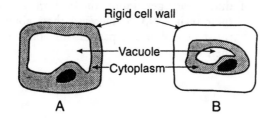

The change in appearance of the cell resulted from

1 more salt moving out of the cell than into the cell
2 more salt moving into the cell than out of the cell
3 more water moving into the cell than out of the cell
4 more water moving out of the cell than into the cell

3 Which statement describing the cells in a body system is correct?

1 Each cell in the system is identical to the other cells in the system, and each cell works independently of the other cells.
2 Some cells in the system may be different from the other cells in the system, but all cells are coordinated and work together.
3 Each cell in the system is different from the other cells in the system, and each cell works independently of the other cells.
4 All cells in the system are identical to each other and work together.

4 The process of active transport requires the most direct use of

(1) carbon dioxide   (3) ATP
(2) amino acids   (4) glucose

5 Which substances may form in the human body due to invaders entering the blood?

1 nutrients   3 antibodies
2 vaccines   4 red blood cells

6 To communicate between cells, many multicellular animals use

1 nerve signals and respiratory gases
2 respiratory gases and hormones
3 bones and muscles
4 nerve signals and hormones

7 The diagram to the right can be used to illustrate a process directly involved in

1 tissue repair
2 meiosis
3 recombination
4 sexual reproduction

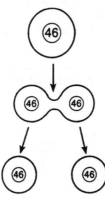

8 The function of the coded instructions contained in the body cells of an organism is to

1 form a variety of gametes that will pass on hereditary information
2 direct the synthesis of proteins necessary for proper cell function
3 synthesize different kinds of amino acids in a specific sequence
4 produce the inorganic molecules needed for normal cell growth

9 Which characteristic allows enzymes to function in a specific way?

1 Enzymes are complex compounds composed of starch.
2 Each enzyme has a characteristic shape.
3 Enzymes are long, complex fats.
4 Each enzyme is made up of four subunits.

10 Flower color in primrose plants is controlled by an individual gene. The sudden appearance of one white flowering primrose in a plant breeder's field of red primrose plants is most likely due to

1 a change in the amount of glucose produced during photosynthesis
2 the use of a new natural fertilizer on the field
3 rapid mitotic divisions within the developing seeds
4 a random change in the structure of DNA during meiosis

11 White short-horned cattle and Black Angus cattle have been crossed to produce offspring with superior beef and rapid growth qualities. This process of choosing organisms with the most desirable traits for mating is known as

1 cloning   3 selective breeding
2 biodiversity   4 genetic engineering

12 When the antibiotic penicillin was first introduced, it was immediately effective in combating staphylococcus bacterial infections. After a number of years, there were outbreaks of staphylococcal infections that did not respond to treatment with penicillin. The best explanation for this situation is that

1 members of the original population of bacteria that were penicillin resistant survived and reproduced, creating a more resistant population
2 the bacteria that survived exposure to penicillin learned to avoid it
3 the bacteria that caused the new outbreaks were from populations that had never been exposed to penicillin
4 during each generation, the bacteria modified their own DNA to increase their ability to resist penicillin and passed this ability on to their descendants

13 The diagram below illustrates some key steps of a procedure in one area of biotechnology.

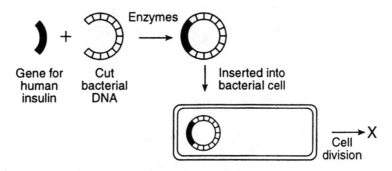

The letter *X* most likely represents

1 bacterial cells that are unable to synthesize insulin
2 human cells that are able to synthesize antibodies
3 bacterial cells that are able to synthesize insulin
4 human cells that are unable to resist antibiotics

14 Which statement about the rates of evolution for different species is in agreement with the theory of evolution?

1 They are identical, since the species live on the same planet.
2 They are identical, since each species is at risk of becoming extinct.
3 They are different, since each species has different adaptations that function within a changing environment.
4 They are different, since each species has access to unlimited resources within its environment.

15 Which concept is not a part of the theory of evolution?

1 Present-day species developed from earlier species.
2 Some species die out when environmental changes occur.
3 Complex organisms develop from simple organisms over time.
4 Change occurs according to the needs of an individual organism to survive.

16 Warts result when certain viruses cause skin cells to reproduce at a high rate. This rapid reproduction of skin cells is due to the viruses stimulating

1 cellular digestion   3 synthesis processes
2 mitotic cell division   4 meiotic cell division

17 Even though the environment changes, a population that occupies a given geographic area will most likely continue to be found in this area if the

1 variations in the population decrease over time
2 members of the population decrease in number
3 members of the population exceed the carrying capacity
4 population passes on those genes that result in favorable adaptations

18 The diagram below represents a reproductive process that takes place in humans.

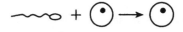

Which statement does *not* correctly describe this process?

1 The normal species chromosome number is restored.
2 Males and females each contribute DNA to the offspring.
3 The zygote will develop to become identical to the dominant parent.
4 The sex of the zygote is determined by DNA in the gametes.

19 The diagrams below represent some events in a cell undergoing normal meiotic cell division.

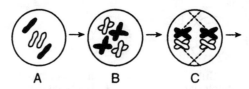

Which diagram most likely represents a new cell resulting from meiotic cell division of the cell shown above?

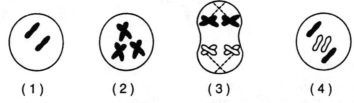

(1)   (2)   (3)   (4)

20 When a pregnant woman ingests toxins such as alcohol and nicotine, the embryo is put at risk because these toxins can

1 diffuse from the mother's blood into the embryo's blood within the placenta
2 enter the embryo when it eats
3 transfer to the embryo since the mother's blood normally mixes with the embryo's blood in the placenta
4 enter the uterus through the mother's navel

21 The energy found in ATP molecules synthesized in animal cells comes directly from

1 sunlight
2 organic molecules
3 minerals
4 inorganic molecules

22 Which substances are necessary for the synthesis of most materials in an organism?

1 hormones   3 antibodies
2 carbohydrates 4 enzymes

23 A certain mutant bacterial cell cannot produce substance X. The mutation was most likely the result of a change in the

1 structure of the cell membrane
2 ability of the DNA to replicate
3 amino acid sequence of DNA
4 gene that codes for a specific protein

24 Which statement best describes an immune response?

1 It always produces antibiotics.
2 It usually involves the recognition and destruction of pathogens.
3 It stimulates asexual reproduction and resistance in pathogens.
4 It releases red blood cells that destroy parasites.

25 Which statement describes a feedback mechanism involving the human pancreas?

1 The production of estrogen stimulates the formation of gametes for sexual reproduction.
2 The level of oxygen in the blood is related to heart rate.
3 The level of sugar in the blood is affected by the amount of insulin in the blood.
4 The production of urine allows for excretion of cell waste.

26 A green plant is kept in a brightly lighted area for 48 hours. What will most likely occur if the light intensity is reduced slightly during the next 48 hours?

1 Photosynthesis will stop completely.
2 The rate at which nitrogen is used by the plant will increase.
3 The rate at which oxygen is released from the plant will decrease.
4 Glucose production inside each plant cell will increase.

27 Which sequence shows a correct pathway for the flow of energy in a food chain?

1 bacteria → grass → fox → owl
2 grass → grasshopper → frog → snake
3 fungi → beetle → algae → mouse
4 algae → snake → duck → deer

28 Before it was banned, the insecticide DDT was used to combat an organism called the red mite. An unexpected result of the use of DDT was that the population of the red mite increased rather than decreased, while the population of insect predators of the red mite decreased. What can be inferred from this situation?

1 Environmental changes that affect one population can affect other populations.
2 The red mite and its insect predators were all competing for the same resources.
3 The red mites were immune to the effects of insecticides.
4 Using insecticides is a reliable way to eliminate all insect predators.

29 Chittenango Falls State Park in central New York State is the only known habitat for an endangered species of aquatic snail. Contamination of its water supply and reduction of its habitat have threatened the future of this snail. Which step could be taken to protect this species of snail?

1 banning human activities that damaged the habitat
2 introducing a new snail predator into the habitat
3 transferring the snail to a terrestrial environment
4 crossbreeding the snail with another species

30 When humans use more ground water for industry than is being replaced, the soil above the ground water may collapse and disrupt natural habitats. This human activity is an example of

1 species exploitation
2 renewal of natural resources
3 a disposal problem
4 poor use of finite resources

31 Decomposition and decay of organic matter are accomplished by the action of

1 green plants   3 viruses and algae
2 bacteria and fungi   4 scavengers

32 For many decades, certain areas of New York State have remained as hardwood forests containing predominantly oak and hickory trees. These forested areas will most likely

1 remain indefinitely and not be affected by environmental influences
2 reach maturity and change in the near future
3 be destroyed by environmental changes and never return to their present forms
4 continue in their present forms unless affected by environmental factors

33 What is a characteristic of a stable environment?

1 It usually contains only one type of producer.
2 It usually contains a great diversity of species.
3 It contains simple food chains that have more consumers than producers.
4 It contains complex food webs that have more heterotrophs than autotrophs.

34 Which human activity has probably contributed most to the acidification of lakes in the Adirondack region?

1 passing environmental protection laws
2 establishing reforestation projects in lumbered areas
3 burning fossil fuels that produce air pollutants containing sulfur and nitrogen
4 using pesticides for the control of insects that feed on trees

35 To ensure environmental quality for the future, each individual should

1 acquire and apply knowledge of ecological principles
2 continue to take part in deforestation
3 use Earth's finite resources
4 add and take away organisms from ecosystems

Part B

Answer all 27 questions in this part. [30]

For those questions that are followed by four choices, record the answers on the separate answer paper in accordance with the directions on the front page of this booklet. For all other questions in this part, record your answers in accordance with the directions given in the question.

Base your answers to questions 36 through 38 on the information and data table below and on your knowledge of biology.

In an investigation, three seeds of the same species were allowed to germinate and grow in three different locations. Each seedling was grown in the same amount and type of soil, and each received the same amount of water during a 6-day period. At the end of the investigation, the height of each seedling and the color of its leaves were recorded. The results are shown in the data table to the right.

Data Table		
Location	**Height (cm)**	**Leaf Color**
Sunny windowsill	7	green
Indirect sunlight	9	green
Closed closet	11	whitish yellow

36 Which hypothesis was most likely being tested in this investigation?

1 A plant grown in the dark will not be green.
2 The type of soil a plant is grown in influences how tall it will be.
3 Plants need water to grow.
4 Plants grown in red light are taller than plants grown in green light.

37 State *two* ways that this investigation could be modified to lead to a more reliable conclusion. [2]

38 Which statement correctly explains why chlorophyll production *decreased* in the seedlings kept in the closet?

1 Lack of sunlight altered the expression of the gene for chlorophyll production.
2 The enzymes involved in chlorophyll production mutate in cooler temperatures.
3 Chloroplasts migrate to the center of the cell when light is not available.
4 Chlorophyll is converted to another pigment when light is not present.

39 A coverslip should be used for preparing a

1 frog for dissection
2 solution of iodine for food testing
3 wet mount of elodea (a simple plant)
4 test to determine the pH of a solution

40 A sample of food containing one type of a large molecule was treated with a specific digestive enzyme. Nutrient tests performed on the resulting products showed the presence of simple sugars, only. Based on these test results, the original large molecules contained in the sample were molecules of

(1) protein   (3) starch
(2) glucose   (4) DNA

41 A television commercial for a weight-loss pill claims that it has been "scientifically tested." The advertisement includes statements from 10 people who say that the pill worked for them. State *two* reasons why someone should question the claims made in this advertisement. [2]

42 When HIV, which causes AIDS, invades the body of a person, that person often develops diseases. These diseases are caused by organisms that usually do not harm people who are not infected with HIV. Explain why the organisms are more harmful to people with HIV than to people without HIV. [1]

Base your answers to questions 43 through 45 on the diagram below and on your knowledge of biology.

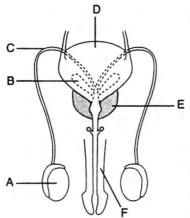

43 Which letter indicates a structure that secretes a hormone that promotes maturation of gametes? [1]

44 Which letter indicates a structure that is *not* involved in the production or delivery of gametes? [1]

45 Structures *B* and *E* provide nutrients and fluid for the gametes. Why are these substances necessary for fertilization? [1]

_____

46 Describe *one* error that was made in the preparation of the graph shown below. [1]

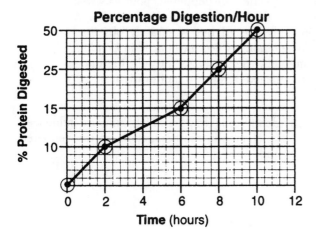

Base your answers to questions 47 through 49 on the diagram below and on your knowledge of biology.

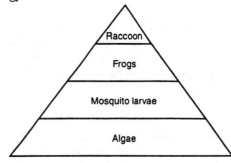

47 State *one* reason that algae form the base of this pyramid. [1]

48 Which term best describes the mosquito larvae?

1 producer   3 carnivore
2 parasite   4 consumer

49 Explain why each level of the pyramid *decreases* in area from bottom to top. [1]

_____

50 Describe the role of scavengers in an ecosystem. [1]

51 Explain how carbohydrates provide energy for life functions. [1]

52 In the demonstration shown below, which process performed by the peas when they start to grow causes the drop of liquid to move to the left?

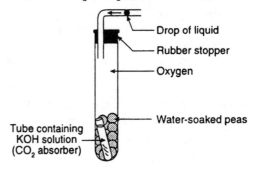

1 protein synthesis   3 digestion
2 photosynthesis   4 cellular respiration

Base your answers to questions 53 through 56 on the information below and on your knowledge of biology.

Organ Transplants of the Future

While most people take good health for granted, thousands of others desperately need to replace a failing organ with one that is healthy. Most healthy organs come from people who agreed to donate them upon their death, although it is possible to remove some tissue and organs (such as kidneys and bone marrow) from living donors. Unfortunately, organs for transplant are in short supply. As of 1992, over 22,000 Americans were waiting for a transplant.

Although increasingly common, transplants are risky procedures. During the operation, veins and arteries must be blocked to prevent blood loss. This deprives parts of the body of oxygen and nutrients and may result in permanent damage. In addition, the body may recognize the transplanted organ as foreign and mount an immune response in which specialized white blood cells (T-cells) attack the transplanted organ.

Drugs called immunosuppressants are given to transplant patients to prevent their immune system from rejecting the transplanted organ. However, these drugs weaken the ability of the body to fight disease and leave the patient less able to fight infection.

Scientists are exploring new technology for producing transplant tissues and organs. Unspecialized cells called stem cells are removed from the patient and then grown in a laboratory. Treating stem cells with the appropriate chemicals causes them to differentiate into various specialized tissues. In the future, scientists hope to develop chemical treatments that will cause stem cells to grow into complete organs needed for transplants. Transplants produced by this process would not be foreign material and, therefore, would not be rejected by the immune system of the patient.

53 Explain why a transplant might be dangerous to the health of a patient.   [1]

54 State *one* reason that transplant patients might take an immunosuppressant drug.   [1]

55 State *one* specific *disadvantage* of taking an immunosuppressant drug.   [1]

56 Explain why doctors would consider using tissues or organs that have been grown from stem cells.   [1]

Base your answers to questions 57 and 58 on the information below and on your knowledge of biology.

Before the Industrial Revolution, a light-colored variety of peppered moth was well camouflaged among light-colored lichens that grew on the bark of trees around London. A dark-colored variety of the peppered moth probably existed but was rarely observed because it was so easily seen by birds and eaten. When industry was introduced in London, soot killed the pollution-sensitive lichens, exposing dark tree bark. As a result, the dark-colored variety of the moth became the better camouflaged of the two moth varieties.

57 In this situation, what is the relationship between the birds and the moths?

1 producer-consumer
2 predator-prey
3 parasite-host
4 autotroph-heterotroph

58 Identify *one* way in which humans influenced the change in the populations of the peppered moth.   [1]

Base your answers to questions 59 through 62 on the information and data table below and on your knowledge of biology.

A student studied the effect of gibberellin (a plant hormone) on the growth of corn seedlings of the same height and species. A different concentration of gibberellin in a fixed volume of water was applied to 7 groups of 10 plants each maintained under the same environmental conditions for the duration of the experiment. At the end of this period, the height of each plant was measured. The data are shown in the table at the right.

Data Table

Micrograms of Gibberellin in a Water Solution	Average Height (cm)
0.00	20
0.05	40
0.10	60
0.25	70
0.50	75
1.00	80
2.00	80

Directions (59–61): Using the information in the data table, construct a line graph on the grid provided *on your answer paper,* following the directions below. The grid below is provided for practice purposes only. Be sure your final answer appears *on your answer paper.*

59 Write an appropriate title for this graph in the space provided.   [1]

60 Mark an appropriate scale on each labeled axis.   [2]

61 Plot the data on the grid. Surround each point with a small circle and connect the points.   [1]

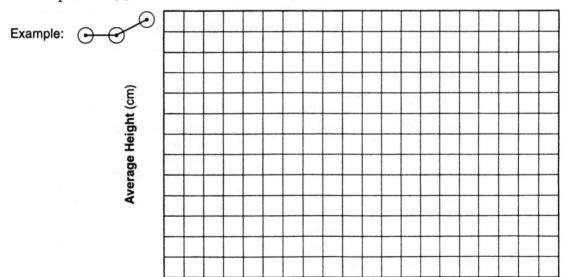

Example:

Average Height (cm)

Amount of Gibberellin (micrograms)

62 Explain the effect on corn seedling height of increasing the application amount of gibberellin from 0.05 to 0.50 microgram.   [1]

Part C
Answer all 7 questions in this part.   [20]

Answers to the following questions are to be written on paper provided by the school.

63 The food web below shows some of the relationships that exist between organisms in a field and pond ecosystem.

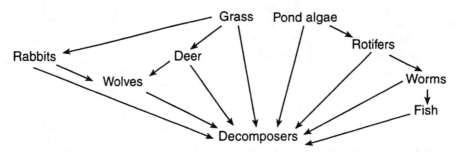

   a Write one or more paragraphs describing some of the relationships in this food web. In your answer, be sure to:
- identify a carnivore from the food web   [1]
- describe the complete path of energy from the Sun to that carnivore   [1]
- explain why decomposers are necessary in this food web   [1]

   b A significant decrease in the wolf population occurs. After a period of one year, what change in the grass population would most likely be observed?   [1]

   c A farmer sprayed pesticides on a field next to the pond. Using one or more complete sentences, explain why several years later the fish population would contain higher pesticide levels than any other pond organisms would contain.   [1]

---

64 All living things carry out a variety of life functions such as coordination, excretion, digestion, circulation, and synthesis. Select *two* of the life functions listed. Define the two life functions you selected and explain how they interact to keep an organism alive.   [4]

65 When Charles Darwin was developing his theory of evolution, he considered variations in a population important. However, he could not explain how the variations occurred. Name *two* processes that can result in variation in a population. Explain how these processes actually cause variation.   [4]

66 Write one or more paragraphs that compare the two methods of reproduction, asexual and sexual. Your answer must include at least:
- *one* similarity between the two methods   [1]
- *one* difference between the two methods   [1]
- *one* example of an organism that reproduces by asexual reproduction   [1]
- *one* example of an organism that reproduces by sexual reproduction   [1]

Base your answers to questions 67 through 69 on the information below.

In a rural area, there is a swamp with a large population of mosquitos. Nearby residents are concerned because the mosquitos are always annoying and occasionally carry diseases. The community decides to have an insecticide sprayed from an airplane on the area during the prime mosquito season. Whenever they stop spraying, the mosquito population quickly rebounds to a higher level than existed before the spraying program began. After 10 years, the spraying became much less effective at reducing the mosquito population. Higher doses of insecticide were required to accomplish the same population decreases.

67 State *one* possible *disadvantage* of spraying the insecticide from an airplane.   [1]

68 State *one* alternative method of mosquito control that may have a more lasting impact on the mosquito population.   [1]

69 Give *one* positive effect or *one* negative effect, other than killing mosquitos, of the alternative method of mosquito control you stated in question 68.   [1]

LIVING ENVIRONMENT
JUNE 2000

ANSWER PAPER

Student . . . .

Teacher . . . . School . . . .

Record your answers on this answer paper in accordance with the instructions on the front cover of the test booklet.

Part A (35 credits)
Answer all questions in Part A.

1	1	2	3	4	13	1	2	3	4	25	1	2	3	4
2	1	2	3	4	14	1	2	3	4	26	1	2	3	4
3	1	2	3	4	15	1	2	3	4	27	1	2	3	4
4	1	2	3	4	16	1	2	3	4	28	1	2	3	4
5	1	2	3	4	17	1	2	3	4	29	1	2	3	4
6	1	2	3	4	18	1	2	3	4	30	1	2	3	4
7	1	2	3	4	19	1	2	3	4	31	1	2	3	4
8	1	2	3	4	20	1	2	3	4	32	1	2	3	4
9	1	2	3	4	21	1	2	3	4	33	1	2	3	4
10	1	2	3	4	22	1	2	3	4	34	1	2	3	4
11	1	2	3	4	23	1	2	3	4	35	1	2	3	4
12	1	2	3	4	24	1	2	3	4					

36   1   2   3   4

37 _____

      _____

      _____

      _____

38   1   2   3   4

39   1   2   3   4

40   1   2   3   4

41 _____

      _____

      _____

      _____

42 _____

      _____

43 _____

44 _____

45 _____

      _____

46 _____

      _____

47 _____

_____

48   1   2   3   4

49 _____

_____

50 _____

_____

51 _____

_____

52   1   2   3   4

53 _____

_____

54 _____

_____

55 _____

_____

56 _____

_____

57   1   2   3   4

58 _____

_____

59 _____

_____

60–61

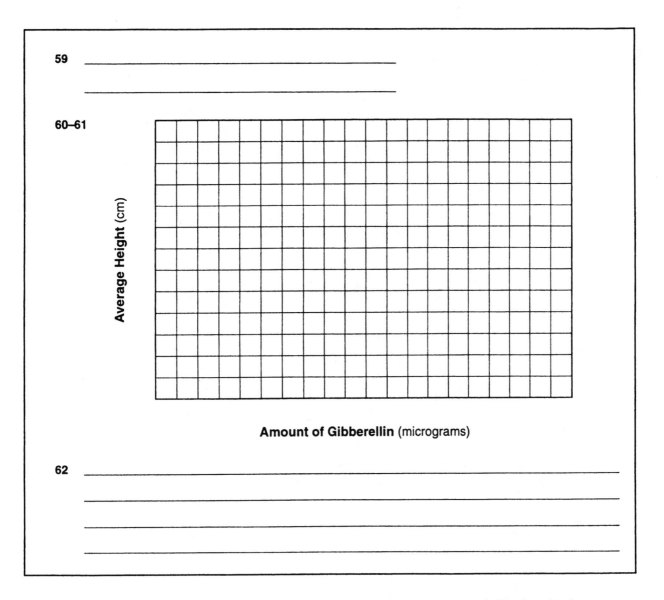

Amount of Gibberellin (micrograms)

62 _____

_____

_____

_____

Note: Answers to Part C are to be written on separate answer paper provided by the school.

LIVING ENVIRONMENT
JUNE 2001

Part A

Answer all 35 questions in this part. [35]

Directions (1–35): For *each* statement or question, write on the separate answer sheet the number of the word or expression that, of those given, best completes the statement or answers the question.

1 Diagrams, tables, and graphs are used by scientists mainly to
   (1) design a research plan for an experiment
   (2) test a hypothesis
   (3) organize data
   (4) predict the independent variable

2 A scientist tested a hypothesis that white-tailed deer would prefer apples over corn as a primary food source. The findings of the test, in which the scientist claimed that the deer preferred apples, were published. Which research technique, if used by the scientist, might result in this claim being questioned?
   (1) The scientist observed four deer in different locations at various times of the day.
   (2) The scientist observed a total of 500 deer in 20 different locations at various times of the day.
   (3) The scientist observed 200 deer in various natural settings, but none in captivity.
   (4) The scientist observed 300 deer in various locations in captivity, but none in natural settings.

3 What happens to certain nutrient molecules after they pass into muscle cells?
   (1) They are replicated in the nucleus.
   (2) They are acted on by enzymes and release the energy they contain.
   (3) They are changed into tissues and organs in the cytoplasm.
   (4) They enter chloroplasts, where they can absorb light energy.

4 A medical test indicates that a patient has a defective protein. This condition is most likely due to a change in the directions coded in the
   (1) number of hydrogen atoms in starch molecules
   (2) sequence of inorganic molecules
   (3) number of carbon atoms in sugar molecules
   (4) sequence of subunits in DNA

5 If a human system fails to function properly, what is the most likely result?
   (1) a stable rate of metabolism
   (2) a disturbance in homeostasis
   (3) a change in the method of cellular respiration
   (4) a change in the function of DNA

6 Which statement regarding the functioning of the cell membrane of all organisms is *not* correct?
   (1) The cell membrane forms a boundary that separates the cellular contents from the outside environment.
   (2) The cell membrane is capable of receiving and recognizing chemical signals.
   (3) The cell membrane forms a barrier that keeps all substances that might harm the cell from entering the cell.
   (4) The cell membrane controls the movement of molecules into and out of the cell.

7 In multicellular organisms, cells must be able to communicate with each other. Structures that enable most cells to communicate with each other are known as
   (1) pathogenic agents   (3) antibiotics
   (2) chloroplasts   (4) receptor molecules

8 Every single-celled organism is able to survive because it carries out
   (1) metabolic activities
   (2) autotrophic nutrition
   (3) heterotrophic nutrition
   (4) sexual reproduction

9 The shape of a protein molecule is influenced by
   (1) whether it is organic or inorganic
   (2) the sequence of amino acids in it
   (3) the number of genes found in the nucleus
   (4) the number of chromosomes in the cell

10 The data table below summarizes the results of an investigation in which seeds from the same plant were grown under different conditions of temperature and relative humidity.

Temperature: 20°C Relative Humidity: 20%		Temperature: 31°C Relative Humidity: 95%	
Genes Present in Cells of Organism	Appearance of Organism	Genes Present in Cells of Organism	Appearance of Organism
AA	red	AA	white
Aa	red	Aa	white
aa	white	aa	white

Which conclusion can be drawn from the information in the data table?

(1) Color in this species is determined by genes, only.
(2) Many characteristics are not inherited.
(3) Mutations occur only when plants are grown at low temperatures.
(4) There is an interaction between environment and heredity.

11 The diagram below represents a change that occurred in a pair of chromosomes during the formation of an egg cell. The letters represent genes on the pair of chromosomes.

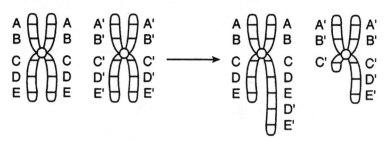

The alteration that occurred will most likely

(1) be passed on to every cell that develops from the egg cell
(2) change the chromosome number of the body cells that develop from the egg cell
(3) convert sex cells into body cells
(4) trigger the production of pathogens

12 A small amount of DNA was taken from a fossil of a mammoth found frozen in glacial ice. Genetic technology can be used to produce a large quantity of identical DNA from this mammoth's DNA. In this technology, the original DNA sample is used to

(1) stimulate differentiation in other mammoth cells
(2) provide fragments to replace certain human body chemicals
(3) act as a template for repeated replication
(4) trigger mitosis to obtain new base sequences

13 Many diabetics are now using insulin that was made by certain bacteria. The ability of these bacteria to produce insulin was most likely the result of

(1) deleting many DNA segments from bacterial DNA
(2) genetic mapping of bacterial DNA to activate the gene for insulin production
(3) inserting a portion of human DNA into the ring-shaped DNA of bacteria
(4) using radiation to trigger mutations

14 Which situation would most directly affect future generations naturally produced by a maple tree?

(1) Ultraviolet radiation changes the DNA sequence within some leaves of the tree.

(2) Ultraviolet radiation changes the DNA sequence within the gametes of some flowers of the tree.

(3) An increase in temperature reduces the number of cell divisions in the roots.

(4) Rapidly growing cells just under the bark are exposed to radiation, causing changes in genetic material.

15 Which statement is best supported by fossil records?

(1) Many organisms that lived in the past are now extinct.

(2) Species occupying the same habitat have identical environmental needs.

(3) The struggle for existence between organisms results in changes in populations.

(4) Structures such as leg bones and wing bones can originate from the same type of tissue found in embryos.

16 The first life-forms to appear on Earth were most likely

(1) complex single-celled organisms
(2) complex multicellular organisms
(3) simple single-celled organisms
(4) simple multicellular organisms

17 One explanation for the variety of organisms present on Earth today is that over time

(1) new species have adapted to fill available niches in the environment

(2) evolution has caused the appearance of organisms that are similar to each other

(3) each niche has changed to support a certain variety of organism

(4) the environment has remained unchanged, causing rapid evolution

18 Within which structure in the human body does specialization of parts of the developing baby take place?

(1) ovary   (3) testis
(2) uterus   (4) pancreas

19 Which statement best explains the significance of meiosis in the process of evolution within a species?

(1) The gametes produced by meiosis ensure the continuation of any particular species by asexual reproduction.

(2) Equal numbers of eggs and sperm are produced by meiosis.

(3) Meiosis produces eggs and sperm that are alike.

(4) Meiosis provides for variation in the gametes produced by an organism.

20 The diagram below represents chromosomes in a zygote.

Which diagrams best illustrate the daughter cells that result from normal mitotic cell division of this zygote?

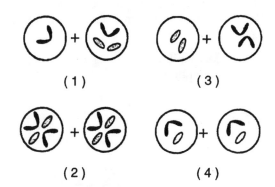

21 During the last months of pregnancy, the brain of a human embryo undergoes an essential "growth spurt." Which action by the mother would most likely pose the greatest threat to the normal development of the nervous system of the embryo at this time?

(1) spraying pesticides in the garden
(2) taking prescribed vitamins on a daily basis
(3) maintaining a diet high in fiber and low in fat
(4) not exercising

22 The diagram below illustrates a biochemical process that occurs in organisms.

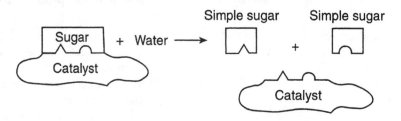

The substance labeled "catalyst" is also known as

(1) a hormone   (3) an antibody
(2) an enzyme   (4) an inorganic compound

23 Which phrase best describes cellular respiration, a process that occurs continuously in the cells of organisms?

(1) removal of oxygen from the cells of an organism
(2) conversion of light energy into the chemical bond energy of organic molecules
(3) transport of materials within cells and throughout the bodies of multicellular organisms
(4) changing of stored chemical energy in food molecules to a form usable by organisms

24 A food pyramid representing relationships in a pond community is shown below.

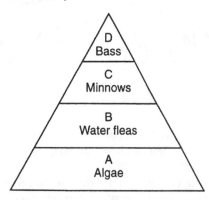

The energy of the Sun is made available to the pond community through the activities of the organisms at level

(1) *A*   (3) *C*
(2) *B*   (4) *D*

25 Eating a sweet potato provides energy for human metabolic processes. The original source of this energy is the energy

(1) in protein molecules stored within the potato
(2) from starch molecules absorbed by the potato plant
(3) made available by photosynthesis
(4) in vitamins and minerals found in the soil

26 Which statement does *not* identify a characteristic of antibodies?

(1) They are produced by the body in response to the presence of foreign substances.
(2) They may be produced in response to an antigen.
(3) They are nonspecific, acting against any foreign substance in the body.
(4) They may be produced by white blood cells.

27 The blood of newborn babies is tested to determine whether a certain substance is present. This substance indicates the presence of the disorder known as PKU, which may result in mental retardation. Babies with this disorder are put on a special diet to prevent mental retardation. In this situation, which action is usually taken first?

(1) treating the expression of the disorder
(2) preventing the expression of the disorder
(3) controlling the disorder
(4) diagnosing the disorder

28 The graph below provides information about the population of deer in a given area between 1900 and 1945.

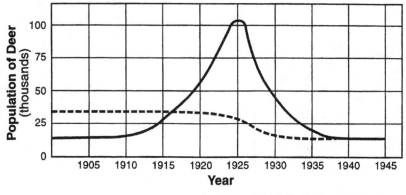

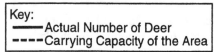

Which statement identifies the most likely reason that the carrying capacity of the area to support deer decreased between 1925 and 1930?

(1) The deer population decreased in 1926.
(2) The number of predators increased between 1915 and 1925.
(3) The deer population became too large.
(4) An unusually cold winter occurred in 1918.

---

29 An increase in the level of insulin in the blood would most directly result in

(1) a decrease in the amount of glucose in the blood
(2) a decrease in the amount of protein in the blood
(3) an increase in the amount of fat in cells
(4) an increase in the amount of carbon dioxide in cells

30 Compared to a natural forest, the wheat field of a farmer *lacks*

(1) heterotrophs
(2) significant biodiversity
(3) autotrophs
(4) stored energy

31 Human impact on the environment is often more dramatic than the impact of most other living things because humans have a greater

(1) need for water
(2) need for food
(3) ability to adapt to change
(4) ability to alter the environment

32 Which factor is *not* considered by ecologists when they evaluate the impact of human activities on an ecosystem?

(1) amount of energy released from the Sun
(2) quality of the atmosphere
(3) degree of biodiversity
(4) location of power plants

33 What will most likely result after a fire or other natural disaster damages an ecosystem in a certain area?

(1) The area will remain uninhabited for an indefinite number of centuries.
(2) A stable ecosystem will be reestablished after one year.
(3) An ecosystem similar to the original one will eventually be reestablished if the climate is stable.
(4) The stable ecosystem that becomes reestablished in the area will be different from the original.

34 The chart below shows the environmental functions that some organisms perform in a stable ecosystem.

Environmental Functions	Performed By
Pollination	bees, bats
Biodegradation	microorganisms
Soil aeration	earthworms
Recycling of atoms	soil bacteria
$CO_2 - O_2$ exchange	plants
Water storage	plants

How would a decrease in the number of organisms that perform these functions most likely affect the ecosystem?

(1) The interactions between other organisms would stop immediately.
(2) The functions carried out by these organisms would no longer be necessary.
(3) The ecosystem would remain stable.
(4) The ecosystem would become less stable.

35 A new type of fuel gives off excessive amounts of smoke. Before this type of fuel is widely used, an ecologist would most likely want to know

(1) what effect the smoke will have on the environment
(2) how much it will cost to produce the fuel
(3) how long it will take to produce the fuel
(4) if the fuel will be widely accepted by consumers

Part B

Answer all questions in this part

Directions (36–64): For those questions that are followed by four choices, circle the number of the choice that best completes the statement or answers the question. For all other questions in this part, follow the directions given in the question and record your answers in the spaces provided.   [30]

36 A food web is shown below.

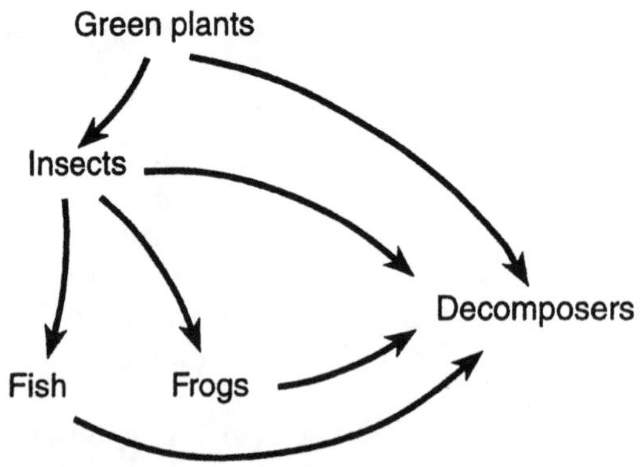

For Teacher Use Only

Green plants

Insects

Fish   Frogs

Decomposers

State what would happen to the plant population if the number of decomposers decreased and explain why this would happen.   [1]

_____

_____

_____

36

Directions (37–39): For each description in questions 37 through 39, select the interaction, *chosen from the list below*, that is most closely associated with that description. Then record its *number* in the space below the description. An answer may be used more than once or not at all.

Interactions

(1) Organism A ———————➤ Organism B
    Organism B ———————➤ Organism A

(2) Organism A – – – – ➤ Organism B
    Organism B ———————➤ Organism A

(3) Organism A ·············➤ Organism B
    Organism B ———————➤ Organism A

(4) Organism A – – – – ➤ Organism B
    Organism B – – – – ➤ Organism A

Key	
———————	= Positive effect
– – – – –	= Negative effect
·············	= No effect

37 The rhinoceros bird (organism *A*) feeds on parasites that live on the body of a rhinoceros (organism *B*). The rhinoceros allows the birds to feed on the parasites.

_____

37 ☐

38 Ants (organism *A*) defend acacia trees (organism *B*) from attacks by insects that are herbivores. The ants live in the hollow thorns of the trees.

_____

38 ☐

39 Wasp larvae (organism *A*) obtain nutrition from tomato hornworms (organism *B*). The tomato hornworms do *not* survive.

_____

39 ☐

Base your answers to questions 40 through 44 on the information and data table below and on your knowledge of biology.

The rate of respiration of a freshwater sunfish was determined at different temperatures. The rate of respiration was determined by counting the number of times the gill covers of the fish opened and closed during 1-minute intervals at the various temperatures. The following data were collected.

Data Table

Temperature (°C)	Gill Cover Opening and Closing Per Minute
10	15
15	25
18	30
20	38
23	60
25	57
27	25

Directions (40–42): Using the information in the data table, construct a line graph on the grid provided on the next page, following the directions below.

40 Label the *x*-axis and indicate the units.   [1]

41 Mark an appropriate scale on each axis.   [1]

42 Plot the data from the data table. Surround each point with a small circle and connect the points.   [1]

Example:

40–42

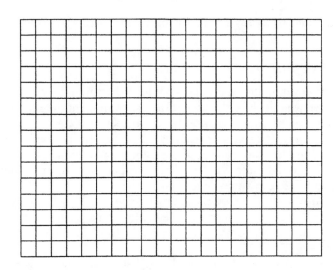

Number of Times Gill Covers
Opened and Closed per Minute

40 ☐

41 ☐

42 ☐

43 According to the data, as the temperature increases, the rate of respiration of the sunfish

(1) increases steadily

(2) decreases steadily

(3) increases, then decreases

(4) decreases, then increases

43 ☐

44 Which title is appropriate for this graph?

(1) The Effect of Temperature on Rate of Respiration in Sunfish

(2) The Effect of Gill Movement on Rate of Respiration in Sunfish

(3) The Relationship Between Temperature and Dissolved Oxygen

(4) The Relationship Between Sunfish Population and Temperature Change in Freshwater Habitats

44 ☐

Base your answers to questions 45 through 48 on the passage below and on your knowledge of biology.

To Tan or Not To Tan

Around 1870, scientists discovered that sunshine could kill bacteria. In 1903, Niels Finsen, an Icelandic researcher, won the Nobel Prize for the use of sunlight therapy against infectious diseases. Sunbathing then came into wide use as a treatment for tuberculosis, Hodgkin's disease (a form of cancer), and common wounds. The discovery of vitamin D, the "sunshine vitamin," reinforced the healthful image of the Sun. People learned that it was better to live in a sun-filled home than in a dark dwelling. At that time, the relationship between skin cancer and exposure to the Sun was not known.

In the early twentieth century, many people believed that a deep tan was a sign of good health. However, in the 1940s, the rate of skin cancer began to increase and reached significant proportions by the 1970s. At this time, scientists began to realize how damaging those deep tans could really be.

Tanning occurs when ultraviolet radiation is absorbed by the skin, causing an increase in the activity of melanocytes, cells that produce the pigment melanin. As the melanin is produced, it is absorbed by cells in the upper region of the skin, resulting in the formation of a tan. In reality, the skin is building up protection against damage caused by the ultraviolet radiation. Exposure to more sunlight means more damage to the cells of the skin. Research has shown that, although people usually do not get skin cancer as children, each time a child is exposed to the Sun without protection, the chance of that child getting skin cancer as an adult increases.

Knowledge connecting the Sun to skin cancer has greatly increased since the late 1800s. Currently, it is estimated that ultraviolet radiation is responsible for more than 90% of skin cancers. Yet, even with this knowledge, about two million Americans use tanning parlors. A recent survey showed that at least 10% of these people would continue to do so even if they knew for certain that it would give them skin cancer.

Many of the deaths due to this type of cancer can be prevented. The cure rate for skin cancer is almost 100% when treated early. Reducing exposure to harmful ultraviolet radiation helps to prevent it. During the past 15 years, scientists have tried to undo the tanning myth. If the word "healthy" is separated from the word "tan," maybe the occurrence of skin cancer will be reduced.

45 State *one* known benefit of daily exposure to the Sun. [1]

_____

_____

_____

45 ☐

46 Explain what is meant by the phrase "the tanning myth." [1]

_____

_____

_____

46 ☐

47 Which statement concerning tanning is correct?

  (1) Tanning causes a decrease in the ability of the skin to regulate body temperature.

  (2) Radiation from the Sun is the only radiation that causes tanning.

  (3) The production of melanin, which causes tanning, increases when skin cells are exposed to the Sun.

  (4) Melanocytes decrease their activity as exposure to the Sun increases, causing a protective coloration on the skin.

47 ☐

48 Which statement concerning ultraviolet radiation is *not* correct?

  (1) It may damage the skin.

  (2) It stimulates the skin to produce antibodies.

  (3) It is absorbed by the skin.

  (4) It may stimulate the skin to produce excess pigment.

48 ☐

49 The diagram below represents a function of the thyroid gland.

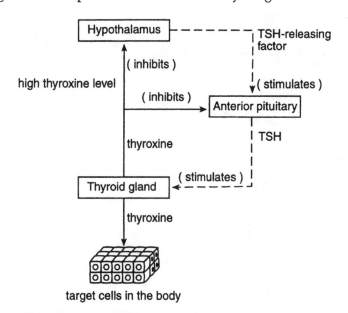

target cells in the body

State *one* effect of an increasing level of TSH-releasing factor.   [1]

_____

_____

_____

49 ☐

50 Although human muscle cells and nerve cells have the same genetic information, they perform different functions. Explain how this is possible.   [1]

_____

_____

_____

50 ☐

Base your answers to questions 51 through 54 on the graphs below and on your knowledge of biology. The graphs show the relative population size of two closely related species of microorganisms grown under identical conditions in culture dishes.

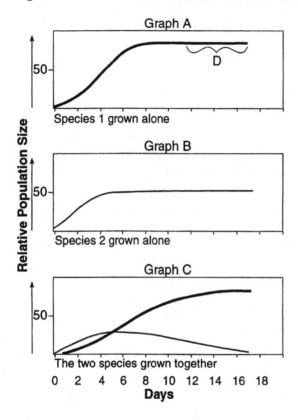

51 Give *one* possible reason for the difference in final population size indicated in graph *A* and graph *B*.   [1]

_____

_____

_____

51 ☐

52 In graph A, what causes the population to level off at letter D?   [1]

_____

_____

_____

52 ☐

53 Give *one* possible explanation for the results shown in graph C.   [1]

_____

_____

_____

53 ☐

54 What will most likely happen if the culture containing the two species together (graph C) is maintained for an additional week?   [1]

_____

_____

_____

_____

54 ☐

55 Explain why people with AIDS often develop many other infectious diseases.   [1]

_____

_____

_____

55 ☐

56 An unknown microorganism was observed with a compound light microscope. Identify the structure that, if observed in the organism, would indicate that it is an autotroph.   [1]

_____

56 ☐

Base your answers to questions 57 and 58 on the information and graph below and on your knowledge of biology.

A small community that is heavily infested with mosquitoes was sprayed weekly with the insecticide DDT for several months. Daily counts providing information on mosquito population size are represented in the graph below.

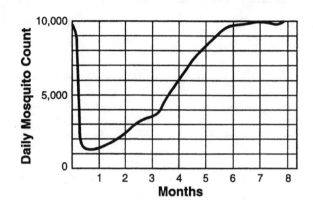

57 Which statement best explains why some mosquitoes survived the first spraying?

(1) The weather in early summer was probably cool.

(2) Most of the mosquitoes were of reproductive age.

(3) Environmental factors varied slightly as the summer progressed.

(4) Natural variation existed within the population.

57 ☐

58 What is the most probable reason for the decreased effectiveness of the DDT?

(1) DDT caused mutations in the mosquitoes, which resulted in immunity.

(2) DDT was only sprayed once.

(3) Mosquitoes resistant to DDT lived and produced offspring.

(4) DDT chemically reacted with the DNA of the mosquitoes.

58 ☐

59 A student placed a solution of glucose and yeast in a vacuum bottle and sealed it with a two-hole stopper as shown in the diagram below. The temperature of the yeast-glucose solution increased gradually with time, and the color of the indicator was observed and recorded throughout a 2-day period.

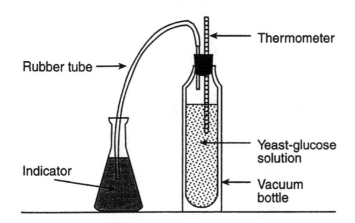

The purpose of the investigation was most likely to

(1) study the relationship between temperature and pressure

(2) demonstrate the release of energy by a chemical process

(3) show that proteins are produced by yeast

(4) study autotrophic nutrition in yeast

59 ☐

60 The diagram below shows two setups that were used to study bacterial growth. Each setup initially contained an equal number of the bacterium *E. coli* in different carbohydrate solutions. After one hour, a 1-milliliter sample was drawn from each tube and analyzed. The number of bacteria found in the sample from test tube 1 was higher than the number in test tube 2.

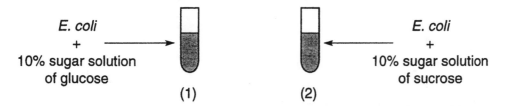

Which conclusion regarding this investigation is *not* valid?

(1) All bacteria grow best in a solution of glucose.

(2) *E. coli* grows better in a 10% solution of glucose than in a 10% solution of sucrose.

(3) The type of sugar solution will make a difference in the rate of growth of *E. coli*.

(4) The rate of growth of *E. coli* depends on the type of carbohydrate present.

60 ☐

Base your answers to questions 61 and 62 on the information below and on your knowledge of biology.

A small green plant was placed in a flask as shown below. A sensor that measures the CO_2 content of the air in the flask was inserted, and then the flask was sealed with a rubber stopper. The other end of the sensor was connected to a computer to monitor and record CO_2 levels in the flask over a period of time.

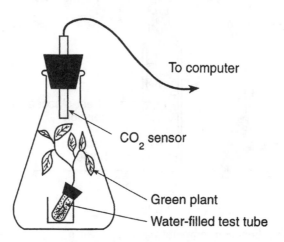

For part of the time the flask was placed in bright light and for part of the time it was placed in total darkness. The graph below shows data that were recorded by the sensor over a period of time.

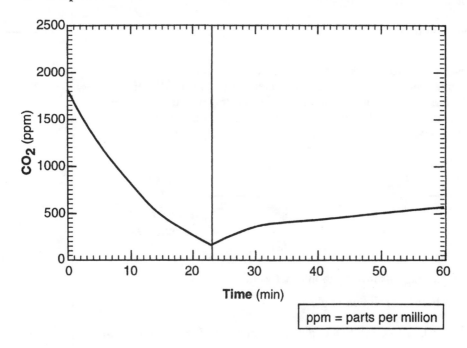

61 Which condition most likely produced the effect on CO_2 level over the first 23 minutes?

(1) The light was on for the entire 23 minutes.

(2) The light was off for the entire 23 minutes.

(3) The light was off at the start and turned on after 10 minutes.

(4) The light could have been either on or off because it would have had no effect on the CO_2 level.

62 Which process most likely caused the change in CO_2 level in the flask over the last 37 minutes?

(1) photosynthesis

(2) respiration

(3) active transport

(4) circulation

63 The data table below contains information on the growth of eight white pine trees, planted in eight different locations, after a period of time.

Data Table

Tree Number	Trunk Diameter 1.2 Meters Above Soil Surface (m)	Soil pH	Elevation Above Sea Level (ft)
1	0.54	4.0	1,200
2	0.79	6.5	1,650
3	0.64	4.5	1,400
4	1.04	5.0	1,350
5	0.96	5.0	1,350
6	0.82	4.5	1,250
7	0.80	5.5	1,400
8	0.52	5.0	1,600

Which statement is best supported by the data in the table?

(1) White pines grow best at higher elevations.

(2) White pines are not found at elevations below 1,000 feet.

(3) White pines have a long life span.

(4) White pines can grow in acidic soil.

64 In the table below, identify *two* body activities that would change in response to an increase in muscle activity *and* describe how each would change.   [2]

Activity	Change in Response to Muscle Activity
1. _____ _____	1. _____ _____
2. _____ _____	2. _____ _____

64 ☐

☐

**Total Score
for Part B**

Part C

Answer all questions in Part C

Directions (65–73): Record your answers in the spaces provided in this examination booklet.

Base your answer to question 65 on the information below and on your knowledge of biology.

> You are the head of the research division of the Leafy Lettuce Company. Your company is experimenting with growing lettuce using hydroponic technology. Hydroponic technology involves growing plants in containers of growth solution in a greenhouse. No soil is used. The growth solution that the company uses contains water, nitrogen, and phosphorus. The company wants to know if adding iron to this formula will improve lettuce growth.

65 Briefly describe how to test the effect of the formula with iron added. In your description, be sure to:

- state a hypothesis to be tested in the new experiment   [1]
- state how the control group will be treated differently from the experimental group [1]
- identify *two* factors that must be kept the same in both the experimental and control groups   [2]
- state what type of data should be collected to support or refute the hypothesis   [1]

65

Base your answers to questions 66 through 68 on the information below and on your knowledge of biology.

> The planning board of a community held a public hearing in response to complaints by residents concerning a waste-recycling plant. These residents claim that the waste-hauling trucks were polluting air, land, and water and that the garbage has brought an increase in rats, mice, and pathogenic bacteria to the area. The residents were insistent that the waste-recycling plant be closed permanently.
>
> Other residents recognized the health risks but felt that the benefits of waste recycling outweighed the health issues.

66 Identify *two* specific health problems that could result from living near the waste-recycling plant.   [2]

_____

_____

_____

_____

_____

_____

_____

_____

66 ☐

67 State *one* cause of a health problem that can be associated with the presence of the waste-recycling plant.   [1]

_____

_____

_____

67 ☐

68 State *one* ecological benefit of recycling wastes.   [1]

_____

_____

_____

_____

68 ☐

Base your answers to questions 69 through 71 on the information below and on your knowledge of biology.

Children must be vaccinated against certain diseases before they can enter school. Some parents feel that vaccinations are dangerous.

69 Explain to these parents what a vaccine is and what it does in the body.   [2]

_____

_____

_____

_____

_____

_____

70 State *one* way a child could develop an immunity to a certain disease without being vaccinated.   [1]

_____

_____

_____

71 Identify *one* part of a research plan that must be followed when developing a new vaccine.   [1]

_____

_____

_____

_____

72 Ladybugs were introduced as predators into an agricultural area of the United States to reduce the number of aphids (pests that feed on grain crops). Describe the positive and negative effects of this method of pest control. Your response must include at least:

- *two* advantages of this method of pest control   [2]
- *two* possible dangers of using this method of pest control   [2]

_____

_____

_____

_____

_____

_____

_____

_____

_____

73 Some people claim that certain carnivores should be destroyed because they kill beneficial animals. Explain why these carnivores should be protected. Your answer must include information concerning:

- prey population growth   [1]
- extinction   [1]
- importance of carnivores in an ecosystem   [1]

_____

_____

_____

_____

_____

_____

_____

_____

LIVING ENVIRONMENT
JUNE 2001

Part	Maximum Score	Student's Score
A	35	
B	30	
C	20	
Total Raw Score (maximum Raw Score: 85)		
Final Score (from conversion chart)		

Raters' Initials

Rater 1 . . . .   Rater 2 . . . .

ANSWER SHEET

Student . . . .

Teacher . . . .

School . . . . Grade . . . .

Record your answers to Part A on this answer sheet.

Part A

1	13	25 . . . . .
2	14	26 . . . . .
3	15	27 . . . . .
4	16	28 . . . . .
5	17	29 . . . . .
6	18	30 . . . . .
7	19	31 . . . . .
8	20	32 . . . . .
9	21	33 . . . . .
10	22	34 . . . . .
11	23	35 . . . . .
12	24	

LIVING ENVIRONMENT
AUGUST 2001

Part A

Answer all 35 questions in this part. [35]

Directions (1–35): For *each* statement or question, write on the separate answer sheet the *number* of the word or expression, that, of those given, best completes the statement or answers the question.

1 Which statement describes the best procedure to determine if a vaccine for a disease in a certain bird species is effective?

(1) Vaccinate 100 birds and expose all 100 to the disease.
(2) Vaccinate 100 birds and expose only 50 of them to the disease.
(3) Vaccinate 50 birds, do not vaccinate 50 other birds, and expose all 100 to the disease.
(4) Vaccinate 50 birds, do not vaccinate 50 other birds, and expose only the vaccinated birds to the disease.

2 Scientists have cloned sheep but have not yet cloned a human. The best explanation for this situation is that

(1) the technology to clone humans has not been explored
(2) human reproduction is very different from that of other mammals
(3) there are many ethical problems involved in cloning humans
(4) cloning humans would take too long

3 In an ecosystem, what happens to the atoms of certain chemical elements such as carbon, oxygen, and nitrogen?

(1) They move into and out of living systems.
(2) They are never found in living systems.
(3) They move out of living systems and never return.
(4) They move into living systems and remain there.

4 The main function of the human digestive system is to

(1) rid the body of cellular waste materials
(2) process organic molecules so they can enter cells
(3) break down glucose in order to release energy
(4) change amino acids into proteins and carbohydrates

5 The normal sodium level in human blood is 135 mEq/L. If a blood test taken immediately after a meal reveals a sodium level of 150 mEq/L, what will most likely result?

(1) Antibody production will increase.
(2) The person will move to an ecosystem with a lower sodium level.
(3) The nutritional relationships between humans and other organisms will change.
(4) An adjustment within the human body will be made to restore homeostasis.

6 The diagram below represents a process that occurs within a cell in the human pancreas.

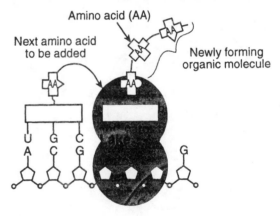

This process is known as

(1) digestion by enzymes
(2) protein synthesis
(3) energy production
(4) replication of DNA

7 When a person's teeth are being x rayed, other body parts of this person are covered with a protective lead blanket to prevent

(1) loss of hair
(2) increase in cell size
(3) changes in DNA molecules
(4) changes in glucose structure

8 The diagrams below represent portions of the genes that code for wing structure in two organisms of the same species. Gene 1 was taken from the cells of a female with normal wings, and gene 2 was taken from the cells of a female with abnormal wings.

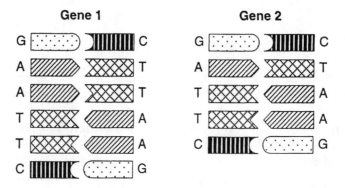

The abnormal wing structure was most likely due to

(1) an insertion

(2) a substitution

(3) a deletion

(4) normal replication

9 The diagram below represents a cell in water. Formulas of molecules that can move freely across the cell membrane are shown. Some molecules are located inside the cell and others are in the water outside the cell.

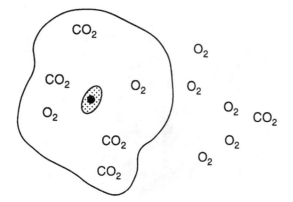

Based on the distribution of these molecules, what would most likely happen after a period of time?

(1) The concentration of O_2 will increase inside the cell.

(2) The concentration of CO_2 will remain the same inside the cell.

(3) The concentration of O_2 will remain the same outside the cell.

(4) The concentration of CO_2 will decrease outside the cell.

10 During the warm temperatures of summer, the arctic fox produces enzymes that cause its fur to become reddish brown. During the cold temperatures of winter, these enzymes do not function. As a result, the fox has a white coat that blends into the snowy background. This change in fur color shows that

(1) the genes of a fox are made of unstable DNA

(2) mutations can be caused by temperature extremes

(3) random alteration of DNA can occur on certain chromosomes

(4) the expression of certain genes is affected by temperature

11 Which phrases best identify characteristics of asexual reproduction?

(1) one parent, union of gametes, offspring similar to but not genetically identical to the parent

(2) one parent, no union of gametes, offspring genetically identical to parents

(3) two parents, union of gametes, offspring similar to but not genetically identical to parents

(4) two parents, no union of gametes, offspring genetically identical to parents

12 To determine the identity of their biological parents, adopted children sometimes request DNA tests. These tests involve comparing DNA samples from the child to DNA samples taken from the likely parents. Possible relationships may be determined from these tests because the

   (1) base sequence of the father determines the base sequence of the offspring

   (2) DNA of parents and their offspring is more similar than the DNA of nonfamily members

   (3) position of the genes on each chromosome is unique to each family

   (4) mutation rate is the same in closely related individuals

13 Although all the body cells in an animal contain the same hereditary information, they do not all look and function the same way. The cause of this difference is that during differentiation

   (1) embryonic cells use different portions of their genetic information

   (2) the number of genes increases as embryonic cells move to new locations

   (3) embryonic cells delete portions of chromosomes

   (4) genes in embryonic body cells mutate rapidly

14 According to the theory of natural selection, why are some individuals more likely than others to survive and reproduce?

   (1) Some individuals pass on to their offspring new characteristics they have acquired during their lifetimes.

   (2) Some individuals are better adapted to exist in their environment than others are.

   (3) Some individuals do not pass on to their offspring new characteristics they have acquired during their lifetimes.

   (4) Some individuals tend to produce fewer offspring than others in the same environment.

15 The energy an organism requires to transport materials and eliminate wastes is obtained directly from

   (1) DNA   (3) hormones

   (2) starch   (4) ATP

16 New inheritable characteristics would be *least* likely to result from

   (1) mutations which occur in muscle cells and skin cells

   (2) mutations which occur in male gametes

   (3) mutations which occur in female gametes

   (4) the sorting and recombination of existing genes during meiosis and fertilization

17 The diagram below shows the human female reproductive system.

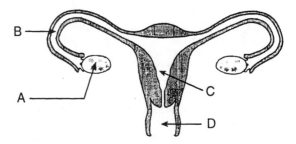

The fetus normally develops within structure

   (1) *A*   (3) *C*

   (2) *B*   (4) *D*

18 One way to produce large numbers of genetically identical offspring is by

   (1) cloning

   (2) fertilization

   (3) changing genes by agents such as radiation or chemicals

   (4) inserting a DNA segment into a different DNA molecule

19 Most cells in the body of a fruit fly contain eight chromosomes. How many of these chromosomes were contributed by each parent of the fruit fly?

   (1) 8   (3) 16

   (2) 2   (4) 4

20 Which disease damages the human immune system, leaving the body open to certain infectious agents?

   (1) flu   (3) chicken pox

   (2) AIDS   (4) pneumonia

21 According to the interpretation of the fossil record by many scientists, during which time interval shown on the time line below did increasingly complex multicellular organisms appear on Earth?

Time Line

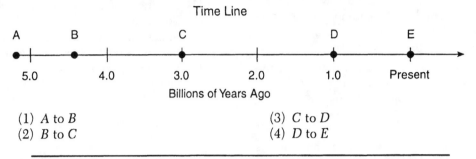

Billions of Years Ago

(1) A to B (3) C to D
(2) B to C (4) D to E

22 Which characteristic of sexual reproduction has specifically favored the survival of animals that live on land?

(1) fusion of gametes in the outside environment
(2) male gametes that may be carried by the wind
(3) fertilization within the body of the female
(4) female gametes that develop within ovaries

23 What usually results when an organism fails to maintain homeostasis?

(1) Growth rates within organs become equal.
(2) The organism becomes ill or may die.
(3) A constant sugar supply for the cells is produced.
(4) The water balance in the tissues of the organism stabilizes.

24 Which activity is *not* a response of human white blood cells to pathogens?

(1) engulfing and destroying bacteria
(2) producing antibodies
(3) identifying invaders for destruction
(4) removing carbon dioxide

25 In some individuals, the immune system attacks substances such as grass pollen that are usually harmless, resulting in

(1) an allergic reaction
(2) a form of cancer
(3) an insulin imbalance
(4) a mutation

26 A characteristic shared by all enzymes, hormones, and antibodies is that their function is determined by the

(1) shape of their molecules
(2) DNA they contain
(3) inorganic molecules they contain
(4) organelles present in their structure

27 The diagram below shows the relationships between the organisms in and around a pond.

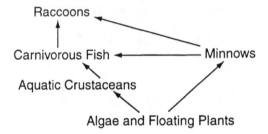

One additional biotic factor needed to make this a stable ecosystem is the presence of

(1) producers (3) decomposers
(2) herbivores (4) consumers

28 What is the major environmental factor limiting the numbers of autotrophs at great depths in the ocean?

(1) type of seafloor
(2) amount of light
(3) availability of minerals
(4) absence of biotic factors

29 The diagram below shows a food chain.

Grasses   ⟶   Rabbits   ⟶   Bobcats

If the population of bobcats decreases, what will most likely be the long-term effect on the rabbit population?

(1) It will increase, only.
(2) It will decrease, only.
(3) It will increase and then decrease.
(4) It will decrease and then increase.

30 An owl cannot entirely digest the animals upon which it preys. Therefore, each day it expels from its mouth a pellet composed of materials such as fur, bones, and cartilage. By examining owl pellets, ecologists are able to determine the

(1) autotrophs that owls prefer
(2) organisms that feed on owls
(3) pathogens that affect owls
(4) consumers that owls prefer

31 In some areas, foresters plant one tree for every tree they cut. This activity is an example of

(1) lack of management of nonrenewable natural resources
(2) a good conservation practice for renewable natural resources
(3) a good conservation practice for nonrenewable natural resources
(4) lack of concern for renewable natural resources

32 To minimize negative environmental impact, a community should

(1) approve the weekly spraying of pesticides on the plants in a local park
(2) grant a permit to a chemical manufacturing company to build a factory by one of its lakes, with no restrictions on waste disposal
(3) make a decision about building a new road in a hiking area based only on the economic advantages
(4) set policy after considering both the risks and benefits involved in building a toxic waste site within its boundaries

33 Deforestation would most immediately result in

(1) the disappearance of native species
(2) industrialization of an area
(3) the depletion of the ozone shield
(4) global warming

34 El Niño is a short-term climatic change that causes ocean waters to remain warm when they should normally be cool. The warmer temperatures disrupt food webs and alter weather patterns. Which occurrence would most likely result from these changes?

(1) Some species would become extinct, and other species would evolve to take their place.
(2) Some populations in affected areas would be reduced, while other populations would increase temporarily.
(3) The flow of energy through the ecosystem would remain unchanged.
(4) The genes of individual organisms would mutate to adapt to the new environmental conditions.

35 Toxic chemicals called PCBs, produced as a result of manufacturing processes, were dumped into the Hudson River. What was most likely a result of this action on fish in the Hudson River?

(1) Some fish became unfit to eat.
(2) The fish populations increased.
(3) Thermal pollution of the river increased, decreasing the fish population.
(4) The carrying capacity for fish increased in the river.

Part B

Answer all questions in this part

Directions (36–63): For those questions that are followed by four choices, circle the number of the choice that best completes the statement or answers the question. For all other questions in this part, follow the directions given in the question and record your answers in the spaces provided. [30].

Base your answers to questions 36 through 38 on the diagram below, which shows some of the specialized organelles in a single-celled organism, and on your knowledge of biology.

For Teacher Use Only

A (contains food)

C (contains DNA)

B (contains liquid wastes)

D (contains receptors)

36 Write the letter of *one* of the labeled organelles and state the name of that organelle. [1]

_____

36 ☐

37 Explain how the function of the organelle you selected in question 36 assists in the maintenance of homeostasis. [1]

_____

_____

_____

37 ☐

38 Identify a system in the human body that performs a function similar to that of the organelle you selected in question 36. [1]

_____

_____

38 ☐

Base your answers to questions 39 through 42 on the information and data table below and on your knowledge of biology.

A student counted the total number of leaves in a group of duckweed plants (*Lemna gibba*) over a 5-day period. The data collected are shown in the table below.

Growth of Duckweed Leaves

Time in Days	Number of Leaves
0	15
1	20
2	25
3	40
4	60
5	80

Directions (39–40): Using the information in the data table, construct a line graph on the grid provided on the next page following the directions below.

39 Mark an appropriate scale on each labeled axis.   [1]

40 Plot the data from the data table. Surround each point with a small circle and connect the points.   [1]

Example:

39-40

Growth of Duckweed Leaves

Number of Leaves

Time in Days

39 ☐

40 ☐

41 The time it takes for the number of leaves to increase from 15 to 30 is approximately

(1) 2.0 days

(2) 2.3 days

(3) 2.9 days

(4) 3.2 days

41 ☐

42 State what would most likely happen to the production of oxygen by duckweed plants if the intensity and duration of exposure to light were increased.   [1]

_____

_____

_____

42 ☐

_____

Base your answers to questions 43 through 47 on the passage below and on your knowledge of biology.

Help Wanted — Bacteria for Environmental Cleanup

The location of a former fuel storage depot and packaging operation in the industrial port of Toronto, Canada, is the proposed site of a sports arena and entertainment complex. The problem is that the soil in this area was contaminated with gasoline, diesel fuel, home heating oil, and grease from the operation of the previous facility. Unless these substances are removed, the project cannot proceed.

The traditional method of cleaning up such sites is the "dig and dump" method, in which the contaminated soil is removed, deposited in landfills, and replaced with clean soil. This "dig and dump" method is messy and costly and adds to landfills that are already overloaded. A technique known as bio-remediation, which was used to help in the cleanup of the *Exxon Valdez* oil spill in Alaska, offered a relatively inexpensive way of dealing with this pollution problem. This cleanup process cost $1.4 million, one-third of the cost of the "dig and dump" method, and involved encasing 85,000 tons of soil in a plastic "biocell" the size of a football field. This plastic-encased soil contained naturally occurring bacteria that would eventually have cleaned up the area after 50 years or more with the amounts of oxygen and nutrients naturally found in the soil. Air, water, and fertilizer were piped into the biocell, stimulating the bacteria to reproduce rapidly and speed up the process. The cleanup by this technique was begun in August and completed in November of the same year. The bacteria attack parts of the contaminating molecules by breaking the carbon-to-carbon bonds that hold them together. This helps to change these molecules in the soil into carbon dioxide and water.

Although this method is effective for cleaning up some forms of pollution, bio-remediation is not effective for inorganic materials such as lead or other heavy metals since these wastes are already in a base state that cannot be degraded any further.

43 The use of bio-remediation by humans is an example of

    (1) interfering with nature so that natural processes cannot take place

    (2) using a completely unnatural method to solve a problem

    (3) solving a problem by speeding up natural processes

    (4) being unaware of and not using natural processes

44 The bacteria convert the contaminants into

    (1) carbon dioxide and water

    (2) toxic substances

    (3) proteins and fats

    (4) diesel fuel and grease

For Teacher Use Only

43 ☐

44 ☐

45 State an ecological drawback to the use of the "dig and dump" method. [1]

_____

_____

_____

45 □

46 Explain why the cleanup took only 3 months. [1]

_____

_____

_____

46 □

47 Bio-remediation is *not* an effective method for breaking down

(1) grease

(2) gasoline

(3) fuel for diesel engines and furnaces

(4) heavy metals such as lead

47 □

Base your answer to question 48 on the information and data table below and on your knowledge of biology.

Two species of fish were subjected to a series of treatments. The number of red blood cells flowing per minute through one capillary in the tail of each fish was counted and the average calculated. The data table below shows the treatments given to each species of fish and the results of the various treatments.

Data Table

Treatment	Species of Fish	Number of Fish Used	Average Number of Red Blood Cells
Adrenaline added (1:10,000 solution)	Trout	10	35
Adrenaline added (1:1,000 solution)	Trout	10	50
50% alcohol solution added	Trout	5	78
Temperature reduced (25°C to 4°C)	Trout	6	30
Lactic acid added (1:5,000 solution)	Sunfish	6	90
25% alcohol solution added	Sunfish	6	89
Adrenaline added (1:10,000 solution)	Sunfish	6	17
Temperature reduced (25°C to 4°C)	Sunfish	6	14
Temperature increased (15°C to 25°C)	Sunfish	6	22

48 State *two* errors in this investigation.   [2]

_____

_____

_____

_____   48 ☐

_____

49 Meiosis occurs in the development of sex cells. Mitosis occurs in most other cells. Identify *two* additional differences between these processes.   [2]

_____

_____

_____

_____   49 ☐

50 The chart below shows information about the relationship between the age of the mother and the occurrence of Down syndrome in the child.

Age of Mother	Occurrence of Down Syndrome per 1000 Births
25	0.8
30	1.0
35	3.0
40	10.0
45	30.0
50	80.0

State *one* conclusion that can be drawn from the chart concerning the relationship between the age of the mother and the chance of her having a child with Down syndrome. [1]

_____

_____

_____

50

51 Using *one* specific example, identify *one* action taken by a mother that could have a negative effect on the embryonic development of her baby. [1]

_____

_____

_____

51

52 In desert environments, organisms that cannot maintain a constant internal body temperature, such as snakes and lizards, rarely go out during the hot, sunny daylight hours. They stay in the shade, under rocks, or in burrows during the day. Explain how this behavior helps maintain homeostasis in these organisms. [1]

_____

_____

_____

52

53 In the early 1980s, scientists discovered holes in the ozone shield surrounding Earth. State *one* negative effect this environmental change could have on humans.   [1]

_____

_____

_____

For Teacher Use Only

53 ☐

54 In an investigation, students determined the average rate of movement of gill covers of a species of freshwater fish at different temperatures. The results are shown in the data table below.

Data Table

Group	Number of Fish	Temperature (°C)	Average Rate of Movement of Gill Covers per Minute
1	5	10	15
2	6	15	25
3	4	18	30
4	7	20	38
5	6	23	60
6	4	25	57
7	4	27	25

Which labeled axes should be used to graph the relationship between the two variables?

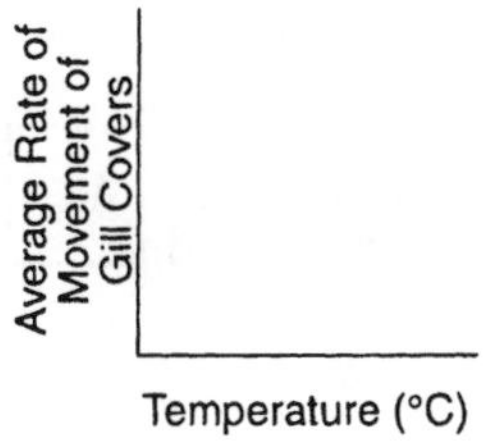

Average Rate of Movement of Gill Covers (y-axis) vs. Temperature (°C) (x-axis)

(1)

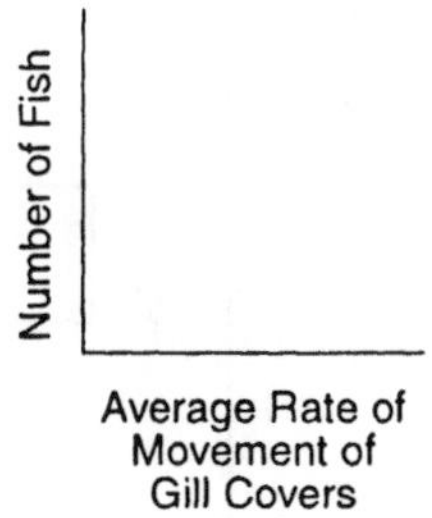

Group (y-axis) vs. Average Rate of Movement of Gill Covers (x-axis)

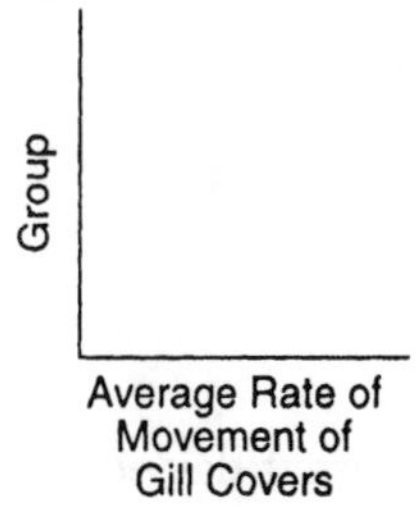

(3)

Number of Fish (y-axis) vs. Average Rate of Movement of Gill Covers (x-axis)

(2)

Number of Fish (y-axis) vs. Temperature (°C) (x-axis)

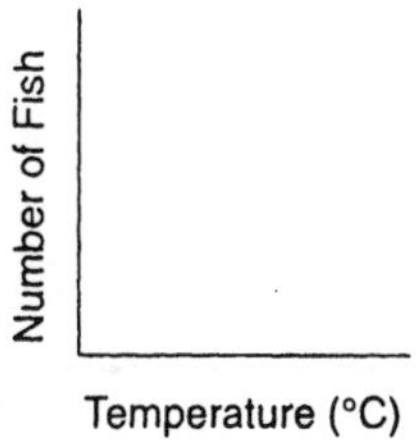

(4)

54 ☐

Base your answers to questions 55 through 57 on the diagram below and on your knowledge of biology. The diagram shows an interpretation of relationships based on evolutionary theory. The letters represent different species.

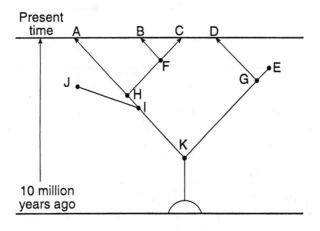

55 Explain why species *B* and *C* are more closely related than species *A* and *C* are.   [1]

_____

_____

_____

55 [ ]

56 The diagram indicates that a common ancestor for species *C* and *E* is species

(1) *F*

(2) *G*

(3) *H*

(4) *K*

56 [ ]

57 Which species are *least* likely to be vital parts of a present-day ecosystem?

(1) *A* and *E*

(2) *C* and *D*

(3) *E* and *J*

(4) *B* and *F*

57 [ ]

58 Hemoglobin is a complex protein molecule found in red blood cells. Hemoglobin with the normal sequence of amino acids is able to carry oxygen to body cells effectively. In the disorder known as sickle-cell anemia, one amino acid is substituted for another in the hemoglobin. One characteristic of this disorder is poor distribution of oxygen to the body cells. Explain how the change in amino acid sequence of this protein could cause the results described.   [1]

_____

_____

_____

58 □

59 Recently, scientists have been sent to rain forest areas by pharmaceutical and agricultural corporations to bring back samples of seeds, fruits, and leaves before these densely vegetated areas are destroyed. State *one* reason these corporations are interested in obtaining these samples.   [1]

_____

_____

_____

59 □

60 Two species of microorganisms were placed in the same culture dish, which included basic materials necessary for life. The size of each population increased during the first three days. After one week, the population size of one species began to decline each day. State *one* possible reason for this decline.   [1]

_____

_____

_____

60 □

61 State what could happen to a species in a changing environment if the members of that species do not express any genetic variations.   [1]

_____

_____

_____

61 □

62 In certain areas of the United States, the populations of wolves and other predators have decreased. As a result, deer populations in these areas have increased. Describe *one* way that an increase in the deer population can be harmful to humans.   [1]

_____

_____

_____   62 ☐

63 State *one* environmental impact of reduced funding for public transportation (trains, city buses, school buses, etc.) on future generations. Explain your answer.   [1]

_____

_____

_____   63 ☐

_____

☐

**Total Score
for Part B**

Part C

Answer all questions in Part C.

Directions (64–71): Record your answers in the spaces provided in this examination booklet.

Base your answers to questions 64 through 66 on the information below and on your knowledge of biology.

An investigation was performed to determine the effects of enzyme *X* on three different disaccharides (double sugars) at 37°C. Three test tubes were set up as shown in the diagram below.

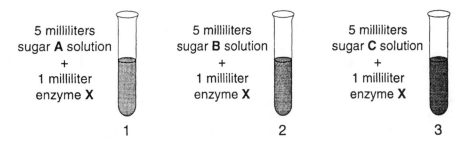

At the end of 5 minutes, the solution in each test tube was tested for the presence of disaccharides (double sugars) and monosaccharides (simple sugars). The results of these tests are shown in the table below.

	Test Tube 1	Test Tube 2	Test Tube 3
Monosaccharide	not present	not present	present
Disaccharide	present	present	not present

64 What can be concluded about the activity of enzyme *X* from the data table?   [1]

_____

_____

_____

64

65 With only the materials list supplied below and common laboratory equipment, design an investigation that would show how a change in pH would affect the activity of enzyme X. Your design need only include detailed procedure and a data table.   [3]

Materials

Enzyme X
Sugar C solution
Indicators
Substances of various pH values —
    vinegar (acidic)
    water (neutral)
    baking soda (basic)

Procedure:

_____

_____

_____

_____

_____

_____

_____

Data Table:

65

66 State *one* safety precaution that should be used during the investigation. [1]

_____

_____

_____

_____   66 ☐

_____

67 For many years, humans have used a variety of techniques that have influenced the genetic makeup of organisms. These techniques have led to the production of new varieties of organisms that possess characteristics that are useful to humans. Identify *one* technique presently being used to alter the genetic makeup of an organism, and explain how humans can benefit from this change. Your answer must include at least:

• the name of the technique used to alter the genetic makeup   [1]

• a brief description of what is involved in this technique   [1]

• *one* specific example of how this technique has been used   [1]

• a statement of how humans have benefited from the production of this new variety of organism   [1]

_____

_____

_____

_____

_____

_____

_____

_____

_____

_____

_____   67 ☐

68 All living organisms are dependent on a stable environment.

  a Describe how humans have made the environment less stable by:
  • changing the chemical composition of air, soil, and water   [1]
  • reducing the biodiversity of an area   [1]
  • introducing technologies   [1]

_____

_____

_____

_____

_____

_____

_____

_____

  b Describe *two* specific ways recently used by humans to reduce the amount of chemicals being added to the environment.   [2]

_____

_____

_____

_____

_____

_____

68

69 A European species of rabbit was released on a ranch in Victoria, Australia. The species thrived and reproduced rapidly. The rabbits overgrazed the land, reducing the food supply for the sheep. The *Myxoma sp.* virus was used to kill the rabbits. The first time this virus was applied, it killed 99.8% of the rabbits. When the rabbits became a problem again, the virus was applied a second time. This time, only 90% of the rabbits were killed. When the rabbits became a problem a third time, the virus was applied once again, and only 50% of the rabbits were killed. Today, this virus has little or no effect on this species of rabbit.

Explain what happened to the species of rabbit as a result of the use of this virus. You must *include* and *circle* the following terms in your answer.   [4]

- gene
- adaptive value *or* adaptation *or* adapted
- variation
- survival of the fittest

_____

_____

_____

_____

_____

_____

_____

_____

_____

_____

_____

Base your answers to questions 70 and 71 on the information in the newspaper article below and on your knowledge of biology.

Patients to test tumor fighter

Boston—Endostatin, the highly publicized experimental cancer drug that wiped out tumors in mice and raised the hopes of cancer patients, will be tested on patients this year.

"I think it's exciting, but ... you always have the risk that something will fail in testing," said Dr. Judah Folkman, the Harvard University researcher whose assistant, Michael O'Reilly, discovered endostatin.

Endostatin and a sister protein, angiostatin, destroy the tumors' ability to sprout new blood vessels. This makes cancer fall dormant in lab animals, but no one knows if that will happen in humans.

The Associated Press

70 Explain why it is necessary to test these experimental drugs on human volunteers as well as on test animals.   [1]

_____

_____

_____   70 ☐

71 State *one* reason that mice are often used by scientists for testing experimental drugs that may be used by humans.   [1]

_____

_____

_____   71 ☐

☐

**Total Score
for Part C**

LIVING ENVIRONMENT
August 2001

Part	Maximum Score	Student's Score
A	35	
B	30	
C	20	
Total Raw Score (maximum Raw Score: 85)		
Final Score (from conversion chart)		

Raters' Initials

Rater 1 . . . .   Rater 2 . . . .

ANSWER SHEET

Student . . . .

Teacher . . . .

School . . . . Grade . . . .

Record your answers to Part A on this answer sheet.

Part A

1	13	25 . . . . . .
2	14	26 . . . . . .
3	15	27 . . . . . .
4	16	28 . . . . . .
5	17	29 . . . . . .
6	18	30 . . . . . .
7	19	31 . . . . . .
8	20	32 . . . . . .
9	21	33 . . . . . .
10	22	34 . . . . . .
11	23	35 . . . . . .
12	24	